MAR
IN HELPLESSNESS . . .

Convulsions tore through Paul's body. Marguerite ran around the partition wall to her cousin. Perhaps Johnny could help.

He couldn't.

Marguerite froze when she saw him. Her cousin Johnny floated three feet above the bed. From his eyes blazed beams of harsh white light. From his mouth a thousand voices came.

He turned to Marguerite, transfixing her with his glowing eyes, and a voice from within the voices spoke.

"We must all be together when the dream friend comes," it said.

Marguerite screamed.

"Gripping . . . chilling . . . totally absorbing."
—***Quill & Quire***

*

"Startling and memorable."
—***St. John's Evening Telegram***

*

Also by
Garfield Reeves-Stevens

BLOODSHIFT

Published by
POPULAR LIBRARY

GARFIELD REEVES-STEVENS

POPULAR LIBRARY

An Imprint of Warner Books, Inc

A Time Warner Company

POPULAR LIBRARY EDITION

This Popular Library Edition is published by arrangement with the author.

Cover illustration by Lisa Falkenstern

Popular Library books are published by
Warner Books, Inc.
666 Fifth Avenue
New York, N.Y. 10103

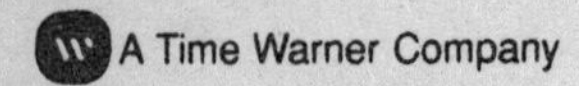

Printed in the United States of America

First Popular Library Printing: October, 1990

10 9 8 7 6 5 4 3 2 1

For
Evelyn Reeves
M.F.M.I.L.
with love

TRANSCRIPT

MAY 1992

Subject: James Michael Estevez, age 13
Attending Psychiatrist: Rosalind Torchia, Yorkwoods Institute
11:02 AM TRANSCRIPT BEGINS

Dr. Torchia: What's your name today?
Estevez: Jamie
Dr: Do you know where you are today, Jamie?
E: Jail.
Dr: Oh, no. This isn't a jail, Jamie. This is more like a hospital. This is a place where we help people get better. Especially children. Do you know why you are here, Jamie?
E: (unintelligible)
Dr: Why did you kill your mother and father, Jamie?
E: (unintelligible)
Dr: I'm sorry. I couldn't hear you.
E: I want to go back to my room.
Dr: Remember our talk about following rules, Jamie? You may go back to your room when the hour is up. Let's try again. How did you kill your mother and father?
E: With the knife.
Dr: I see. Do you remember what we've said about the knife before? I know I've talked about it with you before, and with most of the others as well. You should all know about the knife by now, don't you think?

E: I killed my mother and father with the knife.

Dr: I'll tell you one more time, Jamie. The police have special doctors who work for them. These doctors are very smart and can find out all sorts of things that most people would never think of. These doctors examined the bodies of your parents. They say you can't have killed your parents with the knife because when you stabbed your parents, they had already been dead for at least three hours. So I ask you again, Jamie, how did you kill your mother and father?

E: Ask the special doctors.

Dr: They don't know, Jamie. They've looked at everything. Your parents were in the kitchen. Your father had a glass in his hand. Your mother had just made up some Shake and Bake, and then they both fell to the floor and died. About three hours later, after you had eaten the Shake and Bake, you just stabbed your parents over and over and then called 911. All you would say was that they had been fighting and that you had gotten mad. Do you remember that?

E: Yes.

Dr: Then why were they on the floor? What happened to them?

E: I killed them.

Dr: How did you kill them?

E: With the knife.

Dr: They were already dead when you stabbed them, Jamie.

E: I killed them. I killed them. I (unintelligible)

Dr: (unintelligible) I'm sorry, Jamie. I shouldn't have raised my voice like that. Here, take some Kleenex. We'll try again, all right? Now, once more, why did you kill your parents? Did the dream friend tell you to do it?

E: No way.

Dr: You seem very sure about that. The dream friend has told you to do other things, though, hasn't he? Are you sure he didn't tell you to kill your parents?

E: He doesn't tell me to do things like that.

Dr: What does he tell you?

E: Not that.

Dr: But when he comes to you, Jamie, what does he tell you to do?

E: He doesn't come to me. He's not here yet. Don't you

understand anything? He's coming for me but he's not here yet.

Dr: But you tell me you talk to him. How can you talk to him if he's not here? How can he tell—

E: (unintelligible)

Dr: Don't do that with your eyes, Jamie.

E: I want to go back to my room now.

Dr: Not until the hour is up. Now once again, what does the dream friend say—

E: I'm going back to my room.

Dr: Sit down. Tell me what he says to you.

E: Jamie's gone back to his room, Dr. Torchia.

Dr: (unintelligible) Who am I talking to?

E: I'm Paul.

Dr: Yes, Paul. We've talked before. Do you know what the dream friend says to Jamie?

E: I have something to say to you.

Dr: Go ahead.

E: No more questions.

Dr: What do you mean?

E: You're not supposed to ask any more questions. Jamie doesn't like you. I don't like you. None of the others like you.

Dr: Jamie—I mean, Paul—I have to ask questions to help you. I have to—no, please sit down until the hour is—

E: No. Now you (unintelligible)

Dr: (unintelligible)

E: If there's anyone listening behind that big mirror, you better come quick. Dr. Torchia needs help and I want to go back to my room.

Dr: (unintelligible)

11:09 AM TRANSCRIPT ENDS

THE KINGDOM

JUNE/JULY

ONE

The dying scream of Johnny Matches echoed meaninglessly from the walls of the surrounding burned-out buildings, repeated and replayed a dozen times. But it did not make his first death any easier.

His scream was followed by liquid rasps. The twitching of his arms and legs fluttered errantly into stillness. Then the only movement was of the creeping mist, cast up from the warm currents that pulsed unseen through deep sewers like the blood that once flowed in Johnny's veins. The teenage boys who stood in the lot watched this and did nothing.

Billows of pale vapor vented from sewer grates and eddied across the shattered bricks and shapeless rubble of what once had been a building and now was an empty lot. Above the vapor's tendrils, slow drops of Johnny's blood trembled on the tip of a switchblade, then fell and were lost. The sputtering light from a single flickering streetlamp cast an orange glow onto the river of mist, as if the blood had stained it. The teenage boys said nothing and the night returned to silence.

The children's eyes were fixed on the huddled form of *El Niño* as he hugged the lifeless body of Johnny Matches closer to his chest, as if to completely enwrap and absorb it. That was all they saw. From one dark and vacant overlooking window, the brief reflection of the streetlamp in the dull lens of a light-intensifying nightscope went unnoticed.

There were twenty-seven of them in the lot this night, twenty-seven with shoulder chains gripped tightly and hidden knives held ready. Fifteen were Night Stalkers. Twelve, and the body of Johnny Matches, were Silver Kings. The treaty meeting had not worked out as planned. Now, all waited for what *El Niño* would say, for what he would tell them to do.

Finally, long after the gouts of dark blood had ended, *El Niño* stirred. Those closest to him could see his dark eyes shift quickly over the lot, assessing the positions of his followers and his enemies. The boys tensed with expectation. The time was *now*. When at last his eyes stopped moving, they seemed to look directly through the night and into the lens of Detective Julian Burch's nightscope.

"Touchdown! Touchdown!" Burch screamed the code word into the pencil-thin VOX microphone suspended before his mouth. He pulled the nightscope away from his face an instant before it flared brilliant green as the searchlights atop the surrounding buildings blasted the lot with light like the dayside of the moon. Tires squealed in the distance as police vehicles and ambulances converged.

"Damn," Burch snorted. "He was looking right at me and I missed it. I wanted to see his face when he *realized* what's going down." Burch's knees creaked as he and his partner stood up and stretched for the first time in four hours.

Special Detective Jim Hyams brushed concrete powder from his jeans and jacket and said nothing. He was only twenty-four, not even a graduate officer. Even if he said something, Burch would ignore him. Hyams thought his partner's vendetta against the gangs, and *El Niño* in particular, was too charged and too personal and he wanted nothing more to do with it. The end of Operation Superbowl simply meant that the six-month special assignment was over. On Monday morning, Hyams would turn in his badge and go back to the Academy to complete his training. Over and out.

The young man watched impassively as thirty-eight SWAT officers bounded across the rubble of the lot, flak jackets bouncing like circus clown stomachs, to surround the twenty-seven unresisting teenagers. And a body, Hyams thought. Mustn't forget about the body of Johnny Matches. At the beginning of the operation, when Hyams had been pulled from class and offered this special assignment, he had wondered how it would feel to work first as an undercover detective and then go back to graduate as a rookie. Now, at the operation's finish, he wondered if he still wanted to be a police officer at all. Burch's little maneuver tonight had entrapment written all over it. It wasn't the kind of police work in which Hyams had hoped to be trained.

Burch stowed the 'scope in its battered case and hoisted the strap over his beefy shoulder. With his other hand, he flicked on a six-battery flashlight and used it to pick out the path that led through the rubble to the stairwell. He began walking toward it without waiting to see if Hyams was ready.

"You get what you wanted out of this?" Hyams finally asked as he stepped carefully in the dim light reflecting back from the flashlight's beam.

"Damn right I did," Burch muttered. If he had noticed the cynicism in Hyams's question, he didn't acknowledge it. He was tracking in his own groove now. Hyams could tell that nothing mattered to Burch but what waited for him outside, in the lot.

"First," Burch explained, "we got Ramirez on at least manslaughter for sticking Johnny Matches. I saw it clear as day in the 'scope. A few words. A shoving match, and then Ramirez flicks out his blade and does a slice and dice. Second, *El*-fuckin'-*Niño* is present so we can hang him up for a few months as an accessory." Burch grunted to himself, piglike, brutal, and pleased.

The detectives came to the stairs and cautiously made their way down through the debris. What the hell, Hyams thought. It's not as if Burch can fire me now.

"*First*," Hyams said, "they're all juveniles so they're all going to walk. Even if you get convictions—a year from now if you're lucky—they're still all going to walk. And second—"

Burch spun on the stairs. Bits of plaster clattered into the darkness. He pointed the flashlight at Hyams's face, the spillover glare lighting his own from below like a distorted rubber mask.

"Whose side are you on, asshole?" he spit at Hyams. "What sort of crap are they shoveling at the Academy? Candy-asses like you get so concerned with 'points of law' that you can't see that those animals out there play by different rules. *El Niño* is a *threat*, kid. In the past year he's made treaties with twelve other gangs. And those treaties have stuck! Tonight, he was going to get the Stalkers on his side. At the rate he's going, by August he'll have every fuckin' gang in the city on his side." Burch pointed his flashlight to the stairs. His voice softened. "It won't be *gang* warfare then, kid. It will just be *war*. And we won't have thirty little Ayatollahs taking care of business with each other anymore. We'll just have *one*. And he's not going to be distracted."

"We're police officers, Julian. The gangs don't play by rules but we have to. Whatever you get against those kids out there, you have to make it stick. By the rules." For a moment, Hyams almost felt sorry for Burch.

"What's this 'we' crap, kid? We hauled you out of kindergarten 'cause we needed a fuckin' baby face that wouldn't be recognized on the streets. Next week you go back to mama, but I'm going to start playing by different rules. The real ones. The ones they go by on the streets. Sure *El Niño*'s going to walk in a few days. But not before I put out word that he was the one who set up Ramirez."

"No one will believe that."

"Why not, kid? Out in that lot we got the whole Special Task Force taking out a gang summit. A *secret* gang summit. With Matches stiffed, no one will know who our source was. So why not *El Niño*? We'll say he was having trouble making Ramirez see things his way, so he cuts a deal with the cops, sacrifices his pal Matches so we can get Ramirez on a murder rap, and then he's free to take over the Stalkers on his own. We don't need things to stick by *our* rules, kid. That story will make it stick by *his* rules. As soon as *El Niño*'s back on the street, he's dogmeat."

Burch continued down the stairs. Hyams followed. Twisted as Burch's scheme was, he had to admit it just might work—though he didn't know if, in the long run, thirty little Ayatollahs *were* easier to cope with than one big one.

Voices garbled by static crackled from half a dozen walkie-talkies as Burch and Hyams stepped through the rubble to the center of the lot. From sidewalk-parked patrol cars, blue and red bubble lights sent slow arcs of color against the sides of the surrounding derelict structures. The SWAT officers were calm and at ease in the loose circle they had formed around their captives. No one had even tried to escape. It had been an easy night's work. From the corner of his eye, Hyams saw two teams of paramedics leaning against their ambulances, smoking and talking as if they weren't needed. He didn't think anything of it. He hadn't seen what Burch had seen in the 'scope.

"Any trouble, Mansfield?" Burch asked the SWAT commander as he approached the perimeter of officers.

"Unfortunately, no." The commander was disappointed.

"None of them budged once the lights came on," an officer on the perimeter added. "Great planning, Jules. Twenty-eight punks down without working up a sweat."

Burch slapped the officer on his Kevlar-armored shoulder, grinning. "Twenty-seven and a body bag, you mean."

The other officer glanced at Burch with a questioning look. "Someone get hurt, Jules?" he asked.

"Fuckin' had his throat ripped out," Burch said with surprise.

Mansfield stepped up to Burch. "Say what?"

"You guys jerking me around or what?" Burch sputtered. The other officers had only blank concern in their eyes.

"Right over there!" Burch said angrily. He plunged through the SWAT perimeter and into the still forms of the gang members, striped in bands of harsh blue and deep black from the overlapping beams and shadows of the searchlights.

Without a word, Burch pushed unresisting gang members aside as he waded into the center of their circle. Without a word, he scanned the mist-shrouded rubble for the lifeless form he had seen fall there. Without a word, he slowly raised his head and looked into the eyes of the boy who stood before him.

It was Johnny Matches.

Matches smiled at Burch. His eyes gleamed in the brilliance of the searchlights. Burch's hand shot out and twisted through the boy's short hair, forcing his head back and exposing his neck to the light. It was unmarked.

Burch trembled. "I saw you *die*," he whispered. "I saw you—"

Another, smaller hand reached out and eased Burch's away from Johnny Matches.

"Got a problem here, officer?" *El Niño* asked.

Burch's face went white as his anger and hatred focused within him. *El Niño* began to laugh: a thin, dark, fourteen-year-old's face with shadowed eyes, splitting into a smile that Burch could only see as evil. The detective raised his hand to strike. The leader of all the gangs did not stop him. He did not flinch.

"Burch, no!" shouted Hyams as he pulled his partner back from *El Niño* and a multi-million-dollar assault suit.

Burch wrenched himself from Hyams's grip. His breath came in gasps.

"I *saw* it, kid. I saw the knife go in. I saw the blood. I saw—"

"You saw it in the 'scope, Jules. It couldn't have been that clear. You saw what you wanted to see. Let it go."

Now the rest of the gang members began to laugh. Burch snapped his head back and forth like a trapped animal. His hand reached for the inside of his jacket, for his holster. Hyams jumped him. Two SWAT officers helped. When Burch lay still, they carefully helped him up and led him away.

The laughter stopped. *El Niño* walked over to Commander Mansfield.

"So, like, can me and my friends get back to our game of football here or what?" the boy asked. "Or do you have something you want to charge us with?"

Mansfield could not bring himself to talk with the animal before him. He strode away, ordering his team to stand down. With some confusion, they did.

Hyams lit a Marlboro Light as he stood by the patrol car in which his partner sat, not under arrest but not allowed to leave. Hyams observed intently as the gang members gathered around *El Niño*, and Matches, and Ramirez. One little Ayatollah, Hyams thought, undistracted. Dangerous, to be sure, but still no excuse for what Burch had done out there. The rules were still the best way to go. *If* I go back to the Academy.

He tossed the half-smoked cigarette into a steaming sewer grate and climbed into the car. He supposed that the question wasn't so much his future with the NYPD as Burch's future. When the chief heard that a major surveillance operation had been compromised before an indictable offense had been committed, Burch was going to be lucky to be reassigned to traffic.

Eventually, the searchlights were dismantled, all the police had withdrawn, and out in the lot, the final negotiations were privately, and successfully, concluded. Once again, the treaty had grown. Peacefully, with knives and chains forgotten, the Stalkers and the Silver Kings made their separate ways into the night. *El Niño* and Matches alone remained, standing in mist and darkness.

El Niño shivered. The night breeze chilled him where it blew against the clinging dampness of his shirt and denim jacket, a clinging dampness that Burch had not checked for: the dying blood of Johnny Matches.

Matches put his arm around his friend. "Time to go, man?" he asked.

El Niño nodded. Then something unfamiliar seemed to move behind his eyes. He looked at Matches without appearing to see him.

"I want to go back to my room, now, Johnny," he said.

Matches nodded. He had seen that look before. Ever since the dream friend had started to speak to *El Niño* and the treaty-making had begun.

"Sure, Paul. We'll go back to your room now."

Gently, and with love, Johnny Matches led his friend into the darkened streets. In the lot, the mist filled in the disturbance of their passing and soon the night was silent once again.

TWO

White sheers billowed out from the window like blowing clouds. The sunlight shining through them dappled the richly broadloomed floor of the bedroom. Dean Fuller awoke with a start and slid his hand over the rumpled linen of the bed. His wife was gone.

He sighed, pushed back the covers, and sat for a moment on the side of the bed. At sixty-two, he no longer bounded out to meet the days as he once had. With the election coming up, his Washington securities investment business would soon be entering its quadrennial madness: divestments and blind trusts for the winners, cashing in for the losers. It had always been good to him in the past, but this time, he wondered how he was going to face up to it.

Fuller took a deep breath and groped for his gold-rimmed bifocals on the nightstand. He slipped them on and the hands on his Rolex appeared as if by magic. Almost seven. "Getting lazy in my old age," he muttered to himself.

From the moment he had felt the breeze, he knew where Barbara-Jane had gone. He put on his robe and went to the sliding glass door that led to the garden patio. He could see her standing by the pool, hair in a scattered white frizz, nightgown floating around her like the sheers in the window. That far down the yard, Fuller knew the neighbors could see her, too, but he had long since stopped worrying about it. The neighbors were used to it by now. It was part of the legend. The world had come to expect it.

For a few seconds he stayed at the door. He never looked forward to disturbing her during these incidents, her "seeing times," as she called them. He looked over to the trophy wall of the bedroom and saw dozens of younger versions of his wife staring back. Most were in photographs with her clients and notable friends. Johnson was there. So were Ford, Carter, Reagan, and the President—she had never liked Nixon. There were her friends in "the business"—Jeanne Dixon, an old shot of Maurice Woodruff—and her friends in entertainment, too. Johnny Carson had signed his photo of the two of them on the occasion of her twentieth appearance on his show. Most of the other Hollywood people were represented by covers from the tabloids that ran her columns. A few legitimate newspaper front pages were also framed there—her gallery of "greatest hits." Sputnik. Both Kennedys. An eruption or two. *Apollo I*. Nixon's resignation. But nothing major since '73. Fuller shook his head. She had never figured that out, the way the sure things dried up on her back then.

He turned again to the yard and the present. He went out to his wife.

* * *

After he was sure he would not startle her, Fuller took her hand. It was icy cold. He squeezed but there was no response. He began calling her name, calling her back.

Five more minutes passed. He saw drapes being moved over at the Kruppenheims'. They were probably already on the phone to the other neighbors. Rose, the Fullers' housekeeper since the dawn of time, came out with a robe for Barbara-Jane. Fuller took it from her and sent her waddling back to finish preparing breakfast.

When Barbara-Jane suddenly shuddered in his arms, Fuller realized he had lost track of how long he had been standing there. She shuddered again.

"Barbara-Jane, Barbara-Jane," he whispered softly. "You're at home. You're all right. Can you hear me?"

She turned to him, eyes at last seeing the here and now. Tears filled them.

Fuller saw those tears and felt his heart ache. Her face was rounder these days and no amount of makeup could hide her years, but he had aged with her and his love for her had grown with each passing day. It was why he hated the things on the walls and the story they told of what he had allowed to happen to her.

"There, there, honey. You're home now. You're with me, now." He held her tightly, felt her tremble with sobs. He could see the Kruppenheims standing in their windows, making no effort at all to be discreet. Fuller protectively led Barbara-Jane indoors.

They tracked green slivers of cut grass across the broadloom. He lovingly wiped her feet before he swung her legs back into the bed. Rose brought a tray with a silver pot of tea and left without being asked. He sweetened the tea with honey. Then, when Barbara-Jane breathed normally, though he hated to do it, he asked her what she had seen. Hesitatingly, she told him.

"I was in a great hall. It was huge. The walls were so dark, so far away, I couldn't see them. It was a place of judgment, I think. A place where all the souls of the world could watch and I had to do something . . . something . . ." She began to cry again. Fuller felt his insides being torn out. This wasn't supposed to keep happening. This was supposed to have ended. That was the deal he had made.

"What did you have to do, honey?" He could feel tears building in his own eyes.

"I don't know. I'm not sure. But you were there, too."

"Was *I* supposed to do something?"

"It wasn't clear. But it doesn't matter because there was nothing that could be done. It was all over. Nobody could do anything."

"What was over, honey?"

Barbara-Jane blinked her eyes hard. She took a deep breath. She squeezed her husband's hand. But she couldn't bring herself to look at him.

"There was a clock there, Dean, with big, red numbers. So I would know exactly."

"Know what?"

"Ten fifty-two P.M., August twenty-ninth."

"What happens then?"

"The world will end."

Fuller didn't know whether to feel relieved or more worried. This wasn't like the other times, wasn't rooted in politics. This was a fantasy. He hugged Barbara-Jane.

"I don't think there's much chance of the world ending in three months, honey," he said, trying to keep a light tone in his voice.

"But it will," she replied. She looked at her trophy wall. "I'm . . . always right."

Fuller looked at the trophy wall, too, and loathed everything on it. He thought quickly. His voice stayed gentle and calm. "Maybe you saw the time and date for the end of the world a million years from now. Maybe you saw—"

"It was *this* year, Dean."

"*How* can you be sure it was this year? How can you be sure you saw the end of the world?"

"It was this year because I *know* it was this year. It was the end of the world because of the man who was with me."

"Who was with you?"

Barbara-Jane tightened her hand around her husband's and shook her head. "Oh, Dean, I hate telling you this."

"Who was it?"

"The President." She struggled to keep her words coherent. "There's going to be a war, Dean." She paused. "*The* war."

For Dean Fuller, the anger would come later. But at that moment, he held nothing but the clear and lucid thought that they had lied to him. They had promised that it was over and now, without even consulting him, it had begun again. He patted his wife's hands.

"It's the end of something, all right, honey. Not the world, but something else. I promise you that."

But Barbara-Jane didn't hear him. He could sense her mind racing with what she thought was the awesome responsibility of her gift.

"I have to tell the President, Dean. So he can prepare."

He had known she was going to say that. He was struggling to find the words that might stop her. Out of all the thousands of self-styled psychics and seers and astrologers in the world, Barbara-Jane Fuller had Washington connections. Barbara-Jane Fuller could phone the White House and her call would be returned.

Dean Fuller didn't want that to happen. He didn't want his wife telling the President that she had foreseen him taking part in the final war and the end of the world. Dear God almighty, he thought, that madman would believe her.

THREE

Even on the ninth floor the fire trucks lumbering across West Seventy-ninth sounded like ocean liners bellowing as they came into port. The frosted glass window in Susan Foster's bathroom rattled for a moment as a siren screamed past. She looked at the window, though there was nothing to see, and traced out the web of interconnections that led to its rattling. She saw an early morning fire, an alarm, a rush at the fire hall, a diesel engine driving an alternator, an electric siren, vibrations, sound waves, glass in a window not quite closed, all coming together to vibrate cilia in her inner ear and leading to the sensation of hearing. She turned back to the mirror, saw herself naked within it, and saw the vial of white tablets whose web of interconnections would lead to her having no more sensations forever.

She had had the tablets a long time. Gradually, they had made their way from the jewelry box she hid behind a loose panel in a kitchen cupboard, to the medicine cabinet, and now to the edge of the sink, neatly in place beside a Colgate pump and a bottle of Clinique astringent. She thought of the tablets, it seemed, in inverse relation to the healing of the scar that blazed across her abdomen. No more bikinis, I'm afraid, her doctor had apologized. Of course not, doc, she had wanted to say, bad taste to be buried in a swimsuit after all.

She hefted the vial in her hand, heard the tablets rattle inside. Will they send a fire truck for me? she thought. After the tablets rattle inside me will the bathroom window rattle one more time when I can't hear it? A simple way to kill the cancer, doc. Just kill the patient.

She squeezed the vial and stared at herself. Damn, I look good, she thought. A living reward for no red meat, regular aerobics, plenty of grains and vegetables. Thirty-six but mistaken for late twenties. No sags, no unsightly lumps or bumps. A perfect body for a perfect disease.

Detached, an observer of an observer, she wondered if the tears running down her reflection's face were a sign that today was not the day to take the tablets, or a sign that the decision was already made. Maybe I'll just open the childproof top today, she thought. Maybe I'll just feel the weight of them in my hands and that will be it for today.

The phone rang.

She squeezed the arrows on the plastic top together and twisted. Two more twists and the top was off. She stuck her finger into the batting.

The phone rang again.

Don't be an ass, her reflection said. Maybe it's the hospital. Maybe a one-in-a-million accident happened last month and they got your ovaries mixed up with somebody else's. Maybe some other woman should be standing in front of her mirror with an open vial of little white tablets, a seventy-eight-year-old woman who's had her shot at life. Not you. Anyone else but you. Maybe it's God phoning up to apologize.

She answered the phone on the fifth ring.

"Hello, Susan, it's Father Panati."

She wanted to laugh. She did.

"Surely you don't find me that amusing," Panati said. His voice was deep and friendly, but she could catch the uncertainty in it. Why not? She had laughed at his name.

"I'm sorry, Father. Believe it or not, I was just thinking of you."

Panati's tone indicated that he wasn't inclined to believe it, but neither would he question her.

"I'm sorry to call you at home, and especially so early, but your service said that you hadn't been picking up your calls and—"

"Just a little vacation, Father."

"Going off somewhere, then?"

Foster smiled, but there was no one she could share the joke with.

"Just come back, actually," she said and the small talk continued.

Eventually Panati came to the point and Foster stopped thinking about his reaction if she told him she was naked and lying back on her bed. Outrageous ideas had been coming to her with almost the same frequency as thoughts about the tablets.

"Well, the fact of the matter is that I've been asked to call you. And I must say that I agree one hundred percent with the suggestion."

The professional side of Foster clicked in automatically. From the new flat tone in Panati's voice, she could tell that he was saying something he had either thought about a great deal or had actually rehearsed.

"As you know, Susan, the Church is always forming study groups to deal with one thing or another, and your name came up at one of the groups I attend."

"In a positive way, I hope." It wouldn't have surprised Foster if Panati had been reading from a script.

"Oh, most assuredly. Many, many people are impressed with your coverage of the Pontifical Academy of Sciences. Starting back with the apology to Galileo. There were a lot of . . . cynical . . . articles written about that. Yours seemed very fair and balanced. It honestly reflected the Church's views."

"That's my job, Father." What's he after here? she thought.

"Well, it is appreciated. Um, now the study group I'm involved in—planning committee, actually—covers a few matters also of . . . a scientific bent, and, because of the fine writing you do for the science magazines, and your . . . understanding of the Church's positions on various matters, we were wondering if you might like to . . . ah, take part?"

"I'm not a Catholic, Father."

"Oh, yes. No problem with that at all. The Church has to exist in a world that isn't Catholic. It certainly doesn't bother us if it doesn't bother you." He laughed a trifle too sincerely.

"And you haven't told me what the group is studying, or planning, and you haven't said what my role would be."

"Well, you would be a scientific advisor, of course."

"I'm not a scientist either, Father."

"Ah, you do have a master's degree from Columbia. Biochemistry, is it not?"

Now Foster was fully alert to every nuance of Panati's words. She tried to think back on every meeting she had had with him. She couldn't remember ever telling him that. Someone had been doing some digging.

"Four credits shy, actually, Father. Surely there are other, more qualified biochemists around."

"This doesn't just involve biochemistry. It involves many fields, and . . . ah . . . public perception of many things. I'm really not able to get too specific, Susan. On the phone at least. Could I just say that the committee . . . *might* . . . be planning for a certain . . . shift in Church policy?"

"Concerning biology?" Foster asked. Reading between the lines, she felt goose bumps on her arms. The tablets in the bathroom disappeared from her mind as she realized what Panati was hinting at.

"I think you understand, Susan," Panati said with obvious relief. "And I'm sure you can understand why I'm not able to go into more detail at the moment. Needless to say, if we could meet, I'm sure I could fill you in a bit more."

A dinner meeting was set up within moments and the call

ended. On her way into the shower, Foster stuffed the batting back into the vial, capped it, and put it back into the cabinet. She was glad the tablets were still there, but not necessary—for the next little while at least. If her interpretation of what Panati had been saying was correct, the Catholic Church might be planning to reverse its prohibition on birth control and Foster had a chance to be on the inside of one of the biggest stories of the twentieth century.

She laughed again as she lathered the shampoo into her short dark hair. She remembered how, as a beginner with more query rejections than she had dollars in the bank, she had said she would die for a byline. And now here she was, living for one.

Later that day, the tablets went back into the jewelry box in the kitchen. For the next little while at least.

FOUR

There was darkness all around him but of course he couldn't know it. Marguerite was his eyes. He was her strength. For years, he had known only that. Until now, when he was learning other things.

Marguerite came into the room. She lit the candles. She crossed herself before the brightly painted wooden statue of the Savior, then went to her cousin.

"Juan, are you awake?"

The boy was in his chair. What shape or form it originally had was long gone under successive layers of scavenged padding and blankets. His face was turned to her, his eyes solid white and unseeing. She could never tell if he was asleep or awake. He said nothing.

Marguerite looked over her shoulder to the doorway, straining to hear if Esperanza was in the hallway. There was no sound but the sputtering of the candles as the shadows of the peeling plaster on the walls and ceiling flickered in the dull orange glow. She knelt beside her cousin and called his name again. There would be trouble if he was not ready by the time Esperanza let in the first of the visitors.

The boy was thirteen, his skin as pale as his olive complexion would allow, his dark hair long and tied back. He did not acknowledge her and she began to worry. It was so unfair that he should have been chosen to do so much for others yet not be able to do anything for himself. She had asked the statue why that should be, many times. No answer had been given.

"Juan, it is almost time. Esperanza is coming. You must wake up." There were footsteps in the hall. Outside in the barrio the visitors would be coming: the crippled and the diseased who had heard from a friend, who had heard a rumor about a blind boy in a rundown house. All they needed was faith. And an offering for Esperanza.

Juan shifted in his chair.

"Is he ready?" Esperanza yelled down the hall.

"*Momentito, Tia,*" Marguerite shouted back. She shook Juan's shoulders. "*Por favor*, Juan. Wake up now!"

"But I am not asleep," Juan said.

"Then you intend for me to get in trouble with our aunt?"

Juan smiled in the direction of Marguerite's voice. "Never."

"Then why didn't you answer me?"

"I had a dream."

"Stop teasing me. How can you dream without being asleep?"

Juan gestured to his ears. "How can I hear voices when no sound is made?"

Marguerite crossed herself. "You hear them again?" she asked.

"No, not for a long time now. But I *saw* things. Wonderful things."

Marguerite looked nervously at the statue on the table. In the flickering lights of the candles the figure seemed to move. What miracles were these?

"You saw nothing," thundered the voice of Esperanza as Marguerite saw her stocky shape appear in the doorway. "What nonsense are you talking about?"

"Nothing, Aunt," Juan said. He had been in this house, this room, this chair, for four years. He knew enough not to argue.

"And you!" Esperanza went on to Marguerite, "why isn't this room prepared? How can the unfortunates maintain their faith with dirty plates and glasses around? And look at all the candles you are using! Do you know how much they cost? You are ruining everything!"

Juan winced as the sound of a slap cut through the close air of the room. When the bulky presence of Esperanza left, Juan reached out and his hands found Marguerite's face and felt the heat of her cheek.

"There, there," he said as the heat evaporated under his touch. "She is right to be concerned. She does so much for us, brings so many people here to be helped. We must understand her anger."

Marguerite allowed herself to be held by her cousin. She couldn't tell him the truth, about how Esperanza charged five hundred dollars for an appointment with Juan. More if she thought she could get it. Five hundred dollars while he was trapped in this room, eating food fit for animals, while Esperanza lived somewhere else, coming and going in her fancy white car as if she were the important one. Esperanza had trapped them here, without money and without documents. How could Marguerite say any of that without having some way to help her cousin? And how could she help someone who could not see and could not walk, and must be cleaned up after like a baby?

There were footsteps in the hall. More than one person was approaching. Marguerite got off her knees and smoothed her worn dress.

"What did you *see*?" she whispered as the footsteps grew louder.

"I saw green fields and blue skies," Juan whispered in reply. He had a strange expression on his face, one Marguerite had not seen before. "I saw white clouds and a golden sun that was too bright to look at. I saw my hand in front of my face. I could move it and cover the clouds. Even the sun."

Marguerite trembled. Juan had been blind at birth. How could he know such things?

"And I saw you, Marguerite. You were there beside me. Your hair shimmered gold like the sun. Your eyes were blue like the sky. And you were . . ." He smiled as if at a private joke. "You are very pretty, Marguerite."

Marguerite turned to leave the room. Her eyes were brown. Her hair was black. And her cousin was teasing her once again. In the hallway, she passed a man with a crutch. She knew it would join the others in the back to be burned when the nights grew cold.

Jennifer Campbell was as furious as a fourteen-year-old girl could be. She had a good mind to button up her blouse and go home. John was being a total spaz.

"Earth calling John," she said into her hand. "Earth calling space cadet John, come in please."

John Danylkiw turned his head suddenly and stared at Jennifer as if seeing her for the first time. Then he stared at her breasts as if seeing them for the first time. Then he realized he felt as if someone had punched him in the stomach. He started to gag.

"I don't *believe* you!" Jennifer squealed. She got up from the blanket and started buttoning her blouse, checking to make sure there was still no one else in the empty field stretching out from the copse of trees. The roofs of Larkin's Mill, Pennsylvania, were far down the valley.

"Hold on, hold on," John said. He also started to get up but the pants bunched around his ankles got in his way. "It must've been something I ate for lunch."

"We didn't eat lunch yet," Jennifer said coldly.

John stared as the culmination of three weeks of carefully plotted dating got dressed and prepared to walk out of his life forever. "I must have fallen asleep then—"

"*Asleep!*" Jennifer squealed. "*I put you to sleep?*"

John thought faster than he ever had in school. They didn't have the same kind of motivation there. "Well, what do you expect. I mean, a total, mutual experience like that? Such a moving and complete physical experience? After such an expression of our, ah, mutuosity, why are you so surprised that you left me completely, and totally, exhausted?"

Jennifer's eyes flickered as she considered his words. At least the ones she understood. John saw the hesitation and thought, Thank you dear Lord. I'll make it up to you.

"I mean," he continued, "how can I not feel that way? Didn't you feel that way? Couldn't you have just stretched out in the sunshine and felt totally relaxed?" He was on his knees before her, both hands resting gently on her lips. Her hands paused on a button.

"Well . . ." she said, dubiously.

"Well, maybe we should try it again and see."

Jennifer looked around again and then sat down on the blanket. She tossed her blond hair back and felt a gentle breeze against her breasts. She watched John's eyes jump back and forth between her own blue eyes and her blouse, which didn't have enough buttons done up on it.

"So *if* you were asleep," she said, "how come your eyes were open and you kept waving your hand around in front of your face?"

John struggled to stay cool. It would not do to start drooling, he told himself, forcing his eyes to stay on Jennifer's face.

"Maybe I was dreaming," he offered.

"About what?" Jennifer asked. She was having a hard time keeping her eyes off his shorts. "Lori Daniels?"

"No," John said, and then his face became serious. Had he been asleep? Had he dreamed? "I was looking at something." Yes, that was it.

"Lori Daniels's boobs?" Jennifer asked, leaning forward so John could get a good look at hers. But the spaz wasn't paying attention!

"No. Not that," he said much too seriously. "I was looking at something but I . . . couldn't see anything. I . . . I was blind. That's what it was. I dreamed I was blind."

A look of overpowering nurturing protection came over Jennifer and she hugged John to her and told him she would see to it that he would never have a bad dream again. As the objects of John's affection came closer, though he couldn't be sure he *had* been asleep, he told himself not to forget the dream of being blind. If it affected Jennifer like this, his mind boggled at the thought of what it would do to Lori Daniels.

FIVE

The saved—truly *saved*—smile of Reverend Bobby Jay appeared in the bank of television monitors like a wall of Cheshire cats.

"Do youuu *believe*?" the smiles drawled. "Do youuu *believe* in Lord Jeee-sus Christ?" The monitors flickered and the reverend's good wife, Louella, appeared. Her lips trembled. Mascara streaked her face like a martyr's tears. This was a face that *believed*.

"Well, brothers and sisters at home, then I have *good news* for you. I have—"

Bobby Jay hit a button on his desk and the audio on the screens died. He looked up at Hank Drummond and smiled. Not a saved smile this time, a carnivore smile. Drummond was in deep shit and he knew it.

"Hank," Bobby Jay began, then shook his head. "Hank, Hank, Hank." Even in the privacy of his office, he kept the timing and modulation that he had learned in his years in the revival tents. He spoke slowly. Then quickly. Softly. Then loudly. No one knew what he was going to say next, when, or how. It kept them on the edge of their seats, straining to hear every word. Now all of Bobby Jay's renowned oral skills were being brought to bear on one lone cameraman from the "Bobby Jay Good News Glory Show." It was no contest.

"You know, Hank," Bobby Jay said, "we all work here under the grace and the glory of *trust*. We believe in the brotherhood of the Lord, don't we, son?"

Hank stammered something inaudible. He sat staring down at the thick wool broadloom. Bobby Jay's walnut desk seemed to sink a good four inches into it.

"Of course we do, of course we do," Bobby Jay said for him. His smile widened under his hawk nose. His small gray eyes glittered like manic jewels in deep caves. "You trust the director and the other boys on the cameras to do their jobs right. I trust you to focus your camera and keep me looking good for our brothers and sisters at home, don't I now? And Lord Jesus trusts me to do a good job for him. Why, Lord Jesus trusts in *all* of us as much as we trust in him. Praise the Lord, Hank. Praise him."

"Oh, yes, sir, Reverend. Praise the Lord. Praise—"

"Hank," Bobby Jay cut in, taking control of the ball and running with it. "Hank, there comes a time when a man—and I'm not saying 'person' here, I'm saying 'man' and I mean 'man'—well, son, there comes a time when a *man's* got to make a choice. A man's got to make a *choice* concerning . . . trust. A man's got to say *who* he's going to trust. A man's got to know *when* his trust is being tested. A man has got to—"

"*I'm sorry*!" Hank sobbed. "Oh God, Reverend Jay, I'm so sorry. I'm so, so sorry." The cameraman leaned forward in his chair and blubbered into his hands.

"Well, of course you are, son. I know you're sorry. Why, Louella knows you're sorry. But the question you have to be asking yourself, the question you have to be looking into your own heart to answer, is . . . does the *Lord* know you're sorry?" Bobby Jay watched the quaking form of the cameraman and felt the excitement start to tingle within him. Louella and he had done it again. Another was saved. He could feel this man before him breaking down all the barriers that stood between him and salvation. Bobby Jay licked his lips with the trembling thrill of it.

"I was so sinful, Reverend Jay. So, so sinful." Hank was twitching like a naked nerve. He hadn't realized that the reverend had yet to accuse him of anything.

"Well, son, that's what I wanted to talk to you about. 'Cause you see, *I* don't think that *you* think that what you did *was* sinful." Reverend Jay liked this next part best of all. He threw a switch on his desk and a motorized track clacked into motion and drew the drapes over the wraparound twenty-story view of the ongoing construction of Bobby Jay's greatest vision. He threw a few more switches and the rerun of his latest show—number 939, taped live at America's Glory—disappeared from the bank of monitors on the far wall. Another image replaced it. For a moment, someone might have mistaken it for another segment of the "Good News Glory Show" because Louella Jay was on the screen, lips trembling and mascara running. But after a few seconds it was apparent that this was nothing that the brothers and sisters at home had ever seen before. Louella Jay was on the screen but she wasn't wearing any clothes, and Hank Drummond, cameraman, was up there with her in the same condition.

"Straighten up there, son, and take a gander. Now, does that *look* as if you thought what you were doing was *sinful?*"

Hank looked up and wiped at his eyes to clear them. He stared at the monitors, trying to decipher what he saw moving there. Bobby Jay hit another switch. Familiar gasps and groans filled the room. Hank Drummond's eyes literally bulged from his head. It was one thing for Reverend Jay to have known, about this, but to have *seen* it . . .

Hank slumped to the floor, clutching at his chest. Moist wheezing sounds struggled from his throat. Bobby Jay shook his head, pulled a bottle of Jack Daniel's out of his desk, and went around to help the poor man back into his chair.

"Now straighten up there, son. You did it once. The sin's no greater for seeing it a second time. Have a drink of this." He held the bottle to Hank's mouth and poured some in. "Praise the Lord now, son, and take a deep breath."

After a minute, Hank sat still upon his chair. His blank face showed a man devoid of all hope, devoid of all sensation. The private revival session he had shared with Louella kept rolling silently past on the monitors but he just didn't see it anymore.

"Feel better now, son?" Bobby Jay asked.

"Yes, sir." Hank's voice was dull and flat.

"Like to talk about it, son?"

"Not much to say, Reverend."

"How about a 'Praise the Lord,' Hank. Things aren't as bad as they seem."

"Sir?"

"Well now, I know what you're probably thinking, Hank. You're thinking, 'How can I go on?' Is that right? You're thinking, 'I've gone and done something terrible sinful. Why, I've gone and done something terrible *stupid*. I've gone and boffed Louella Jay!' Isn't that right, son?"

"Reverend Jay, sir, I—"

"Now don't go interrupting, Hank. Let's not add discourtesy to the list, all right now? As I was saying, you're probably thinking you're finished here at America's Glory. Heck, you're probably thinking you're finished all over television—Christian television, secular television, the whole shebang. But I'm telling you, that . . . might not be the case. I'm telling you . . . you've still got a chance. And your *chance* is to *choose*, Hank Drummond. Remember what I was saying before? Your *chance* is to *choose* . . . the *Lord*. Do you hear me? I said, do you *hear* me?"

"Y . . . yes, sir." Drummond looked at Reverend Jay in wonderment. His face said it all: A chance? A choice? There's a way out?

"Well then, son, *take* that chance! *Make* that choice! Get down, I say, get *down* on your knees and go *up* to Jee-sus. Can you do that, Hank? Can you confess to the Lord Jee-sus? Can you tell Jee-sus *you* are a *sinner*?"

Hank slipped down to his knees and clasped his hands before him. "Oh, yes, Reverend Jay. Oh, yes, I'm a sinner."

"Well don't stop now, son. Keep going. Tell Jee-sus. Tell him what kind of sinner you are." Bobby Jay was on a roll now, pacing back and forth, hands chopping the air, pointing the way for all sinners.

Hank rocked back and forth on his knees. Hank and Louella rocked back and forth on the monitor. Bobby Jay knelt down beside him.

"Keep going, Hank. Keep telling the Lord. *Tell* him what a sinner you are. *Show* him what a sinner you are. Show him, Hank. Look on the television. Look inside your own lustful heart. Show the Lord Jee-sus what a lustful sinner you are."

"I don't understand, Reverend Jay," Hank said. He hadn't heard about 'showing' before. "Help me understand."

With the beneficent smile that brought joy and peace to thousands of brothers and sisters at home every week, Reverend Jay nodded with the blessing of the Lord.

"All you had to do was ask, Hank. I'll help you *find* Jee-sus. I'll help you *show* what a sinner you are. Better take off those clothes, son."

* * *

Louella Jay rewound Drummond's tape on the VCR, ejected it, and slipped it into her purse. It would join the others in their private library in the new studio. Bobby Jay toasted her with a glass of Jack Daniel's.

"Praise the Lord, I say."

"Praise Bobby Jay is what I say," Louella purred as she sat on the reverend's desk.

Bobby Jay admired his wife's thighs as they strained against her dress. "Keep sitting like that, swee'pea, and I'll have to go shutting those curtains again."

Louella turned on her best southern belle. "I suppose whatever you want to do to me would serve me right for being such a sinful temptress." She started to giggle and Bobby Jay joined her. "I never knew it could be so rewarding doing the Lord's work till I met you, Bobby Jay."

Louella leaned over and kissed her husband. When she came up for air she said, "Mmmm. Much better than that horrible Hank Drummond."

"I can see a lot on that tape, swee'pea, but I can't see everything. You're going to have to tell me all about it tonight."

"I'll tell you all about it right now, Bobby Jay."

"Swee'pea," the reverend protested, "I've got to meet with Randolph in five minutes." He took her hands from him. "You just think about who we're going to win over for the Lord next."

Louella leaned back on her elbows, straining even more of herself against her dress. "It has to be that new girl in makeup. Honestly, I don't think personnel checked her background at all. You know she's told me a different story the two times I asked her what church she used to attend before moving down here. The girl has to be brought to the Lord. And it will give you something to tell *me* about, too."

Bobby Jay slipped the bottle of Jack Daniel's back into the drawer and straightened up the files on his desk. "Now, don't you go taking this too lightly, swee'pea. No one comes to the Lord until they've seen the error of their ways. We help them see what depths of degradation are already in their hearts so that they are ready to be saved. This is serious work. There's no pleasure in it till we see their faces uplifted to the Lord."

Louella studied her husband's face carefully. They had been

playing this game so close to the edge for so many years now, she really couldn't tell what he was thinking anymore. Perhaps it wasn't like the traveling show days. Perhaps he really meant it now.

"Of course, Bobby Jay. Why else would we be doing it?" She got off the desk and straightened her clothes. Randolph Dewitt had been producing the "Good News Glory Show" ever since it began four years ago. He was firmly in the Lord's fold and hadn't needed the inspiration that Louella and Bobby Jay so selflessly gave to the other, less fortunate members of their staff. Which, Louella sometimes found herself thinking, was a bit of a shame. Randolph's good looks and thoughtful, calm nature were powerfully appealing to her. To say nothing of her curiosity about what happened to that flame-red hair of his beyond the few little tufts she had seen bristling enticingly over his open shirt collar.

"Are you going to be needing me for this meeting, Bobby Jay?"

"Not today, swee'pea. We're just going over a few equipment lists for the new studio downstairs. Tomorrow, though, we'll be having another planning meeting for the Labor Day special. Sure would be nice if you helped out on that one. Like to get Chuck to get a few new songs written for you."

The chime sounded on the desk phone. The receptionist announced Randolph Dewitt. Louella blew a kiss to her husband and left through the side door just as Randolph came in through the main ones. Bobby Jay pulled the bottle of Jack Daniel's out of the drawer again. Not only was Randolph a good Christian, he also knew how to hold a good meeting.

Over the first shot, Randolph passed across a copy of the equipment list for the new television studio being prepared twenty stories below them in the America's Glory Corporate Center tower, the tallest structure in America's Glory. Production would start to swing over there from the old studio in the basement of the Bible college on the other side of the America's Glory complex by July, and the equipment specifications had been finalized months ago. Bobby Jay just liked to have something to show in case Louella asked how the meeting went.

Over the second shot, Randolph got down to the real business.

"The pledge projections are off again, Bobby Jay. Those damn computer maniacs have started up again." Bobby Jay nodded resignedly. All the Christian shows that relied on public donations faced the problem. Certain misguided souls who thought there was no glory in being called on to give as much as possible to the Lord's work used their home computers to block the Prayer Lines. They wrote programs that instructed their computers to call the Prayer Line numbers twenty-four hours a day. Every time their calls were answered, the computers would disconnect and call again. Not only were the calls costing the organization fifty cents for each toll-free connection, the brothers and sisters at home who tried to call in with their offerings kept getting busy signals. Once a year, it seemed, the phone companies came up with a new way to stop the calls, and, inevitably, about two months later, the hackers would figure out how to defeat it and the calls would begin again.

"Can we trace whoever's doing it this time?" the reverend asked.

"We're working on it, Bobby Jay. Whatever kind of computer is calling is real fast, so we have to rent some equipment that's even faster so we can trace the calls before it disconnects."

"How much?"

"Five thousand a week."

"AT&T has the nerve to charge us five thousand dollars to trace someone interfering with our phone lines?"

"I didn't go to the phone company, Bobby Jay. If they find out about it, we'll have to go to court like Jerry Falwell. I know you like to deal with matters like this in a more direct way, once we know who to go after. Don't you agree?"

Bobby Jay smiled. As always, Randolph was right. "Direct action is the best action. Praise the Lord." The last thing Bobby Jay needed in his organization was contact with a bureaucracy, AT&T, IRS, whatever. The Lord's work was too important to be subject to all the rules and regulations that the rest of the world needed. Why, Bobby Jay had often thought, if we were all Christian we wouldn't need any laws at all. But in the meantime, he reflected, it was a blessing that his organization was large enough to include just the sort of people who could carry out the type of problem solving Randolph was planning. Directly and without recourse to legal channels.

Over the third shot, red cheeks now matching the short curls on his head, Randolph moved on to something a bit more interesting.

"From New York," he said. "We've got a report from a brother in the archdiocese office. If it's true . . ." Randolph shrugged.

"What are our misguided Catholic brothers attempting to do now? Build bingo parlors in Calcutta?"

Randolph slid a file across the reverend's desk. "I think you better read it yourself, Bobby Jay. I'm not even sure I understand half of it."

Bobby Jay opened the file and began to skim. After two pages he looked up and said, "Are you sure this isn't a joke of some kind?" Randolph shook his head. Bobby Jay read seven more pages. He poured a fourth shot. Behind him the sun had set and the naked bulbs strung around the America's Glory construction site twinkled into life.

"They are actually forming a committee to look into this? They actually believe this might be real?" Bobby Jay bit at his lower lip.

Randolph nodded. "Apparently they have technical documentation. They're setting up a committee to examine it and then, if it checks out, report to the Vatican."

Bobby Jay felt the room spin around him. "*This* could be the proof we need, Randolph. This could be the proof the whole *world* needs."

Randolph watched the war of emotions raging across the reverend's face. "What does it mean, Bobby Jay?"

"If it's true, it means that we may be among the most fortunate of people ever to have lived throughout the whole six thousand years of this world's history." Bobby Jay stood up and went to the window. Stars shone above and lights below. "If it's true, brother Randolph, it means that there might be no more history!" The reverend turned back to Randolph. This time his smile was something more than saved, something more than sane. "And won't that be a blessing?"

SIX

After twelve years as a detective, Julian Burch had learned how to plan the perfect murder. Now he was ready to commit it.

Captain Jenkins had suggested that Burch stick to his desk while the investigation into the sudden collapse of the mayor's Special Task Force on Youth Gangs proceeded. Burch's countersuggestion of taking some time off had been gratefully accepted. That gave him the time he needed to set up his alibi, though he doubted it would come to that. *El Niño* had enough enemies on his own before Homicide would start suspecting a cop had nailed him. This was going to work out just fine.

It was just an hour after sunset as Burch crossed over 112th, weaving as he walked. He wore secondhand work clothes and a Goodwill jacket which he had trampled in dirt. He hadn't bathed or shaved for three days and a miasma of Bay Rum hovered around him. From time to time he spoke to the empty air and spat onto the sidewalk. With each jarring step, the piece strapped to his ankle thudded reassuringly. No one gave him a second glance. I love New York, he thought.

Right now, his car was parked outside a condo in Tampa and his Master Card was being used in a bar with lap dancers who wouldn't be inclined to remember a face. The friend who was using the card, who had diligently practiced Burch's signature without asking questions, was also a police officer. A real police officer, Burch thought. Not like that bleeding heart baby face Hyams.

Burch turned down the half-gutted street where *El Niño* kept his headquarters. He figured he would sit on a nearby stoop for a few hours until the leader of all the gangs appeared. Then he'd pop him in a hallway, head back to the Port Authority locker for a change of clothes, hit a Times Square room-by-the-hour for a shower and shave, get a red-eye flight cash ticket, and be back in Tampa in time to be seen having a late breakfast. All over and done with before Forensics had time to finish scraping *El*-fuckin'-*Niño*'s brains off the wall. The detective had to concentrate to keep himself from whistling.

El Niño showed up within the hour. It was Burch's lucky night.

He had come back early because he could feel another attack coming on and he couldn't risk anyone except Johnny seeing him that way. It would undermine all he had set out to do. The gangs would disintegrate and all their energy would be directed against each other once again, instead of their real enemies: the suits and the uniforms and the *anglos* who wore them. Three more months, he had told them, three more months and five more gangs and all the other holdouts would cave in. Then the real negotiations would begin, starting with the mayor. *El Niño* stumbled on the sidewalk as another jolt twisted up the side of his neck and head. Johnny Matches caught his arm and kept him upright.

"Almost there, Paul. Another few feet, man." Matches kept *El Niño* moving. The jolts were coming more frequently. Within minutes his friend would be completely out of it, writhing on the floor and speaking nonsense. Paul had told Johnny that he had looked it up in some books. He said it was epilepsy. He said Julius Caesar had it too, so that it was cool. As long as he didn't break down during negotiations. Once August came around and his position was assured, it didn't matter if anyone found out. Johnny wasn't convinced but whatever *El Niño* said was all right by him.

They came to the building where Paul's parents used to live and where Paul still kept the apartment. He didn't have to pay for it because as long as he was there, the landlord didn't have to worry about things getting broken or burned, including himself. It was a fair arrangement.

Johnny checked the street. It had been a long time since there had been real trouble between the Silver Kings and the other gangs, but the old habits were hard to shake. A couple of kids were leaning against the shell of a completely stripped car. A wino was sleeping it off on a stoop across the street. Everything looked cool.

"Here we are, man," Johnny said. He guided his friend up

the worn stone steps to the lobby doors. The glass had been replaced by plywood years ago, the handles by twisted loops of insulated wire. He wrenched open the doors and half pushed Paul through. The door creaked shut behind them. Across the street, the wino woke up.

In the dim light from a naked twenty-five-watt bulb, Johnny waved to the landlord when he saw the ex-wrestler peering through the crack of his door. The landlord had a baseball bat back there, Johnny knew, black with electrician's tape and bristling with nails. He hadn't had to use it since *El Niño* came to stay. But the old habits were hard to shake for everyone in this city. The landlord's door closed. Paul grimaced again and clutched at his head. Johnny led him to the dark, narrow stairs.

They were one flight up when the lobby doors opened again.

Burch held his gun ready in the ragged pocket of his jacket. He slipped into the lobby and quickly tugged the door closed behind him. He stood for a moment, squinting in the half-light, getting his bearings.

The landlord's door creaked. Burch stumbled around to face it, intent on maintaining his disguise.

"Geddaddaheayabum," the landlord snarled and pulled his door all the way open. The bums were the one thing the gangs couldn't control. But they were usually just a nuisance, not a threat.

The landlord stepped out into the lobby, yellowing undershirt taut over what once had been muscle, the baseball bat weaving back and forth like a dinosaur's spiked tail. Burch assessed the threat coolly and competently. He looked behind the landlord to see if anyone else was behind him. He glanced over to the stairway. The landlord was breathing too noisily for the detective to listen for footsteps, but Burch sensed that they had to have gone up there.

The landlord took another step, then stopped. This bum's eyes weren't yellow and red like a squashed roach. This bum wasn't slouching anymore. This bum was holding something in his pocket.

"Isedgeddaddahea!" the landlord repeated. Some of the conviction was gone from his mucous-clogged voice.

Like a card counter in Vegas, Burch ran a quick assessment of the odds. Then he fired through his pocket, a silenced *phht*. The landlord's brains blossomed from his skull and his body slumped stupidly back to sit against the wall. The business end of the baseball bat prickled through the side of his right leg. Burch was on the stairs before the first drop of blood leaked onto the cracked floor tiles.

The detective stopped on the second floor. Ancient paper, pattern long faded, curled from the wall and rasped against him. He held his breath. Motionless, he listened and observed. His instincts told him they weren't on that floor.

Third floor. The same. Fourth floor. No light in the hall. He looked into the shadows. To the side of his vision where night sensitivity was the greatest, he could see a dangling wire and socket still swinging from the flaking ceiling. A faint glimmer of glass came from the coarse weave of the thread-bare carpet directly beneath it. The bulb had just been broken. He trusted his instincts. It was this floor.

Burch flattened himself against the greasy wall. He held his gun stretched out before him. Slowly, like torturously exquisite foreplay, he eased down the hallway. *El Niño* was his.

After ten feet, he stopped. There was a flimsy wooden door three feet ahead and across from him. Pale light from the street-lamp beyond the dirt-coated window at the end of the hall shone dully. Burch could see that the door's surface was scratched and dented and the number 47 was written on it in chalk. He could also see that the hinges were secure and the door was tight in its frame. If they broke the light, he thought, then they're hiding on this floor. And if they're hiding, then they didn't belong on this floor and they wouldn't have a key to get into an apartment. He moved on, knowing what to look for.

The next door was on his side. It was intact. He moved on. The next door was across from him. The frame was sprung. Burch felt calm move through him. The threat of *El Niño* was ended.

He listened carefully. He heard a muffled thumping noise coming from the apartment. Moving furniture against the door, he thought. He crossed over to the other wall. He reached out his empty hand to touch the door. It moved infinitesimally beneath his touch. It wasn't locked and it wasn't barricaded.

* * *

Johnny looked up as the door slammed open. It was the wino. He should have suspected.

The wino had a gun. Johnny recognized Detective Burch.

"What the fuck are you doing, man?" Johnny screamed at the detective. The boy was kneeling on the floor, Paul's head in his lap. It was Paul's feet that thumped erratically on the floor as his body writhed.

"Well, ain't this cute?" Burch said with delight. "I got me a couple of big tough faggots here. What do you think the Stalkers are going to do when they hear *El*-fuckin'-*Niño* and his best pal are cocksucking little faggots, Matches?" Burch almost wished he had brought a camera for this part. Not that there was anyone to whom he could show the photos.

"He's having an attack, Burch," Johnny said, trying to hold Paul's head still. A piece of wood wrapped in the sleeve of an old shirt was in Paul's mouth. He frothed against it.

"On bad smack, too?" Burch said. "My oh my. Too bad I didn't come here to arrest him."

Johnny tensed as he realized what Burch had just said. The detective was closing the apartment door behind him. There were no other police officers in on this.

"What are you talking about, man?" Paul had stopped writhing. His back was arching as if someone was trying to pick him up by his belt.

"I'm talking about putting your friend out of his misery, Matches. I'm talking about the way you made a fool out of me in the lot last week. How did you do that?"

"Easy to make a fool out of you," Johnny sneered.

Burch sneered back and kicked the boy on the side of his head. Johnny went sprawling across the room.

"I mean how did you manage that little trick out there with Ramirez and the knife?"

Johnny pushed himself up from the floor. His ears rang and he could taste blood in his mouth. Paul was curled up on his side. He was snarling.

"What trick, man?"

"When Ramirez sliced open your fuckin' throat, you little bastard. What was it? A blood bag? A rubber knife? You set me up with that.'' Burch kept his gun trained on Johnny. *El Niño* was no threat to anyone right now.

''I don't know what you're talking about, Burch. You came to me to set up Paul in a drug buy. So I got to Paul and tell him what you're planning and he sets it up so there's no buy and you cops crawl out from under your rocks and blow surveillance. That wasn't no trick.''

''You slimy little maggot,'' Burch said, all calm leaving him. ''You want to find out what it really feels like to have your throat ripped open?'' He raised his gun to fire. *El Niño* sat up like a puppet being jerked to life.

Burch looked over at the sudden movement.

''Holy shit . . .'' he said. His mouth hung open.

El Niño twisted his head around to Burch and stared at him with eyes that were pure and solid white.

''What's *wrong* with him?'' Burch croaked.

El Niño rose slowly from the floor. It took Burch a few seconds to understand that the boy's legs weren't moving. They weren't even in contact with the floor. *El Niño* was floating.

Burch stepped back. He tried to say something more but nothing would come out. He aimed the gun at the thing in the air. Johnny screamed and jumped for Burch's arm. The gun exploded into Johnny's chest.

Burch froze against the wall, as far back as he could be. Somewhere beneath the twice-dead body of Johnny Matches was his gun, lost in the gore. But his instincts told him the gun would be no use against what faced him now.

Five feet before him, two feet off the floor, *El Niño* stood in midair, hovering like an astronaut far from Earth. His eyes blazed white and from his mouth a thousand voices came. Burch felt his bladder go. He couldn't breathe.

The floating boy raised his hand. It blocked the light that streamed from his eyes, fingers causing ripples of light and shadow like sunbeams in deep water.

''I see green fields and blue skies,'' breathed a voice within the voices. ''I see white clouds and a golden sun.''

He lowered his hand. Dark, dark eyes looked out now. The voice within the voices spoke to Burch, entered into him, told him to pick up his gun. Told him what to do with it.

"*Nooo!*" the detective screamed as the words formed ideas within his mind. "*Nooo!*" he pleaded as he knelt to the floor and reached beneath the moist, dripping ruin of Johnny's body. His blood-soaked hands closed on the warm, wet metal of his gun and slipped it from the thickening pool.

"I can move my hand and cover the clouds," the floating boy said.

Burch brought the slick glistening barrel to his mouth. He tasted the blood upon it.

"Even the sun," Burch heard him say.

And then there was only endless silence.

SEVEN

All through dessert, a quiveringly sweet baked pear, Susan Foster thought of the proper way to frame her question—present her suspicions, actually. Father Francis Panati had been an ideal dinner companion, beginning with his choice of restaurant—Carolina's. As a professor of history at St. Joseph's, as well as holding seats on a number of advisory boards, he had a wonderful store of anecdotes—none of which he had repeated from the last time they had met more than a year earlier—and a surprisingly liberal public relations expense account. Unfortunately, although he was trying to offer her an exciting opportunity, as a journalist and, she supposed, as a woman, Foster was convinced that Father Panati was lying through his Catholic teeth.

"Is that pear saying something to you?" she vaguely heard Panati ask.

"Sorry?"

Father Panati laughed. He laughed a great deal. Where some men his age—mid-fifties, Foster guessed—carried the wrinkled legacy of a life of work and worry, Father Panati shamelessly showed the deep lines and friendly crinkles of a lifetime of smiling. He wasn't a handsome man, but the warmth of his face above his Roman collar made that hard to see.

"I didn't think you were all here," he said. "Now, if you were a Catholic, you could claim to be having a vision of the infinite. But I'd guess you were thinking of, oh, redecorating your apartment. Or the book offers you'll get when the committee's work is made public." He winked at her like a favorite uncle.

"Nothing of the sort." Foster looked around to check on other diners. So far, the only other people in the back room of the restaurant were seated on the other side of the central tree. A string of small white lights was entwined in its branches, multiplied in streaks and smears within the slanted glass of the skylight. But the shows would start letting out soon and their privacy wouldn't last.

"Francis, how often do priests have to go to confession?" she asked abruptly. Panati had insisted on the "Francis" and she was still getting used to it.

The priest seemed surprised by the sudden change in topic, although Foster suspected he was used to the conversations he took part in suddenly changing to religious discussions. "Most of us *should* go every day, I would think. Generally though, once a week, a month, or whenever we find it necessary. Why?"

"I was wondering if you'd have to confess what you've been saying to me this evening." Foster leaned forward from the banquette and sipped at her coffee. Panati narrowed his eyes but didn't say anything. That was the moment she knew she was on the right track, even if she didn't know where it was leading.

"I've interviewed a lot of people in my time, Francis. Some are like little kids. I ask them a question and they just spew out all sorts of information because they're so excited that someone takes an interest in their work. A lot of scientists are like that. Then there're the people with something to hide. They're pretty evident because they don't say anything. They won't even talk about the weather. And then, there are people like you."

"And we are?" Panati asked, leaning back in his chair, his face serious despite the smile lines.

"People who try to keep something hidden by misdirection. They don't try to lie about anything, necessarily. But they do tend to obscure things by getting other people—award-winning science writers for example—to pay attention to other information." Foster batted her eyes at him. She held two awards from the American Association for the Advancement of Science for articles which had appeared in national science magazines.

"What do you think I'm trying to obscure, Susan?"

Foster checked the dining room again and leaned closer over the table.

"I think there's as much chance for the Pope to reverse the *Humanae Vitae* encyclical prohibiting artificial birth control as there is a chance for the next Pope to be a woman. I think everything you've told me tonight about the work your planning committee is doing in support of that reversal is a smokescreen so you can pick my brains about the other, *minor* areas of biological research that you say you're conducting as a footnote to your main goal."

Panati regarded Foster with even concentration. "And in what minor area of research do you think the committee's main goal really lies?" he asked without inflection. "—assuming that I *am* trying to misdirect you?" It was the moment of truth. Put up or shut up, he was saying to her.

Foster had three choices, three topics that Panati had glossed over during their discussions as being side issues tenuously connected with a sweeping new Vatican statement on bioscience, concentrating on relaxing the prohibition of artificial birth control. She studied Panati's eyes carefully. She decided his Jesuit training was paying off because, now that he had been warned, he wasn't giving up anything.

She thought back over all he had told her that evening. He had talked about steroid suppression of the immunoresponse in ova. Theoretically, this would allow human sperm to fertilize nonhuman primate eggs. A whole new class of animal could arise, smarter than apes, less than human, a perfect slave for a high-tech world and clearly abhorrent to the Church. Panati had also mentioned cloning as an area under investigation. Specifically, the molecular excision of the genes that control the formation of particular organs so that extra hearts and livers might be grown *in vitro* for transplant back into the donor without fear of rejection. And there was hybridized parthenogenesis. By exposing a human egg to an acid present in sperm, the egg could be induced to begin fission without being fertilized. Individuals could be produced who had genes derived from only one parent. Additionally, by introducing a second egg, it would be possible to produce an individual with genes from two mothers, or from two mothers and two fathers or almost any other combination. Where was the clue that would give one topic weight over another?

Then she had it. Misdirection. It wasn't the topic with the most weight. It was the one with the least. The Catholic Church had absolutely banned the manipulation and misuse of human genetic material in 1987. But aside from the ethical considerations of deciding when to harvest organs, it had never had any problems with the practice of transplants. Why was that included among the committee's goals? Not for the result, but for the method, Foster decided. Time for my best guess, she thought. All or nothing.

"Francis, it is transparently obvious that someone in the Church thinks that somewhere out there, someone else has successfully, and inevitably I must add, produced a set of genetically identical people. Human clones."

Jesuit training or no Jesuit training, nothing could stop the look of surprise that appeared on Panati's face. He took a quick gulp of brandy to kick-start his vocal cords.

"Tell me one thing," he finally said in a subdued voice. "*Am* I that transparent or did someone else get in touch with you?"

Foster could tell that Panati was more concerned with someone else being involved than he was with her being part of it. She answered truthfully.

"I had to work at it, but I did figure it out just from what you told me. You find this very serious, don't you?"

Panati nodded. "Don't you?"

"As I said, I really do think it's inevitable. Cloning's been around since the early sixties. Even earlier, if you read Ira Levin. As I recall, the first organism cloned was a carrot. But from the very beginning there was speculation that the procedure could be adapted to animal cells."

"Which, of course, it was," Panati offered.

"Tadpoles first. Then newts. The big breakthrough came when they were finally able to clone mammalian cells: our little friends, the laboratory mice."

"And if mice can be cloned, why not other mammals? Why not humans?" Panati asked, very seriously.

"This is what you really wanted me for, wasn't it? You wanted to be able to ask a bunch of revealing questions without tipping your hand to a real, live biologist. Right?'' Foster smiled at Panati's embarrassed shrug of admission.

Panati glanced around the room. Another couple had been seated and was obviously discussing various theories concerning why a priest and an attractive woman were leaning over a table and whispering to each other.

''Let's go for a walk,'' Panati suggested and signaled to the waiter for the check.

Foster sat back in the banquette and felt satisfyingly pleased with herself. Whoever would have thought that a dinner date with a priest could be so much fun?

They walked against the show crowds toward Times Square. Though the natural thing to do would have been for one to have taken the other's arm so they could stay close enough to talk while they walked, Foster felt uneasy about compromising Panati's friendship before a group of strangers. His collar placed his every action under unforgiving scrutiny. It seemed to be the right choice, though awkward. But after a few blocks of shared apologies and repetitions, the crowds thinned out and they were able to walk more slowly and speak more clearly. They still drew stares when people passed by.

''Does that bother you at all?'' Foster asked.

''Twenty years ago, it might have. Today, not at all. Those people will think whatever they're thinking even if I float down the street accompanied by angels. I prefer to concentrate on those things I have a chance of accomplishing. However slim.''

''Seems reasonable,'' Foster agreed. ''Is this cloning investigation, or whatever it is, something you feel you have a chance at?''

Panati walked for a few feet in silence, weighing what he would say next.

''Chance has nothing to do with it. It must be done.''

''I thought the Church supported fertility research.''

''Oh, the Church is always eager to increase its flock. Sometimes a bit too eager, if you ask me. But I think this matter goes beyond fertility research. Back in the restaurant, why did you say that the cloning of people was inevitable?''

''Because it is. Foster's first law: anything that can be done will be done. And in this case, I'm assuming, has already been done. It *is* what you're investigating, isn't it?" Foster didn't like talking on the go like this. It made it difficult to watch Panati's face to compare what he was thinking with what he was saying.

"Oh, that's what it is, all right. But, even if you think it is inevitable, why haven't we heard of it being done up to now?"

"Two answers to that one, Francis. The first is technical problems. To clone a tadpole, say, the nucleus is removed from an egg cell and replaced with the nucleus from almost any other cell from the body. A normal egg nucleus has only half the chromosomes needed to produce an individual. Usually a sperm cell provides the other half. In cloning, the egg cell with the transplanted nucleus starts dividing with a full complement of chromosomes from the very beginning and grows into an exact duplicate of the parent. That is, whatever individual supplied the transplanted nucleus."

"So if they can do that with frog cells, what are the technical problems they experience with human cells?"

"Size is the big problem. The human egg is so small that most standard techniques for removing the nucleus, micro-surgery or laser, cause too much damage. The problem is even worse with the donor cells because, small as it is, the egg cell is the largest cell in the human body. Another problem is creating the proper nutrient environment for the cloned cell, assuming the nucleus transplant can be achieved. But that's actually the lesser of the two. A viable cloned cell wouldn't be appreciably different from a normally fertilized zygote. Just pop it into a uterus and nine months later out comes a clone." Foster was pleasantly surprised she was remembering all this. She hadn't written anything about cloning for at least two years.

Panati stopped walking. He turned to Foster. His expression said that she was telling him things he might have already suspected but dreaded having confirmed.

"The same procedure as *in vitro* fertilization you mean? Combining sperm and egg in a petri dish and then replacing them in the mother's body when fertilization occurs?"

"Exactly the same." Foster felt her first suspicion that there was something more than cloning going on in the conversation. "That's the second answer to your question about why it hasn't been tried with humans."

"What answer is that?" Panati acted like a man who had just lost an important fight. His eyes actually looked haunted.

"That human cloning has already been achieved but because of the legal and, I suppose, ethical entanglements, whoever has done it isn't advertising."

"A secret laboratory somewhere?"

"Wouldn't have to be. A single cell doesn't need much to hide it. The work could be carried out in the open at, say, a fertility clinic. Lots of those around these days. Who's to say whether or not all the fertilized egg cells being implanted *are* fertilized egg cells. They could just as easily be clones."

Even under the streetlamps, Foster could tell Panati was turning paler.

"This is really hitting home with you, isn't it, Francis?" She was starting to feel concerned. What else was worrying the Church here?

"How about a chemical method of nucleus transplant?"

The question was so unexpected Foster knew it had to be important. "Is that the procedure supposedly used in the claim you're investigating?" she asked. Panati sighed and nodded.

"It's certainly a method being studied," she continued. "Isolating or creating specific enzymes to dissolve the nucleus of an egg cell and everything but the nucleus of another cell. There wouldn't be any danger of physical damage to the cell or nucleus. I'd say it's as much a possibility as anything else."

"Would it have been a possibility fourteen years ago?"

Foster whistled. They'd be almost full grown if it was true. "I take it you have good documentation for this procedure?" she asked.

"Fourteen-year-old documentation," Panati answered. "*Would* it have been a possibility then? A chemical transplant? Uterine implantation?"

Foster thought for a moment, trying to remember the dates of the research announcements she had discussed. "Unlikely," she finally said. "But not impossible."

"What would be required?"

"In terms of equipment, nothing special. Even for fourteen years ago. All someone would have needed was the technique. A lucky break or an inspired discovery. Either way it definitely would have been possible."

"I think I have to sit down," Panati sighed. "Let's get a taxi."

Despite her earlier reservations, Foster took the priest's arm. He looked as if he needed the support.

"Why is this so important, Francis? How can it be so upsetting? Surely the church has had to come to grips with other scientific breakthroughs. After all, human clones would really be no different from identical twins. They're just more of them." Then it hit her. "How many of them *are* there, Francis?"

"We're not sure," he said like a man in a dream. "Twenty. Thirty. We're trying to track them down."

"But what's the problem with that? How does the Church respond when a woman on fertility drugs gives birth to quintuplets? Septuplets? I don't understand why you're reacting this way to something that, in the end, is really no more than a simple laboratory procedure." Two taxis rushed by while Foster and Panati faced each other on the curb.

"It's not the procedure so much as it's . . . it's the . . . donor. I suppose donor is the proper word."

"The donor? You mean the individual being cloned? What's the problem with that? Is it a criminal? The Pope? Who could it be to upset you this way?"

Father Panati took a deep, deep breath. He held Susan Foster by her shoulders and for the first time in a long time that evening, he looked directly into her eyes. This time, he was obscuring nothing.

"What do you know about a holy relic called the Shroud of Turin?"

Foster started to answer before her brain caught up to what Panati was saying. "Some people claim it's the burial cloth of —"

And then she truly knew what Father Panati was investigating. The world rushed away from her in the impact of that knowledge. There was no city around her, no traffic noise, no sidewalk beneath her feet. Only the tear-filled eyes of a Catholic priest, and she couldn't tell if those tears were of joy or of utter fear.

"Jesus Christ," she whispered.

EIGHT

There were a couple of restaurants called David's in and around Washington, D.C., but the only one that mattered was the David's where the CIA ran the bar. Or so the rumor went.

First and foremost, it was private, a luxurious jewel box of a building, with ornately carved oak walls transported from an eighteenth-century English estate, gleaming brass from three generations of distinguished naval vessels, and Baccarat crystal set up at the bar. After that, the unstated amenities took over. Things like ongoing sweeps of all surfaces and furniture to ensure against electronic eavesdroppers. No windows, so vibrating panes couldn't transmit conversations over inquisitive laser beams. And staff like Max at the bar, a portly white-haired cherub with a security clearance high enough that any minor indiscretion on the part of his clients wouldn't result in an unfortunate incident.

Some people in D.C. had very unforgiving jobs. When those people felt the need to sit in a bar and perhaps have one drink too many, they didn't have to risk a public place. They could come to David's. Though no one had ever met him, it was common knowledge that David was your friend when no one else could be. Dean Fuller hadn't been there in years.

"Good to see you again, sir," Max said as Fuller sat down at the bar. "Glenfiddich?" he asked.

Fuller had cut back on whiskey in the years he hadn't been coming to David's, but he was so impressed with Max's recall that he couldn't say no.

"Thank you, Max. That will be fine," he said and watched as the white-jacketed man, as neat and crisp as any admiral in dress uniform, seemed to pull bottle and glass from thin air.

"You're looking well, Max," Fuller said as his drink was poured.

"Thank you, sir," the bartender replied, then paused for a

moment. "I may not be the Max you're remembering, sir. I believe you haven't been by for a while."

"Almost five years," Fuller said, puzzled.

"Well, then, the Max you're remembering passed away last year, sir."

"I'm sorry to hear that," Fuller said with conviction.

"Yes, sir. We all shared the loss." The bartender nodded sagely as if commenting on some great truth.

"I'm also sorry to have confused you with him," Fuller went on. "I've called you by his name."

"Oh," the bartender suddenly smiled, "it's my name, too, sir. We're all Max here." Max dipped his head in a short salute and moved down the bar to another cluster of stools and clients. Fuller sat alone, trying to avoid thinking how everything had changed, though nothing had. Then the President's assistant chief of staff tapped his shoulder and said his name.

In any other restaurant in the city, the intense good looks of Thomas Jefferson would have caused heads to turn and conversations to buzz. He was seen so often on television, generally standing about three feet back from the President and two feet over, that his movie star features were almost as recognizable as his boss's. His name added even more patriotic strength to his image of up-and-coming senior advisor. But this was David's. He was just another friend looking for a few quiet moments away from the crowd. No one paid him any attention, except for Max.

"Very good to see you again, Dean," Jefferson said.

"It's even better of you to see me at such short notice. I know how busy you must be with the election gearing up." Fuller really was appreciative. Many people would wait weeks, if not months, for a meeting with Jefferson. Fuller had received next-day service.

"This administration has a long memory, Dean. Anytime, and you know it."

They passed a few minutes catching up with each other. Though it was before his time, Jefferson made reference to Fuller's days in Treasury, while making it subtly apparent that he knew where Fuller had really worked. Fuller made the appropriate inquiries about Jefferson's three children and even more appropriate comments about their academic performances in grade school, kindergarten, and nursery school respectively.

"So," Jefferson said after a short pause, "I'm guessing that you called me to talk about Barbara-Jane."

Fuller raised his white eyebrows. "That's about as impressive as Max number two knowing my regular drink," he said.

"It's all on computer these days," Jefferson explained. "I gave your name when I made our reservation. They have all our past transactions recorded in a database. My office has one, too. That's where I found out that your wife called the President two days ago." He saw the unvoiced question in Fuller's eyes. "No, he's still in California. But I know he'll call her back when he returns. I gather you know what the call was about?"

Fuller nodded. "Galahad," he said.

"I've been briefed," Jefferson confirmed. "Not because of our meeting today, though. A couple of years ago, actually. Someone else suggested something similar in Reagan's second term. He had to be told that it had been tried before."

"Did they go ahead with a new operation?" Fuller asked.

"All the money goes to the environment these days. In this case, I gather that's a good thing."

"Probably is," Fuller agreed. "I think she's—no, I *know* she's having recurrences."

"Regularly?"

"Off and on. But the one she had two days ago was powerful. She had a . . . a vision I guess you'd call it."

Jefferson pursed his lips. "And there wasn't a trigger?"

"Not for years, Tom. Last one was in 'seventy-three."

"That's what I had been told. So is the . . . vision . . . why she's calling Number One?"

Fuller nodded. Somehow, he was beginning to feel embarrassed about all this. He should be living in Bermuda now. He and Barbara-Jane certainly had the money. They should be going for walks along the beaches, dressing for dinner, and not bothering the White House over something that had started almost thirty-five years ago.

"How's the New Détente working out?" Fuller asked, as if switching back to polite conversation.

Jefferson shrugged. "As far as Number One is concerned, the Soviets are still the godless monsters they've always been. But if they pull up their socks and get out of Honduras, and a few other places, then they'll be nice enough for us to get rolling on a joint Mars mission. There's an unofficial movement to issue an invitation for an American observer team to visit *Mir* station next year and a more official movement on our side to cut the number of Soviet diplomats in the U.S. by a third. Back and forth, same as always."

"Nothing major in the wind?"

Jefferson's voice became curiously flat. One didn't pump a friend for information in this town. "Nothing I'd know about," he said.

"How about August?" Fuller asked, changing the topic again. "What are the President's plans for August?"

"Campaign starts on Labor Day, Dean," Jefferson answered as if it were painfully obvious. "What do incumbents do in any August of an election year? He'll be all over this country opening everything from power plants to taco stands. What's this about?"

"How about the end of August?" Fuller held up his hand. "Humor me."

"At the end of August he'll be down south getting ready to kick off the campaign at that new Bible college or theme park or whatever it is down in Georgia. Reverend Bobby Jay's place. America's Glory."

"I thought the President intended to distance himself from the fundamentalists? Especially after that 'Sixty Minutes' piece on the New Right."

"Number One intends to win, Dean, and in his mind, forty million right-thinking, God-fearing, flag-waving Americans can't be wrong. Now what's all this about? Did Barbara-Jane see something about the election?"

Fuller thought for a long moment. "Before the election," he said.

Jefferson saw the worried expression on the old man's face. "She wants to tell the President what she saw? Not a Kennedy thing again?" Only a handful of words were not used in David's restaurant. Assassination was one of them.

"Worse," Fuller said.

"What could be worse?" Jefferson asked, eyes widening.

Fuller shifted over to the side of his stool. "How about Armageddon? How about an all-out end-of-the-world war scenario?"

"Soviets?"

"Who else, Tom?"

"End of August?"

"The twenty-ninth. She even saw the time."

"And she wants to tell the President this?"

"Come on, of course she does."

"Anyone else know?"

"Just you and me."

Jefferson sat back in his stool. He waved Max over for another round.

"I want to thank you for telling me this," he told Fuller.

"The President *does* know about the Galahad project, doesn't he?" Fuller asked. That was the crux of the matter. How much weight would the President give to Barbara-Jane's vision?

"I'm certain he would have been briefed on it long ago, but I'll see to it that it's mentioned again before he comes back and finds your wife's message to call." Jefferson was staring blindly into the wall of bottles and crystal behind the bar.

"Tom, it's not true, you know. None of them were ever true." Fuller said that as much to reassure himself as to reassure Jefferson.

Jefferson turned to him and said succinctly, "Your wife's horoscope column runs neck and neck with Jeane Dixon's, doesn't it? Two hundred? Two-fifty newspapers?"

"Oh my God. I didn't even think of that."

"Here's something else you didn't think of: Number One reads it."

Fuller felt sick. "He can't believe in her. He . . . he's the President."

Jefferson shook his head. "He's a man who believes this country needs a moral renewal. A *Christian* moral renewal. I've heard him discuss it. I've even heard him talk about Armageddon and the final war. He' a fine man, Dean. He's a great man who's given a lot to this country and I'm proud to serve him. But . . ."

"But what?" Fuller asked. There was urgency in his voice.

"Can you take Barbara-Jane out of town for a week or two? Take a short vacation? Maybe where the phones are bad?"

"Sure," Fuller said. He was halfway to planning that already.

"I'll get over to the coast so I can come back on Air Force One. That's probably the best time to get to him."

"What are you going to say?"

"I'll tell him that Barbara-Jane called. It'll give me a chance to remind him about Galahad. Set him up for remembering that whatever she tells him, it can't be true. And maybe you can work on Barbara-Jane, too. Tell her about the panic that might ensue. Get her to keep it a secret. Maybe even convince her that the vision was wrong."

"There's only one way I could do that," Fuller said.

"Tell her about Galahad?"

Fuller nodded sadly. "But if she believed me, *if* she believed me, it would destroy her. It would really, completely destroy her."

Jefferson sat quietly for a moment, understanding the grief that the old man was feeling. In his time, Dean Fuller had given a great deal to his country. It might be that he had to give even more.

"Think of the alternative," Jefferson said softly, then reached out and held Fuller's arm.

Max came back for another round. Fuller had to remind himself he was among friends.

NINE

At about ten o'clock on a Friday night in the small town of Larkin's Mill, Pennsylvania, John Danylkiw lay back on Lori Daniels's bed and began drafting his letter to *Penthouse Forum*. He had been dead-on about the effect of describing his dream about being blind. Lori had wanted to comfort him so badly that here he was, *completely naked*! and on her bed. And she was fifteen, a whole year older than he was! God, life could be good sometimes.

"Oh shit, that's my father's car!"

Lori was up and jiggling to the window before John opened his eyes. The sight of her bending over to look under the blind was enough to keep him from immediately comprehending the clear and present danger into which he had suddenly been thrust.

"Hurry! Hurry!" Lori half whispered, half shouted at him. "Get dressed." She threw him items from the common pile on the floor. His bemused realization that he was holding her underwear cost him precious seconds.

His own underwear was nowhere to be found. He pulled his jeans on and delicately tried to fasten the zipper without ripping out what few secondary sexual characteristics he had. Fortunately, the onset of panic had melted him faster than butter in a microwave. Lori threw him his shirt and his Nikes. One of the sneakers thudded to the floor. Both of them froze. They could hear the screen door open downstairs.

"*He'll kill you!*" Lori whispered deafeningly.

"Where can I hide?"

Lori waved to the right as she pulled a sweatshirt over her head. John regretfully said good-bye to his two new friends and obediently headed for the closet.

"Not there!" Lori rasped. "The window! The window!"

John's mouth fell. It was an old house. The bedroom was on the third floor.

Downstairs, Lori's dad came home. They could hear him shout hello.

"Hi, Daddy," Lori shouted back. "Be down in a second." She snapped the blind down. It jumped out of her hand and whacked up against the windowsill. John moaned. He was sure Mr. Daniels was going to come through the door at any second.

"Whacha doing up there, sweetheart?" rumbled the voice from below.

"Jane Fonda Workout, Daddy. Five more minutes!" That was good for a serious attack of the suppressed giggles while the window was opened. They stopped suddenly when John leaned out and stared down the three floors to the ground.

"I can't go out there," he said.

"There's a pipe by the chimney." Lori pointed to something small and rickety in the shadow of the brick flue. "Hurry!"

"I don't hear the music, Sweetheart," shouted Daddy. His voice was closer.

Lori fought the urge to simply push John through the window as he cautiously crawled out on the ledge cut into the slope of the roof, shoes in hand. He looked wistfully back into the only girl's bedroom he had ever been in. Lori was struggling to pull her Walkman earphones over her mussed-up hair. Then she blew him a kiss and pulled down the window and the blind. He was on his own.

"Toss the shoes!"

John heard a hoarse whisper coming from the ground. He could make out the round shape of his buddy, Jason Coyle, hiding in the bushes near the back of the driveway where he had been waiting for the promised blow-by-blow description. John lobbed the Nikes at his friend's hiding place. A poor career decision. One of them bonged onto the hood of Mr. Daniels's silver Audi. But Jason didn't even hesitate for his friend. He bounded out of the bushes like the biggest, fattest rabbit ever seen, grabbed the shoe from the hood, and burrowed back to safety within seconds. A real smooth move, John thought. Too bad I can hear him wheezing from up here.

Then he heard voices coming from behind Lori's bedroom window. He swallowed hard, leaned out into space until his fingers wrapped around the pipe in the shadow, and out he swung.

Like a dream, the first few seconds weren't too bad. He had both hands around the pipe and both feet braced against the angle of the wall and the chimney. Just like Night Crawler, he thought. He removed one hand, placed it lower on the pipe, did the same with the other and then shuffled his bare feet down the brick. By then, the adrenalin had faded and the dream came to an end. His hands ached and his feet stung. What an asshole, he thought. He heard the voices in Lori's bedroom getting louder. Like an argument.

John was able to move down three more feet before he hit the ivy growing up the side of the house. His right foot just slipped off into nothing, feeling as if it left all of its toes behind. Then his other foot lost its grip.

John dropped the length of his arms and snapped against the pipe. He was two and a half floors up, hanging on only by eight fingers wedged between the pipe and the bricks. They felt as if they were being ripped from his hands. He had no choice. He screamed.

Then he heard the chillingly familiar sound of the blind in Lori's bedroom whacking up against the windowsill. He heard the window slide up. He heard Jason muttering a few choice "oh shits" on the ground, and then the voice of doom burst upon his ears.

"What in hell do you think you're doing with my daughter!"

John looked up and saw the apoplectic face of Mr. Daniels looking down. He felt his feet struggle against the ivy, felt himself spin away from the pipe, and then he was down on the driveway tearing off between the houses with Jason wheezing along beside him and the hoarse cries of Mr. Daniels fading into the night.

The boys stopped in a small park three blocks over from Lori's street. They had at least four ways to run if a silver Audi came cruising. John sat down against an old rough tree and laughed and gasped on cool Friday night air. Eventually he noticed that Jason was sitting on the grass five feet away, also gasping but in no way laughing.

"Do you know what you did back there?" Jason asked. His eyes were round little marbles in a pudgy, pimply face.

"I think so," John laughed. "But we're going to have to look it up in your mom's *Joy of Sex* to be sure." He started giggling again. A wild woman, a breathtaking escape—he felt as if he were in a James Bond movie.

"I don't mean Lori, you gonad. I mean when you came out the window."

John blinked at the anger or whatever it was in his friend's voice. "I climbed most of the way down the pipe by the chimney, then Lori's dad stuck his head out the window and I jumped the rest of the way."

Jason shook his head ponderously. "You didn't climb down more than five feet, J.D. You jumped from over the second-floor windows."

John couldn't remember that part, but he and Jason had been buddies since grade three. He didn't think Jason was trying to shit him.

"So, I fell into the bushes. Big deal. Give me my shoes."

"You landed on the driveway, J.D. And you didn't fall." Jason tossed the Nikes over.

"So what did I do, fly?"

Jason's face was as serious as a thirteen-year-old's could get. "It was more like floating."

"Chew the root, Eugene," John explained to his friend.

"You chew it, sphinctoid. How long were you out on the pipe before Mr. Daniels looked out the window? About ten seconds, that's how long. And you just hung there like a humongous snotball for most of the time. Think about it! You didn't have time to climb down more than five feet."

"You're not shitting me, are you, Jase?"

"No way," Jason swore. "You were floating like an X-Man or something. I thought Mr. Daniels was going to have a fit."

All the urge to laugh was gone from John.

"People don't float, Jase," he said softly.

"You did."

John sat quietly for a moment. He thought back to the window ledge. He remembered reaching out into . . . into space and . . . not seeing anything. Like being blind.

Jason squealed.

"Wh-what happened to your *eyes*!"

John looked around. The park had gotten darker. The streetlamps must have gone out. He squinted, trying to force himself to see.

The streetlamps came back on. Jason squealed again.

"What's wrong, Jase?"

"Y-your eyes. They just went all white or something. Oh shit, J.D. I'm getting scared."

The reply came to John without him having to think about it. In a deep, soothing voice he recited, *"There is no reason to be frightened by what you have experienced or will experience. It is important for you to remember that you are not alone."*

Jason screwed up his face. "What did you say? *Did* you say it?"

A certain thoughtful expression had settled on John's face when he had told Jason not to be afraid. It remained after his voice returned to normal. It looked as if he had just had an awesomely good idea.

"Are you feeling okay?" Jason asked. He was nearing his limits, even for friendship.

"Give me your hand," John said. Jason started to back away but John said, *"Don't be afraid,"* and Jason wasn't anymore. "I want to try something. Something . . . I had forgotten." John held out his hand. Jason accepted it.

It took a moment for John to get it right. Then they rose one foot off the ground. And stayed there.

This time, Jason's squeal was more like a squeak. He kicked his feet. They didn't touch anything.

John smiled. It was all coming back to him now. He started to laugh again. Jason joined in, nervously.

"Isn't this neat?" John asked his buddy. "Isn't this godzillous?" He made them spin through the air around the tree and then land gently on the grass.

"How do you do it?" Jason asked. He stamped his feet up and down on the grass, just to make sure Mr. Gravity was back in control again. He was starting to feel giddy.

"I'm not sure," John said. "I just know I can. I know I can do lots of stuff. It's like I've always known but that I've just remembered or something. I don't know how I do it but I *can* do it!" It was a cry of victory.

Jason had seen enough episodes of *The Twilight Zone* to know that it just didn't end there.

"Shouldn't we tell someone, J.D.? The CIA or a newspaper or something? Maybe even your parents?"

John was grinning a grand and glorious smile. This was better than what had happened in Lori Daniels's bedroom.

"I know what we're going to do, Jase. We're best friends so you're with me all the way on this, right?"

Jason nodded excitedly. He knew, without question or doubt, that he could trust John. He had always felt that a little bit. Now he felt it a lot. "Whatever you say, J.D. Whatever you want to do."

John stepped back a bit and spun into the air, laughing and laughing as his plan fell into place. He felt the knowledge of his powers swell within him. All he had ever dreamed of would now be his, and his best friend's. He dropped back to the ground, breathless.

"Next week," he gasped to Jason, "next week we're going to California, man!"

"California?" Jason repeated doubtfully.

"Do you have any idea how much George Lucas would pay for something like this? We can do all his special effects for him. We'll be famous!" John couldn't contain his happiness. He was fourteen years old and his life was making sense!

"Why do we have to wait till next week?" Jason asked. His face said let's go now!

"Because we've been living in this town since we were in third grade and we both know how many assholes are out there, right?"

"Right."

"Well, it's time we started getting even."

Jason basked in the conviction and security radiating from his best friend's face. He liked J.D.'s idea a lot. He liked J.D.'s idea a *whole* lot. Jason was a fat, pimply thirteen-year-old. He had a lot to get even for.

TEN

Forensics was just finishing scraping Julian Burch's brains off the wall when Jim Hyams stepped into the room. He took one look and stepped back out. Despite the swollen blackening of his lips where they had been burned by the cartridge's exhaust, Burch's face was recognizable. But his head was like one of those high-speed photographs of a water balloon, a hundred-thousandth of a second after a bullet has passed through it. Part of it was normal and solid, an encircling fringe of it was tattered and feathery, and the rest of it just wasn't there.

Detective Greg Ioannou of Homicide joined Hyams in the corridor. He was a detective of the old school. In deference to his undercover work, long dark hair framed his face like a hangman's hood; his beard and moustache would suit a Mongol invader. But his eyes gave him away. They never stopped moving, always checking things out, checking things over. In interrogations, the suspects knew that one mistake and it was a body slam to the floor. Ioannou didn't let anything get past him. And he wasn't taking any crap from any weak-kneed rookie who hadn't even graduated from the Academy yet.

The detective settled himself against the wall beside Hyams. He kept his head down and talked to the floor. "Sure doesn't look like you gave your partner much in the way of backup, kid."

"What's that supposed to mean, detective, sir?"

"You tell me, kid."

Hyams pushed away from the wall. "What is this? Mike Hammer? Interrogation 101? If you've got something to ask me, then ask it. Half the cops in half the precincts could recognize Burch in there. You didn't need to call me for an ID."

Two paramedics carried a clanking stretcher to the top of the fourth-floor stairs. They dropped the wheels and rolled it toward the open apartment door. Ioannou held up his hand.

"Be a while yet, boys. Couple of things still to check out."

The paramedics rushed back to watch over their ambulance. It was that kind of neighborhood.

"Can I go now, detective, sir?" Hyams was making no pretense of hiding his annoyance.

Ioannou stepped too close to Hyams. Interrogation worked best when the subject was under pressure.

"There's a good cop dead in there, kid," he said.

Hyams rolled his eyes. "Where the hell do you get your lines? Dirty Harry movies or what?"

Body slam time. Ioannou grabbed Hyams's jacket at the shoulder and shoved him back against the wall, leaning into him, hard.

"I get the feeling you don't want to be a cop anymore," the detective breathed through clenched teeth. "In fact, I'm getting the distinct impression that you don't even want to *help* the cops anymore. And that makes me ask myself, What's this doorknob trying to hide? What's this jerk trying to cover up?"

A uniformed cop stuck his head out the door to see what the thudding sound in the hall was. It was just Ioannou punctuating his discussion with Hyams by repeatedly slamming the rookie against the wall. The cop nodded and went back into the room.

"I want a lawyer," Hyams said. He was furious but he knew better than to try to hit a detective.

Ioannou stepped back suddenly. "So you *are* trying a cover up. You want to hide behind a lawyer." His beard split into a twisted smile. Hyams wouldn't have been surprised to see fangs in there.

"Will you listen for one second!" Hyams shouted. "I was

taken off my assignment more than a week ago. Burch was no longer my partner. Burch wasn't even supposed to have been in the city. He was somewhere in Florida, for God's sake. I get a phone call asking me to come down and ID him. So I come. I see you don't need me to ID him because his face is still in one piece. So I start getting the feeling I'm being railroaded. That's why I want a lawyer, asshole. The only cover-up going on here is what you're saying about Burch. That's no good cop in there. That's something they teach us *never* to be at the Academy." Hyams stopped for breath. Ioannou said nothing. Hyams continued.

"Burch was a bigoted, sloppy policeman who fabricated evidence, lied to his superiors, planned entrapment, and from the looks of things, paid the price."

"You knew all this about your partner, kid?" Ioannou asked innocently. "Entrapment? Fabricated evidence? Lying?"

"Damn right."

"And you never reported it to your Captain or IAD? That could sound like complicity."

Hyams sputtered. Ioannou was playing him back and forth, straight out of the procedures book, and he couldn't get unhooked.

"You think anyone's going to listen to a rookie, detective? That's not the way the system works around here."

"That's the first smart thing you've said since you got here, kid. We *do* have a system here. It's not what they teach you in the Academy. It's not what you see on TV. It's real life. It's a system that works. And it's the system that you're going to work in until we find out who did that to your partner."

"He was my ex-partner."

"Like they say, kid, 'no divorce in the force.' There's no such thing as ex-partners. Only dead ones."

Ioannou sat back on the dingy couch across the room from Burch's body. The ME, photographer, and forensic technicians were sent out to the hall. Ioannou motioned to Hyams to sit down on an equally dingy chair that once had been part of a set with the couch—three rooms of furniture for ten dollars a month, forever.

Detective Sandra Heaslip sat on the arm of the couch. Her

undercover look didn't gibe with her partner's. Where Ioannou was uptown rough, Heaslip looked as if she had stepped from a Soho gallery opening. She wore three unmatched earrings in one ear, four in the other, and if her hair were any shorter she'd be bald. She opened her fuchsia-tinted, transparent plastic shoulder bag and took out a notebook.

"Story time, kiddies," Ioannou announced. "Sandra goes first. How about the mutant in the downstairs lobby?"

"Landlord," Heaslip said. She read the landlord's name and stats from her book. "Killed by a single shot to the head. Low-velocity, small-caliber bullet."

"Sound familiar?" Ioannou asked.

Heaslip looked over at the body against the wall. A blood-soaked gun with an oversized barrel lay in Burch's hand. "Silenced twenty-two," she said.

Ioannou peered over to Hyams. "Sound familiar to *you*, kid?"

"It was his backup piece," Hyams said. "Kept it in an ankle holster. Right leg."

Ioannou nodded to Heaslip. She went over to Burch's body and pushed up his right pants leg with the toe of her silver lamé Maud Frizon slingback. The holster was there.

"Okay," Ioannou said. "Assume Burch killed the landlord. Why?"

"He came here after someone else and the landlord surprised him," Heaslip said.

"Sound good to you, kid?"

Hyams shrugged.

"So who did he come here after?"

"This is the building where *El Niño* lives," Hyams said. "Paul Almagro."

"And he is . . . ?"

"Oh, come off it," Hyams exploded. "It's so bloody obvious. Burch had a vendetta against *El Niño*, the big gang lord everyone's hung up about. The punk aced him into blowing surveillance. Burch decides to even things up. He waits till he sees Paul come home and follows him in. He gets surprised by the landlord, so he drops him, then chases the kid up here."

"Why chased? Why not ambushed?"

"Because this isn't the right apartment. Paul lives up on the seventh floor."

Ioannou looked at Heaslip. She nodded agreement.

"Okay, kid, you're hot. Burch chases this *El Niño* upstairs. *El Niño* hides in here. Burch bursts in to even the score. And then *El Niño* asks Burch politely to blow out his brains for him. It had to have been very politely or Burch might have said no." Ioannou looked at Hyams with disgust. "Think it through, kid! There's something else going on here." He turned back to Heaslip. "How about all the blood?" he asked.

"Definitely two bodies," she said. "From the spray patterns and the smear outline by the rug, it looks like someone took a major chest wound and collapsed before Burch ate it."

Ioannou caught the hesitation in her voice. "*Looks* like it but you're not convinced, right?"

The detective flipped through her notebook. "There's a whole mess of blood down there but it doesn't go anywhere. The second body's been removed but there's no sign of how it was done. No footprints to indicate someone else shifted it. No drag marks to indicate it crawled away by itself." She shrugged.

"So to recap," Ioannou said cheerfully, "we got us a murderous cop who hunts down a fourteen-year-old gang lord so he can blow his *own* brains out. And a body, which may or may not be the gang lord's, which just floats up and out of the room." He turned back to Hyams. "What was it you said, kid? 'Bloody obvious,' was it?"

"What do you want from me?" Hyams said in abject defeat.

Ioannou held up three fingers and checked them off. "First, you fill in *my* partner and me with everything you can tell us about this *El Niño*. Second, you write down every nasty deal you can remember Burch being involved in with *El Niño*. Entrapment, fake evidence, anything else that might float into your mind. Third, you continue with your leave of absence from the Academy and you don't leave the city."

"Am I under arrest?" Hyams asked.

"You've been watching too much TV, kid. Cops don't arrest other cops. We have a better system."

"Which is?"

"I don't think you'd like it. I strongly suggest you don't try anything that might make you find out about it, either."

"And how long is this going to last?"

"Not long," Ioannou said. "Just until we find out why Burch

ate his gun and how a body can float away into neverland. With a hotshot like you working with us, shouldn't take long at all."

ELEVEN

Jamie Estevez opened his eyes to darkness once again, but this time it was the real darkness of his room at night. Not the dream darkness, a darkness so thick and black that it was as if he had never seen anything, ever, in his life. No, the darkness he was seeing now was real. He was hearing something, too. Something that had wakened him.

"Would you like the light turned on?" a voice asked.

"Dr. Torchia . . . ?" Jamie slurred. His mouth felt rubbery. His tongue felt too big.

"Dr. Torchia has gone away," the voice said. There was a click and the light that flooded into Jamie's eyes was so strong the boy thought he had been hit. He covered his eyes with his hands.

"Your pupils are still dilated," the voice explained. "You'll get used to the light in a few minutes."

"Who are you?" Jamie asked, trying to look out from behind his hands. But the light was like walking out of a movie theater into sunlight.

"That's what I was going to ask you," the voice said. "Who am I talking to now?"

"I'm Jamie."

"I'm Dr. Hadrian, Jamie."

"Where's Dr. Torchia?"

"Don't you remember?"

"Remember what?"

"Don't you remember what happened to Dr. Torchia?"

Jamie thought for a few seconds. When was it? Weeks ago? Months ago? "Did she get mad at me?" he asked, unsure.

"Not really. Did you get mad at her?"

"No." Jamie was sure of that. He liked Dr. Torchia best of

all the people in this jail they kept calling a hospital. Most of the time, at least.

"Then why did you hurt her the way you did?" the doctor asked.

Jamie remembered. "I didn't hurt her," he said.

"Then who did?"

Jamie tried not to speak, but he said, "Paul did."

"And Paul is the leader, right?"

"Sometimes." Jamie tried peeking out from his hands again. He could almost focus on a thin man in a white coat sitting in a chair by the nightstand. He was holding something in his hand. Something that looked scary.

"Did Paul kill your parents, Jamie? Was it Paul who didn't want them to fight anymore?"

Jamie didn't want to say anything. He knew he shouldn't say anything. But there was something about the doctor's voice, something about the way his own mouth was so rubbery and his head felt so heavy. Jamie *had* to answer.

"Yes."

"Did Paul kill your parents the way he hurt Dr. Torchia? Did he *tell* them to die?"

"Yes." Jamie was starting to cry. He didn't want to, but he was telling on Paul.

"And after Paul had killed your parents, you stabbed them so it would look as if *you* had killed them. That way, no one would know that Paul had done it. You didn't want Paul to get into trouble, right?"

"Y-yes."

"Where is Paul now, Jamie? May I talk to Paul?"

"No."

"Why not, Jamie? Paul's there, isn't he? Isn't Paul inside you now?"

Jamie could only sob.

"Why can't Paul come out and talk to me?"

"He . . . he had to run away," Jamie said.

"Does Paul know he's been bad?" the doctor asked. Jamie was vaguely aware of a tone of excitement in the man's voice.

Jamie nodded his head, sniffing.

"Because he killed your parents?" Jamie saw Dr. Hadrian leaning forward in the chair. The bad thing was still in his hand.

"No," Jamie burbled. "Because of the policeman." He heard the doctor sit back in the chair.

"What policeman?" Dr. Hadrian asked.

"The policeman he killed. The way he killed my parents." Jamie said.

Dr. Hadrian's voice didn't sound as smooth as it had a few moments ago. "When . . . when did you—I mean Paul—kill a policeman?"

Jamie rocked his head back and forth on his pillow. He was telling *everything*. Paul wouldn't be his friend anymore.

"Last night," Jamie cried.

The doctor whispered something Jamie couldn't hear. He sounded disappointed.

Jamie heard the doctor stand up. He looked out through his hands at what the doctor carried.

"Is that a gun?" the boy asked, terrified of the answer.

Hadrian looked down at the device he held. "It's not a real gun," he explained. "It's a special hypodermic air gun. Just in case I have to give you a shot so you can go back to sleep. Don't be afraid."

"*There is no reason to be frightened by what you have experienced or will experience*," Jamie recited. "*It is important for you to remember that you are not alone*."

"What did you say?" Dr. Hadrian asked. His voice sounded even rougher.

"I didn't say it," Jamie cried. He was certain the doctor was going to shoot him for telling on Paul.

"*Who* said it?" Hadrian leaned over Jamie.

"The dream friend! The dream friend!" Jamie screamed. "Don't shoot me! Don't kill me!" And then the doctor must have turned out the light again because everything went dark.

In the darkness, Jamie knew he had to get away from the doctor who was trying to shoot him. He struggled up into the darkness, trying to leave the doctor behind.

He heard the doctor shout out a bad word, the kind of word his mom and dad never liked him to say. Then he heard a whooshing sound and felt something sting his arm.

Jamie fell down into the darkness. This time, it was the deep dream darkness. From very far away, Jamie could hear Dr.

Hadrian shouting even more things at him. Or was it Esperanza he heard?

Jamie wasn't sure. But, as he went back to sleep, he wasn't worried, either. He knew his cousin would help him escape from Esperanza. Part of him knew he could always count on Marguerite.

TWELVE

Bobby Jay's golden construction helmet glittered in the brilliant spots of the location lighting. He found his footing in the mud, looked into the camera, and said his lines again.

"I am standing in what the architects tell me is going to be a three-hundred-foot-long and seventy-five-foot-wide reflecting pool." He smiled for the brothers and sisters at home. Shucks, he was saying, I don't know nothing about all this high-falutin' stuff. I'm just a simple man of God.

"Now you might be asking yourself—I know I am—just what it is that's going to be reflecting in this pool. Well, maybe we can get Hank on the camera to just sort of look down past my shoulder to where all those construction workers are." Bobby Jay stepped back, trying hard not to slip in the mud again and have to stay around for a third take. Hank Drummond, wooden-looking but newly born again, praise the Lord, slowly panned and zoomed his camera at a sprawling, half-built structure two hundred yards away.

"That's good," the location producer called out. "We'll insert the close-ups from there. Pull back, Hank. And you're on . . . Bobby!"

Bobby Jay held his microphone closer so he could drop his voice to a whisper.

"That there is going to be the main hotel building," he said. "That there is going to have more than two hundred and fifty hotel rooms." He shook his head at the wonder of it all. "It's going to have a the-ay-tor, for motion pictures *and* live presentations. It's going to even have an old-fashioned down-home ice cream parlor. I tell you, it's almost going to be a whole city in there. And right above it, brothers and sisters, high, high above it, to welcome all of you who come down to visit America's Glory, whether to take part in our ongoing Bible courses, or just to come down for a weekend for some old-fashioned family fellowship, what you're going to see up there is the symbol that made this country great.'' He edged the microphone farther away as his voice grew louder. ''The symbol that reaches out and calls to each and every one of us. A fifty-five-foot-tall *e-lec-tro-lum-in-escent* cross! Praise the Lord! Won't that be beautiful? They tell me we'll be able to see that from near twenty miles away. What a sign! What a symbol! And that's what going to be reflecting in this pool!'' He paused for the glory of that vision to sink in, then added, ''But, as we all know, all those wonderful things cost money.''

''Cut!'' the location director called. ''Very good, Bobby Jay. We'll take it from there when you're back with the studio audience. Pack it up, please.''

The generator was cut and the crew started dismantling the lights and reflectors. Bobby Jay handed his helmet back to the prop girl—newly born again in the Lord last November, he recalled—and checked with the director that the wind hadn't played too much havoc with the mike. Only then, when he was absolutely sure that his organization could continue in the next five minutes without him, did he slurp through the muddy construction site to see what his producer had for him.

''You don't seem to be smiling with the inner light of the Lord today, Randolph,'' Bobby Jay said. He slapped his old friend on the shoulder. Randolph was a worrier, he knew. Most of the top people in his organization were. Probably a good thing, too, he thought. It made it easier for Bobby Jay to run forward with the Lord, without doubts or worries of his own. Bobby Jay had the fire and the dream of the Lord and combined with the MBAs and the LLDs of his management team, there wasn't anything that could stand in the way of God's Kingdom on Earth. Praise the Lord.

Randolph slapped Bobby Jay's shoulder back. ''Just wondering if it's a good time to be starting another fund drive, Bobby Jay. Especially after the 'Christmas Miracle.' "

The reverend nodded. His friend had a good point. "We'll explain that to the brothers and sisters, Randolph. The money was there at Christmastime, sure enough. But the building costs skyrocketed when the Lord directed us to add the children's village. When a family comes here on a fellowship retreat, sometimes the best thing for Mom and Dad is to have a little time to themselves. The children's village is a good thing, Randolph."

"I know that, Bobby Jay. It's just that I'm thinking that we do have the money in the other accounts, so why—"

Bobby Jay stopped Randolph with the cold, dark expression that came to his face. "Randolph, the money to which you are referring was given to us by the brothers and sisters to fund our mission work in Africa and that's where that money is going. If God is giving me the choice of honoring the brothers' and sisters' trust in me and bringing a few pitiful meals and a few words of hope to the desperate overseas *or* opening America's Glory with every tree and roll of sod in place, you know what I'm going to choose."

"I'm thinking that it might not look too good to have the President's motorcade come plowing through a sea of mud come Labor Day, is all," Randolph tried to explain.

"Randolph, I appreciate your concern. I truly do. But you have to remember that the President and I go way back. Why, when I was preaching in a torn old tent and he was just a congressman, he'd come to visit most every time I was in the state. He swore to me then he'd never forget the simple word of God among all the complex words of government. And he hasn't. The President's not going to mind a bit of mud if it means the Lord's work's being done among the less fortunate in Africa. And neither should you."

Randolph agreed and, as usual, appeared to be embarrassed for ever having thought something that Bobby Jay didn't agree with.

"'Sides," said Bobby Jay, "you think the President's party is going to let him start his reelection campaign from a sea of mud? If the landscaping does seem to be underfunded by the middle of the summer, I think we can count on a few dollars from Washington." Bobby Jay chuckled at that. "Of course, as the lawyers say, all this worrying might be moot. Have you heard from our sheep among the wolves?" He referred to the brother who worked within the diocese of New York.

Randolph nodded. "The planning committee had a meeting last weekend. They had some science writer there who was filling them in on the details. Our brother taped it."

"And have you heard the tape?"

"Not yet. But from what our brother told me about it, I think the Catholics have been indulging in their sacramental wine a bit too freely."

Bobby Jay's smile was as brilliant as his golden helmet had been. "I have a tape deck in my office, brother Randolph. Let's hear what our fallen brothers have to say."

The bottle of Jack Daniel's was more than half gone by the time the tape was finished.

"Oooo-eeee," Bobby Jay said as he slumped in his high-backed kid leather executive chair. He had kicked off his shoes and rested both feet on the corner of his desk. Small, gray droplets of dried mud clung to his pants legs.

Randolph looked up from the matching leather couch where he sat beneath a gallery of Bobby Jay's honorary degrees and framed letters from political notables.

"You don't believe it, do you?" the producer asked. His tone told Bobby Jay what his opinion was: stupid as teats on a bull.

"Almost," Bobby Jay said, staring into the glass cradled in his hands. "What I do believe is what the first priest said about the confession. I have no doubt that the late Dr. Wyndham came to church, made his last confession, and then told his story and started this whole ball of wax rolling. I have no doubt that the papers the committee are referring to, the papers which Dr. Wyndham left with the priest, are real. What I need now is for the Lord to tell me if the story those papers tell is true."

"I don't think any of it is true. It can't be," Randolph said.

"That Foster woman seemed to make a good case for this cloning thing to be possible."

"But from bloodstains that are almost two thousand years old?"

Bobby Jay looked over at his producer. "Randolph, I don't

think you were listening to what those people were saying on that tape. I think they're approaching things the right way. Strange as that might seem for Catholics, I hasten to add."

The reverend stretched and got up from his chair to stare out the window at the half-built America's Glory.

"Go over it again, son. First, they're conceding that human cloning is possible. Second, they're conceding that Dr. Wyndham *was* on Cardinal Pellegrino's scientific committee as far back as 1969 and that he had access to the shroud on a number of occasions between then and that mysterious fire in 1972. Given those assumptions, they're left with what that Father Panati called the three big questions." Bobby Jay turned back to Randolph.

"Number one," he said, striding across the thick broadloom of his office, voice going up and down as if he were in the studio. "Is it possible to reconstruct a human being's genetic structure from dried blood? Foster says that, theoretically, the answer is yes, but she wants to examine Dr. Wyndham's procedural notes. Sounds like the proper thing to do. Then there's number two. Are the reddish-brown stains on the Shroud of Turin actually bloodstains? Panati says maybe yes, maybe no. He's arranging to get the research results of the big studies from '78 and '89."

Bobby Jay sat down beside Randolph and looked him in the eye with all the fervent intensity of a backwoods revivalist. "And that leaves the big number three, brother. Given that cloning is possible. Assuming that the genetic structure required for cloning can be reconstructed from dried blood, and assuming that Dr. Wyndham did indeed reconstruct such a genetic structure from organic material found on the Shroud of Turin, is the shroud what a lot of people think it is—the burial cloth of our Lord Jesus of Nazareth?"

"So what if it is?" Randolph protested.

"Well then, Randolph, as Father Panati said, somewhere out there in the great big world, there are twenty to thirty exact duplicates of Jee-sus, alive and well and walking among us." Bobby Jay couldn't understand how Randolph wasn't picking up on the implications of all this.

"But none of them *are* the Lord!" Randolph said. "How could they be?"

"Randolph, you're starting to sound as stodgy as those Catholics on the tape." Bobby Jay put his hands on his hips and imitated Father Panati in a singsong voice. " 'Was Jesus an ordinary human being, special only because of his relationship with God on a spiritual level or was Jesus special because, in addition to his spiritual relationship with God, he was physically different from ordinary people as well?' Jehosaphat, Randolph! Don't even consider that kind of intellectual Jesuit horseshit! Jesus was Jesus because God was within him. There might be thirty copies of him out there but I guarantee you, the Holy Spirit won't be anywhere near them." He narrowed his eyes. "But something else will be."

"What will be?"

"Think of Revelation, brother! Ever since Israel was reborn the signs have been gathering. There's the evil atheistic empire in the East. There's sin and depravity raging in the West. God has sent a plague among the sexual deviates. He has caused mountains to erupt! Seas to rage! The time of the end is almost here, brother Randolph. There's only one thing missing. A leader for the forces of darkness. The Antichrist!"

Randolph's face screwed up. "You think one of the duplicates might be the Antichrist, Bobby Jay?" This was starting to smack of old-fashioned hellfire and brimstone.

"Jehosaphat, no! I think they *all* are the Antichrist!" Bobby Jay was on a holy roll once more. He closed his eyes as if listening to a faraway voice. "I can see it all now, Randolph. It's all so clear. A perfect plan of the devil's. Jesus was born to Mary as a miracle of God! Praise the Lord. But these duplicates, these false Christs, are born of an abomination of a scientist. Evolutionists, Randolph! *Se-cu-lar* humanists! Satan's pawns, all of them. There was only *one* Jee-sus to spread the *one* truth of the *one* God. The devil knows he's in trouble, Randolph. The devil knows he needs reinforcements against the Lord. So he's created *thirty* of them. Just like the pieces of silver . . ."

"But, Bobby Jay," Randolph jumped in as soon as he had the chance. "There's got to be more to the End Times than that. There's got to be the Rapture, there's got to be—"

"All in good time, Randolph. All in good time." Bobby Jay held up his hand and Randolph fell silent, just as if he were in church. "Those things will come."

"When?"

"On the eve of Armageddon, Randolph. The final war which

will destroy all evil and prepare the way for the millennium of Jee-sus. That time is near. These satanic duplicates are the proof."

Randolph's forehead was creased with concentration. When Bobby Jay explained something, it usually didn't matter if all the words and logic were understood. What counted was conviction. Bobby Jay had it, so, of course, Randolph knew he must, too.

"What are we going to do, Bobby Jay?"

"We're going to *preempt* the devil, Randolph!" Bobby Jay clapped his hands sharply in triumph. "Prepare ye the way for the coming of the Lord. Hallelujah! Prepare ye the way for the final war."

"Preempt? How?" Randolph croaked.

"Make the truth be known," Bobby Jay said. "That's pretty simple now, isn't it? The truth shall make you free."

"I guess so," Randolph agreed without enthusiasm. "Whatever you say, Bobby Jay."

"Oh, it's not me talking at you. It's the Lord." Bobby Jay went back To his window, spread his arms out, and pressed his hands against the glass. "Yessir, he's answered me. He's shown me the way. Told me what to do. First off, we got to get us some of those duplicates. Stare the devil right in his face and *spit* at him."

"I thought you said you still weren't sure if the story was true?" Randolph asked. There was a tinge of fear in his voice.

"That was before," Bobby Jay said. His breath fogged the glass so that America's Glory seemed to float in a mist of heavenly clouds. "I *know* the truth now. God has spoken *through* me and *to* me. The way is clear. We must act first before the devil's plans are realized."

Randolph sat silently for a few long moments. At last Bobby Jay turned back from the window. His eyes were burning. Randolph felt the hair on the back of his neck bristle in response. Perhaps the Spirit *was* within the room. Something was making his hair stand on end.

"Very fitting, don't you think," Bobby Jay asked, "that the very first day of America's Glory should be the very last day for this tired old world, and the very first day of God's own eternity? I think the President's going to find that very fitting when he comes to our grand opening come Labor Day, don't you Randolph?''

It was then that Randolph understood what Bobby Jay was thinking. The President. The man who controlled the weapons of Armageddon. Preempt. Dear, sweet Jesus.

''Amen,'' Randolph said. But, he realized, it wasn't the Holy Spirit that was making his hair bristle. It was fear.

THIRTEEN

It was a dead man's apartment. Each piece of furniture, each book unshelved, had that weight to it. Johnathan Wyndham had moved each item into the place it occupied and then Johnathan Wyndham had died. Nothing here would ever move again, except to be packed up, discarded, or investigated.

The door creaked open in the still, close air. The chain stopped it after four inches. Father Panati's hand reached in, holding a small brass key. The chain dropped out of its lock. Panati and Susan Foster walked in.

The feeling that they were stepping into a tomb was strong in Father Panati. He crossed himself and said a few words for Wyndham. He noticed that all the plant pots in the living room were empty.

Foster opened the curtains. New Jersey sunlight appeared in thick, dusty shafts. Foster waved the dust from the curtains away from her face and looked around. The apartment was neat in the way that people arrange things when they leave on a vacation and there's the morbid chance that the next people to enter their home might be strangers. Wyndham had known he was going away.

In the kitchen, Father Panati found a box with two small bowls, a hand can opener, and a stack of cat food tins. The refrigerator held two small containers of chocolate pudding, a half-pound of butter in a plastic keeper, a plastic container of distilled water, and two Hershey bars. The garbage bag holder under the sink had a fresh garbage bag in it. It was empty.

Foster studied the photos that hung on two walls above the stuffed bookshelves. Of the photos with people in them, one man appeared many times. She assumed he was Wyndham. He stood in front of a valley so green it could only be tropical. He sat at a restaurant table with other men with shiny faces. The wine bottles on the table had wicker wrapped around them. He stood before medieval-looking buildings. He sat in the chair near the windows of his apartment with a white-pawed black cat on his lap. There were several pictures of the cat. In none of the photographs was Wyndham smiling. As the clothing styles in the pictures became more recent, the doctor became slimmer.

Panati went into the bedroom. Foster started opening drawers in the desk against a wall in what other people would have used as the dining area. It appeared to have been Wyndham's office. In one drawer, she found meticulous files of charge card bills, car repair receipts, tax forms, utility bills, and other financial detritus. In another, health care receipts from the Doncaster Pet Clinic for "Spats" Wyndham. The last receipt was fifty dollars for euthanasia. Wyndham had known he was going away and that he wasn't coming back.

Later, Panati and Foster sat at a small butcher-block table in the kitchen. Panati was worried for Foster. Since entering the dead man's apartment, she had seemed preoccupied and jumpy, almost as if this place had some connection to her. But he couldn't think of a way to ask her about it.

"Did the priest Wyndham confessed to know him at all?" Foster asked.

Panati shook his head. "No, I'm afraid not. Dr. Wyndham told Father Montgomery that he hadn't been to church for almost ten years. Never had been to St. Mike's at all."

"And all he told Father Montgomery was that the complete records were at his home? Nothing more?"

"Well, I'm sure that's not all he said. He approached Father Montgomery to give his confession and that, of course, is completely confidential. These days, a confession of that nature, returning to the Church after such a long absence, that usually entails a face-to-face meeting. Counseling session, actually. Anyway, Father Montgomery says that Dr. Wyndham stated expressly that what he had to say about his . . . experiment wasn't to be considered part of his confession. He wanted Father Montgomery to be free to talk about it. Both men couldn't even be sure if what he had done was a sin. In any event, Father Montgomery says that as far as the experiment is concerned, there was far more information in Dr. Wyndham's papers than his conversation."

"Lots of information in the outline papers he left at St. Mike's," Foster sighed, "but no details." She looked out into the office area. Despite their attempts to be neat, she and Panati had disrupted the apartment during their two-hour search. "Where would he have kept them?"

Panati got up from the table. "Last thing to do then is to start flipping through all the books in the bookcases, one by one, and look for notes." Foster agreed and they began.

Twenty minutes later, both were so caught up in the repetitive task of removing a book, flipping, and reshelving, that neither of them noticed the front door opening until a small, dry voice said, "Don't move, slimeballs. I got a gun."

Foster dropped the book she was holding and slowly turned her head. Father Panati held up his hands.

"Now, just a minute here," he began.

The woman with the shotgun and a faded flowered dress was bone-thin and seventy. She blinked at Panati's clerical collar.

"You should be ashamed of yourself!" she shouted. "What's the world coming to?" She blinked again at Foster. "And I suppose you're a nun?"

"She's Susan Foster, my associate, and I'm Father Francis Panati. We're here on Church business."

"Church business! Church business! What kind of business is it to go breaking into people's apartments?" The woman gestured with the shotgun as she spoke.

"We didn't break in," Panati explained. "We have keys. Dr. Wyndham passed away and he's left everything to the Church. We're just here to start going through it all. We're completely aboveboard, madam. I assure you."

The woman spat as if she had heard that story from every other priest she had caught committing a B&E.

"I have letters from Dr. Wyndham's lawyers," Panati said. "Madam, *please* put down that gun!"

Eventually they sorted it all out around the kitchen table, though Mrs. Kirby, the superintendent's wife, took a long time to realize that Dr. Wyndham wasn't coming back. After all, his rent was prepaid for three more months and she certainly wasn't about to give a refund.

"Liver cancer killed him, you say?" she asked warily. The shotgun was leaning against the wall in the kitchen, though it was still within easy reach.

"Yes," Panati lied. In truth, he told himself, six more months and the liver cancer would have killed Wyndham. The injection he gave himself just speeded up the process.

"And you say he gave all his stuff to you people?" Mrs. Kirby did not survive to be seventy without developing a healthy respect for cynicism.

"That's right," Panati agreed, for perhaps the eighth time.

"Never took him to be a churchgoer," Mrs. Kirby said. She cocked her head. "I guess you'll be wanting all that crap he's got in storage, too."

"Storage?" Panati and Foster said at the same time.

The basement of the old apartment building was filthy and damp. A haphazard construction of chicken wire and rough pieces of wood created a suggestion of storage lockers along one of the crumbling brick walls. Only two of the cubicles had anything other than a pile of trash in them.

"You want number twenty-three," Mrs. Kirby told them, waving her flashlight in its general direction.

The door to number twenty-three had a padlock on it. Panati looked at it for a second then, without straining, lifted the anchor plate off the door frame. The chicken wire had been pulled back from the frame so it wasn't strictly necessary to open the door to enter the locker, but Panati swung it open anyway.

There were five green-painted metal trunks inside, each twice the size of a large suitcase. Originally, they had been arranged in two stacks but someone had pushed them over. Probably the same person or persons who had smashed their locks.

"Any idea when this happened?" Panati asked Mrs. Kirby.

The woman shrugged. "Kids. All the time kids come in through the windows. Only old papers in there though. Nothing that kids would want."

Foster and Panati looked at each other.

"How do you know what's in the trunks, Mrs. Kirby?" Foster asked wryly.

"Aww, the doctor told me. So you going to take them, or what?"

Panati crouched down beside the closest trunk and pried open its lid. The inside was a rat's nest of papers and file folders and thin blue notebooks. It appeared to have been gone through many times. He asked Mrs. Kirby to move the flashlight closer as he held up a crumpled piece of stationery.

"Harris Fertility Research and Treatment Clinic," he read. He turned to Foster. "Just as you said, Susan."

The basement wasn't the place to dig through the thousands of documents that were in the trunks. Foster and Panati wrestled one of them up the cracked, linoleum-covered wooden stairs to the main floor, then decided to arrange for a van and some assistance from other members of the planning committee.

The priest suggested that Foster take the first trunk back to her apartment and start going through it. "Now that Mrs. Kirby knows the doctor won't be coming back," the priest explained, "I think I'd feel better knowing the locks on the apartment have been changed."

Foster laughed and agreed. Panati phoned Father Montgomery to arrange the pickup of the rest of the trunks and then helped Foster carry the first trunk out to her Prelude and slide it into what passed for a backseat. Just before she climbed in to drive away, Foster hesitated.

"Yes?" Panati asked, guessing a question was coming.

"Just thinking," she said. "Everything in that apartment, the photographs, the books, the furniture, everything up there tells me that Dr. Wyndham was a pretty ordinary person."

"I think he was," Panati said. "Most people are."

"Then why did he do it, Francis? Did he explain that to Father Montgomery?"

Panati looked away and wrinkled his face in the sunlight. "He said he was tired of just believing, poor man. Said he was tired of faith alone. He wanted proof, he said. One way or the other, he wanted to know what the truth is."

"Don't we all," Foster agreed. There was sadness in her face.

"Well, he knows the truth now."

"Do you say that from knowledge or faith, Francis?"

"From faith, of course." He smiled at Foster. "If it were all down in black and white like one of your articles, Susan, if it were all that simple, where would the challenge be? The mystery?"

"Must there be mystery?"

"Show me someone who says he understands God," said Father Panati, "and I'll show you a fool."

FOURTEEN

"Good afternoon, ladies and gentlemen," said a voice struggling to be heard over the roar of the prop, "I'm Captain Lowell and I'd like to thank y'all for choosing San Francisco Airlines. Our cruising altitude today will be about seven hundred feet and our speed will be one hundred and thirty miles an hour. Estimated flight time to San Francisco International is nine minutes, so please, settle back and take a few moments to relax and enjoy the view."

Tom Jefferson settled back in his seat as instructed but found it hard to relax as the seven-passenger Long Ranger rumbled across San Francisco Bay like a robot dragonfly from a Japanese horror film. He slipped out a small black notebook and wrote down the flight distance between Oakland and San Francisco. It was his wife's idea. Ten dollars was riding on her contention that over the course of one year, he would have racked up fifty percent more mileage than the President, simply by going along to the same places the President did. For one reason or another, Jefferson always seemed to miss out on an Air Force One flight and then had to hop around among other airports and commercial flights trying to end up in the same places that the President's plane could fly to directly. Today's itinerary was no exception.

Jefferson had flown from D.C. to Los Angeles, where the previous afternoon the President had revealed major—read preelection—federal funding for a commercial desalinization plant. Upon landing at L.A. International, Jefferson had learned that Air Force One had departed the night before to San Francisco so the President could attend the regular Thursday night presentation at the Bohemian Club. After a few phone calls to make sure the President was still in San Francisco, Jefferson had snagged the first available seat on a commuter flight to the Bay Area, landing at Oakland. It had been worse than the European tour after last fall's summit.

Jefferson ran through the total mileage he had accumulated throughout the year and decided he was going to have to kiss the ten dollars good-bye. Oh well, he thought with a smile, maybe his wife would decide to take it out in trade.

Landing at the helipad, Jefferson could see the sun flare from the silver skin of the presidential 747-100B parked on an isolated section of the apron, attended by both airport and army security vehicles. He estimated that if it stayed put for twenty more minutes, he could make it aboard. The five-and-a-half-hour flight back to D.C. would give him lots of time to jog Number One's memory about the Galahad project and prepare him for Barbara-Jane Fuller's bizarre message.

He had been told early on in his tenure at the White House always to keep a packed carry-on suitcase at the office. The President never waited for luggage so neither should his staff. It was a worthwhile lesson. Without luggage to worry about, Jefferson was at the apron security gate closest to Air Force One within seven minutes of leaving the helicopter.

Imposing in dress blue jacket, gold aiguillette, and white hat, the marine sergeant on duty at the gate recognized Jefferson, greeted him by name, and then formally requested his identification. Jefferson was used to the thoroughness of the procedure and presented his White House photo ID.

"You're not listed today, Mr. Jefferson," the marine said matter-of-factly.

Jefferson glanced at the sergeant's name tag. "Change of

plans, Sergeant Rawlings. Trying to hitch a ride back to save the taxpayers some money."

The sergeant waved over another soldier carrying a cellular phone and called through to the plane. Jefferson listened to the conversation on his side with surprise.

"Sorry about that, Mr. Jefferson," Sergeant Rawlings explained. "Apparently the President has already booked some last-minute guests aboard. Flight's full up."

"Not even room for one more?" Jefferson asked. Air Force One could hold seventy passengers, in addition to the twenty-three crew.

Rawlings shook his head.

Jefferson looked over the sergeant's shoulder to see five stretch limousines, flanked by motorcycles with flashing lights, speed up to the jet.

"Do you happen to know who the President's guests are?" he asked the marine.

"Sorry, sir, but I can't give out that information." The marine was resolute.

"Well, I understand your position, Sergeant Rawlings, but this is mine," Jefferson tried. "I just flew in from D.C. for a chance to meet with the President. Now, I could claim official business and bump one of his guests. But if the guest turns out to be someone who's more important than my business with the President, I could find myself bumped out of a job. How about a hint, Sergeant? Let me know what league I'm in, okay?"

The sergeant looked over his shoulder as if to make sure this wasn't some sort of security test. He decided it wasn't.

"It's that television preacher, Bobby Jay, and some of the people from his staff," Rawlings said.

"Thank you, Sergeant," Jefferson said with a tight smile, "you just saved me a great deal of trouble. Would you happen to know the best way back to the American counter?"

It was just as well that there wasn't room for one more on that flight, Jefferson thought as he walked back through the terminal to the departure level. It was bad enough the President was halfway convinced that an all-out nuclear war might be the battle of Armageddon mentioned in the Bible, when all the nations of the world would be engulfed by war. Even some of the members of the Joint Chiefs of Staff were concerned that the President not continue with that line of thought. But the Reverend Bobby Jay was another matter.

Jefferson had seen some of the reverend's television shows, most of them while sitting up late at night with one or another of the kids during flu season. Bobby Jay wasn't halfway convinced that a nuclear war might be Armageddon, he was one hundred percent certain. If the President ever got wind of Barbara-Jane Fuller's prediction, it would just make it easier for the reverend to pass that certainty on to his followers. Jefferson shivered as he stood on line at the ticket counter. Fanatics, of any persuasion, always made him nervous. To Jefferson, tolerance was what had made America great, and acceptance was what would make it even greater. Tolerance and acceptance, two areas of personal inventory in which the Reverend Bobby Jay was notoriously lacking.

Jefferson advanced through the lineup wondering what Bobby Jay could possibly have to say to the President that had required such a hastily arranged meeting on Air Force One. Whatever it was, Jefferson decided, he probably wouldn't like it.

FIFTEEN

Later that night, Susan Foster had sorted through about half the contents of the green metal trunk when she suddenly found herself thinking of Dr. Wyndham's cat and started to cry.

She sat on her living room floor, Michael Franks singing gently on the stereo, a glass of wine beside her, surrounded by two dozen piles of smoothed-out sheets of correspondence and medical records, and quietly sobbed into her hands. I'm not a crier, she thought, and I don't even like cats. But it all came out despite herself.

The precise neatness of Wyndham's apartment had gotten to her first. Not even her Aunt Emmeline in Kansas was that neat.

She had stood in the apartment that afternoon and pictured the man, already dying, spending a few more hours vacuuming, rearranging, and cleaning—as if any of it mattered—for the people he knew would be coming to his home after he was dead. Despite the cramps that gnawed at her beneath her scar, now coming almost weekly, she had never even thought of doing that in her place.

When she had found the records from the animal clinic, she had seen again the tired man from the photographs, the man who had stood in tropical valleys, eaten with friends in a restaurant, and visited medieval buildings, as he walked along the streets of the city, carrying his beloved cat to be destroyed.

The finality of that act caught at her. Giving a shot to the cat was somehow even worse than taking the tablets for herself. Wyndham's cat would have no idea what was happening. But Wyndham would. And so would she when the time came. How can I tell myself that I would understand what was happening any more than that stupid cat would? she asked herself. Then she stopped trying to stop herself from crying and released all the dark fears and deep pity rooted in the incision in her gut.

The record ended before she did. When she looked up, blinking around at her apartment as if seeing it for the first time, she heard only the relative silence of faraway traffic noise filtered through closed windows. She felt thick and slow, as if she had been wrapped in yards of the batting that filled the vial of white tablets. But she felt more at ease than she had in a while. Whether that was because something had been accomplished by crying, or whether she had run out of emotional energy for the time being, she didn't know. She didn't care either. She went into the bathroom to wash her face.

When Foster came back, face scrubbed pink and hair brushed back, she flipped the record and went back to the trunk. The contents of it were confirming Wyndham's report to his confessor, Father Montgomery, that he had set up a clinic in Manhattan to offer fertility testing, counseling, and artificial insemination. But Foster had not yet found anything to support his claim that, during what women thought were artificial insemination procedures, he had actually implanted viable zygotes with nuclei containing the cloned genetic structure of whoever's blood had stained the Shroud of Turin. However, she thought, there were still four more trunks in the basement of Wyndham's apartment building.

By the time she was finished listening to her fourth album of the night, Foster had every piece of paper from the trunk spread over her floor, her dining table, her coffee table, and most of the kitchen chairs. The piles were divided into various versions of bookkeeping and medical insurance records, supply purchase orders, equipment purchase and maintenance records, staff records for two nurses and two technicians, and patient records split into counseling, testing, referrals, and artificial insemination. Since she hardly expected cloned material from the Shroud of Turin to show up on the business records, Foster concentrated on reading through the medical records for the 498 patients whose files had been in the trunk.

On her second pass through them, she noticed an anomaly on the records of women who had been artificially inseminated. On each treatment chart was a space in which was written the identification number of the sperm lot used. The identification number consisted of two numbers, three letters, and four more numbers. It was the same format as was used for the patient identification numbers filled in below the women's names on the record sheets. Foster concluded it was a patient ID number for the sperm's donor.

Foster flipped quickly through all the records in the "AI" piles. As she expected, many of the forms showed that the sperm donor's ID number was only one digit removed from the recipient's number. Since two patients arriving together would receive consecutive ID numbers, this indicated to Foster that the sperm for those procedures had been donated by the patient's husband, or whoever had accompanied the woman to the clinic. She had identified a pattern.

She found that in about a third of the records the donor's ID number wasn't at all close to the recipient's number. Foster assumed that in those procedures, the women concerned did not have fertile men with whom to conceive, and so were being inseminated with anonymously donated sperm. It was a logical variation on the pattern.

Then there was the anomaly. A single anonymous donor—#72/SXM/4308—had been used to inseminate sixty-seven different women over a two-year period. No other anonymous donor had been used more than six times, an ethical decision intended to reduce the chances that, unknowingly, half brothers and half sisters might meet each other in the future and decide to have children together.

Foster crawled around her living room, digging through the piles, trying to find documents which carried a cross-check reference to any of the sperm donors' numbers. Unfortunately, Wyndham seemed to have split up his records on the basis of sex and there wasn't a single male medical record in the trunk. But Foster wasn't discouraged. There were four more trunks and she had a system of analysis now. If, after going through the other records from Wyndham's basement, she couldn't find a patient record form for donor #72/SXM/4308, then she felt certain those would be the cases to investigate.

She felt a satisfying sense of accomplishment that she hadn't had too often. As a science writer, mostly for magazines and journals, she had rarely been involved in any time-sensitive story requiring investigative skills other than basic research. Ignoring what she had thought of as her uncharacteristic little digression at the beginning of the evening, she felt almost like a real reporter covering a breaking story. She poured herself another glass of wine and put on a Springsteen album to reward herself. She curled her legs under her on the couch and read through the records of the sixty-seven women who had been inseminated by the same donor. It became apparent that another thing those women had in common was an inordinately high rate of miscarriage.

Her door buzzer rang. It was two-thirty in the morning and she lived in New York City. She was extremely thankful for the two dead-bolt locks on her door as she carefully slid the cover from her viewer. It was Father Panati, accompanied by her building's elevator man, who was standing about five feet behind the priest and had his ever-present iron bar dangling from one hand. Foster always tipped well at Christmas.

Foster threw open all the locks and opened the door.

"It's all right, George," she said to the elevator man. "He's a friend."

George looked appraisingly at the priest and then decided that Foster was telling the truth and it wasn't his business any longer.

He shrugged good-night and went back to his elevator. Foster invited Panati in. He looked older than he had that afternoon. His face was pale, eyes shadowed.

"Is something wrong?" she asked and then realized he had been staring at her still-swollen eyes and flushed nose and was about to ask the same thing. But his need to talk was greater.

"Father Montgomery is dead," he said as if he still couldn't believe it.

Without a thought for the shield of his collar, Foster hugged the man.

"Oh, Francis," she said. "What happened?"

Panati's eyes were bleary. He stared at the records spread throughout the apartment. He pointed to them.

"He . . . he was *murdered*," the priest said, as if it were an obscenity too foul to be voiced. "By the people who stole the rest of Dr. Wyndham's records."

SIXTEEN

Father Panati's planning committee meeting was more subdued than the last one Foster had attended. The priest's eyes were swollen as if he hadn't slept the night before. Probably hadn't, Foster thought. He hadn't left her place until four.

Two of the three others at the meeting looked almost as bad. They were all friends or associates of Panati's who had been asked by him to informally examine Dr. Wyndham's revelations to Father Montgomery before an official report was prepared for the bishop and then, perhaps, for Rome. But their purpose was no longer informal, it was deadly serious.

Farthest away from the rest, exiled by his nervous chain-smoking to the end of the meeting table, was Alexander Thorkel. He was a large, balding man with thick rimless glasses. At the first meeting, he had given Foster the impression that he examined everything as if through a microscope. Panati had told her it was a fitting observation. Thorkel had made a fortune in the manufacture of miniaturized electronic components. Over the years, he had shared that fortune graciously with the Church and St. Joseph's University. Panati valued his level-headed advice.

Across from Foster, Father Scott Carey looked shrunken in on himself. He was a lecturer in economics at St. Joe's and, even at the first meeting, had acted unsure and out of place. Now the gray-haired, mousy priest looked as if he were praying to be sent back to his computers and his classrooms. But, again, Panati had said the economist had an uncanny sense of what was going on behind the scenes at the Vatican. Father Carey's insights would be extremely valuable if the committee decided to bring Wyndham's experiments to the attention of the Holy Father.

The one who sat closest to Foster was the one who seemed least affected by the tragedy of Montgomery's death, Andre Delambre. A graduate student in history from one of Panati's seminars, he was young, fat, and possessed of an annoyingly nasal voice. Delambre looked not only as if he had slept soundly the night before but also as if he could sleep soundly right at that moment. His eyes were large and bulbous, giving him a half-lidded look of intense concentration or intense disinterest. Of all the people at the table, the graduate student was the only one for whom Foster had not felt an immediate liking.

The meeting room was five doors down from Panati's office in the wood-paneled walls of the ivy-covered Margot Jeffrey building. Normally, it was used as a staff lounge for people in the history department, but Panati had pinned a worn, hand-printed "In Use" sign to the door before closing it. Now, he stood at the end of the room by a steaming electric kettle and mixed various concoctions of instant Maxwell House, edible oil products, and sugar and sweeteners. It was his ritual for clearing his mind for a meeting.

He distributed Styrofoam cups and orange plastic sticks to everyone, sat at the head of the table, and led a prayer for Father Montgomery and the man who had died with him. His voice wavered. Montgomery had been a good friend. That was why he had come to Panati in the first place, instead of going directly through the Church's bureaucracy. "Things will happen a lot more quickly if we look into it ourselves, Francis," he had said. Unfortunately, Montgomery had been right.

Thorkel was the first one to speak after the prayer. "So what do the police know about this terrible, terrible event, Father?"

Panati's voice was flat. "I spoke with the detective heading the investigation this morning. She feels that the police have developed a 'plausible scenario.' " He quoted the jargon as if it were an insult to his friend's death. "Father Montgomery had his van parked at the back service doors to the apartment building. The doors were propped open. As he and Walter Walker, a young man from his parish, were bringing Dr. Wyndham's trunks up from storage, apparently two, perhaps three, thieves entered the building through the open doors. The police say Father Montgomery and his helper must have surprised the thieves so . . . the thieves killed both of them."

Father Carey muttered something inaudible and crossed himself.

"Do the police know why the thieves took the trunks?" Foster asked. Panati hadn't known any of the details the previous night. He had only identified Father Montgomery's brutally stabbed body and been told to wait for the detective's report. Foster had a hard time understanding how anyone would want to lug the heavy trunks up the narrow basement stairs without looking into them to see if they were worth stealing. And if the thieves *had* looked inside the trunks, why would they want old medical records?

"Detective Fenton said that the area suffers from a great many break-ins. She said that gangs of kids, especially, are always on the lookout for an opportunity and that the propped-open doors would have been an invitation. The kids would have gone in looking for anything they thought was valuable and which they could get at quickly. She thinks that's why the only apartment broken into was Dr. Wyndham's. The kids stole the keys from Father Montgomery."

"But nothing was stolen from the apartment?" Foster continued.

"It's hard to say. I was there this morning and it had certainly been vandalized. When you and I were there yesterday, I don't remember seeing anything of value except perhaps the television set and the stereo system. But both of them were still there. Smashed but still there."

Foster didn't like the sound of that. Too much of a coincidence, she thought. But she didn't say anything more because, if she extrapolated her reasoning, it made good sense not to reveal too much to the other people at the table.

Delambre popped his eyes open and shut a few times. "So the police say that a group of kids just happened to be walking by and killed Father Montgomery and that other fellow so they could smash up what little there was that made sense to steal, and steal four trunks that contained nothing of value?" His adenoidal whine didn't suggest he found flaws in this theory, he was just seeking confirmation.

"What can you say about the kind of animals who would do something like that?" Thorkel boomed from down the table. "Killing a priest! They'd probably have done it for a handful of change as much as for a million dollars." Thorkel lit a new cigarette from the stub of his last.

"That's pretty much what Detective Fenton suggested," Panati said in resignation.

As if realizing that all the others had voiced their concerns about the police's interpretation of events, Father Carey looked nervously around and then said, to no one in particular, "You don't suppose someone was specifically after the trunks, do you?"

"Who would be?" Delambre whined. He reminded Foster of a large insect.

"Dr. Wyndham made it quite clear that the report he left with Father Montgomery was the first and only time he had revealed what he had done," Panati said. "It makes no sense, Scott." Father Carey settled lower in his chair.

There was silence around the table, except for a sudden bout of coughing from Thorkel. "Little punks." He spat into an ashtray after it subsided.

"Well, if there's nothing else," Panati announced, "then I think that we should continue." There were nods of agreement all around. "Susan, perhaps you could explain to the others what you found in the one box of files we managed to retain."

"As it turns out," Foster replied quickly, looking around the table, "nothing." She ignored Panati's expression of surprise and kept talking over his objections. "The trunk contained dribs and drabs of financial and medical records from Wyndham's clinic. I sorted through them last night and thought I found an interesting pattern in a very few of the medical records. But when I looked at them again this morning, it was fairly evident that the pattern owed more to Dr. Wyndham's unique penmanship than anything else. I'm afraid that the records we have don't indicate anything in support of his claims."

Panati obviously wanted to say more, to question Foster on how her interpretation of the records had changed so radically in the space of a few hours, but he didn't pursue it. Foster noticed that the others' questioning expressions indicated that they felt something was going on in the undercurrents, but she hoped they would pass it off to the sad circumstances of Montgomery's death.

The meeting didn't last much longer after Foster's negative report. Thorkel promised he would use his influence to make sure the investigation into the murders proceeded quickly and with as many personnel as possible. Delambre said he would have an abstract covering the Shroud of Turin Research Project's findings to everyone in a matter of days. Father Carey wondered if there were any point to continuing now that they seemed to have hit a dead end. But Father Panati said that Detective Fenton held out hope that the trunks might be recovered, especially if they held nothing that others would think of value. Father Carey offered a brief closing prayer for both Montgomery and the young man who had died with him, and the meeting was adjourned.

Father Panati's office was the archetype of an overworked academic's cubbyhole. In 1920, perhaps, it had been richly appointed with walnut bookshelves, a brass-trimmed desk, and solid, red-leather-covered furniture, but now it exhibited only a shabby layering of decades of scholastic neglect. The most common decoration in it were "Peanuts" cartoon strips, some yellowed and cracking. Foster read a few of the ones closest to her chair as she sat and waited for Panati to finish reading through his phone messages.

"What made you change your mind about the records?" Panati asked as he consigned most of the pink message slips to his overflowing wastebasket. "You seemed so positive last night."

"I haven't changed my mind at all," Foster said. Panati was even more confused and told her so. She described her suspicions.

"Those trunks of Wyndham's must have weighed close to a hundred pounds each. What group of two or three kids is going to haul those things up the stairs, let alone transport them from the scene of the crime? Unless your detective comes up with a better story, I'd say that whoever killed Montgomery and Walker was going after those trunks."

Panati put an elbow on his desk and leaned his head on his hand. "I just can't see that, Susan," he said. "Those records don't mean anything except to us. Who else could want them? And badly enough to kill for them?"

"I've no idea," Foster conceded. "But you have to admit that the timing is suspect. No one else knew about those trunks until we found them yesterday afternoon."

"Mrs. Kirby knew," Panati interrupted.

"She's known for months," Foster said. "Maybe even years. Besides, she's already gone through them. From the mess everything was in, I bet several people have been through them. Kids must have broken in there lots of times, seen the trunks, pawed through them, and then left them. So why did they all of a sudden become worth the trouble to steal—to kill for—within the few hours after you and I had located them?"

Panati leaned back in his chair with a thoughtful expression. "Just a minute, here," he suddenly said. "Are you suggesting that someone in the planning committee had something to do with stealing those trunks? Is that why you didn't say anything in the meeting? You think one of the people in there is a . . . a . . . spy or some such other thing?" Panati was acting astounded by the idea.

At least it's bringing the color back to his cheeks, Foster thought.

"Francis, all I'm saying is that it seems to be a strange coincidence, so what harm is done if we just keep things to ourselves until we find out one way or another?"

"The harm is you're asking me to distrust my friends and colleagues. How can I do that? Alex Thorkel has practically paid the salaries in my department for the past twenty years. I went through seminary with Scott. And Andre is one of my brightest students. I've had him in one course or another for almost four years. I've been his confessor a number of times. I know those people, Susan. That's why I confided in them in the first place.

I knew that confidentiality must be preserved until we decide what to do about it. They are all trustworthy people.'' Panati was clearly shaken.

''Well, then,'' Foster said diplomatically, ''maybe news about the trunks was passed on by someone else you talked to yesterday. *Did* you call anyone else after you spoke with Father Montgomery?''

''No,'' Panati said sullenly.

''Did Father Montgomery talk with anyone?''

''He talked with everyone. He arranged the meeting for today so we could start sorting through the other trunks. When I called everyone last night to tell them what had happened, they all mentioned it. They had all just talked to him that afternoon.''

''He didn't call me,'' Foster said.

''You were there when I talked to him from Mrs. Kirby's phone.''

Foster also realized that Panati hadn't phoned her as he had the others when he had learned of Montgomery's death. He had come to see her instead, at two-thirty in the morning. She decided not to ask him why, but he must have sensed her question.

''I came to see you last night because I wanted to talk to someone about it,'' he said quietly. ''The phone is too impersonal. And somehow, when we were in the apartment yesterday, I had the feeling that there was something about it that was troubling you. I suppose I just wanted to make sure that Father Montgomery wasn't going to be adding to your troubles.''

Simple enough, Foster thought. ''I'm glad you came by.''

''*Is* something troubling you, Susan?'' Panati asked, voice full of concern.

''Nothing major,'' she said with a smile. ''But I think we're getting off the topic here, Francis.''

''Yes, of course,'' he said and his voice returned to a semblance of normal.

''Do you agree that the theft of the trunks is a coincidence that bears looking into?'' she asked.

''I suppose I must.''

''I'm not accusing anyone of anything, you understand.''

''Oh, I'm quite aware of that. You're just being cautious. I'll go along with that for the time being.'' Panati paused for a moment. "Until Detective Fenton says they've found Montgomery's murderers and located the trunks."

"Fair enough," Foster agreed. She noticed that a tension had gone out of the room. "Well . . ." she prompted.

"Well what?"

"Don't you want to know what I put together out of those records I was telling you about last night?" She removed a four-by-five notebook from her shoulder bag.

Father Panati laughed at that. "Yes, I think I've come back to the real world now. Please do."

She had fifteen names, she told him, fifteen women who had been artificially inseminated by donor #72/SXM/4308 and who had not miscarried. Undoubtedly, since Wyndham had suggested that twenty to thirty clones might exist, the names of more women were in the other trunks.

"Any similarities among the women, apart from the donor?" Panati asked.

"What race was Jesus?" Foster asked in return. "Anything known about his ethnic origin?"

Panati looked down at his desk as if reading from notes. "Jewish, of course. Most cultures tend to depict him as one of their own but he would definitely have come from some Middle Eastern line. As in all things about him, there's been considerable research and debate, but no discoveries outside the truths within the Gospels."

"But, he would have had dark skin, dark hair, maybe Arabic features, characteristics like that?" Foster confirmed.

Panati nodded. "As far as anyone knows," he agreed.

"Then there could be another similarity," she said. "Most of these women, by name at least, appear to be from related ethnic backgrounds." She read down the list of names. "Shamir, Massoud, Naguib, Haddad, Nasser, Faron, Sulman. Then there's a grouping of Latin-sounding names: Estevez, Mendoza, Montalva, Almagro, and Guerrera. And then a few oddballs: Danylkiw, Smythe, and Amsden."

"And you think that might be significant because, if a clone from the blood on the shroud was going to produce a child with Mediterranean features, then it was best implanted in women who shared the same appearance, so they would accept it as their own?" Panati ventured.

"Exactly."

"Wouldn't there be a strong chance, however, that the child wouldn't resemble the woman's husband?"

"That would be acceptable," Foster explained, "if the couple involved in the supposed artificial insemination thought that anonymously donated sperm was to be used. I'm not sure how acceptable that procedure would be to people from Middle Eastern or Latin cultural and religious backgrounds, but maybe that's why so few of the implants were done: lack of volunteers. In fact, some of the records indicate that a few of the women were recruited almost as experimental subjects and paid money to have a child. A very questionable practice. Regardless, the couple involved would be free to think that the child resembled its biological father, someone unknown to both mother and father."

"Circumstantial, but I suppose it makes as much sense as anything else," Panati said. "So what do we do now? Track down those women and ask to see their children?"

"More or less," Foster said. "Unfortunately, only one of the women had a New York address. The others are spread out all over the country. And the addresses for all of them are anywhere between twelve and fourteen years old."

"You'll look for the New York woman first then?"

"That's the least expensive way to start," Foster said. "Going after the others is going to take some time and money."

"Well, if you have the time, Alex Thorkel will cover it for you at whatever your rates are. Expenses too."

Foster thanked Panati for that support. She hadn't accepted any new assignments in the past few months, only cashed in a few IRAs. In the back of her mind was the idea that she wouldn't have need of too many more acceptance checks.

"So how will you trace this woman?" Panati asked.

"Start at the library. Look her up in the city directories from fourteen years ago and take it from there. I already checked for her in the phone book this morning, but there's no listing at the old address."

"What's her name?" Panati asked, as though he had just realized that the woman had an identity.

Foster referred to her notebook. "Almagro," she read. "Constance Almagro. One of the women who were recruited.

Her record showed she gave birth to a boy named Paul. He'd be fourteen years old now."

A dreamy look came to Panati's eyes. "I wonder what he would have been like," he said.

"Paul Almagro?"

"No, no," Panati smiled. "Jesus. You know, outside of the Gospels, we have no historical references to him. And except for a brief mention in Luke, the only stories we have of him as a child are apocryphal. I'm afraid it's a bit like debating how many angels can dance on the proverbial pinhead, but I am curious. I wonder what he would have been like at the age of fourteen?"

"Maybe we're about to find out," Foster suggested.

"I hope not," Panati said softly. "I truly hope not."

SEVENTEEN

In one short week, a lot had happened in the small town of Larkin's Mill, Pennsylvania. Police Chief George Taylor had never seen anything like it in twenty-five years on the force. His seven officers were dizzy trying to keep up with a two thousand percent increase in complaints of peeping toms. Many of them were reported looking into second- and third-story windows.

Vandalism had also shot up. Improbable vandalism at that. Twenty-two houses had had their roofs spray-painted with graffiti. Most of it along the lines of "Asshole Acres" and "Nerd Alert." Then there were the cars. Almost all of the teachers at Walt Whitman P.S. had experienced trouble with the electrical systems of their vehicles. Trouble, hell, Taylor thought, their wiring harnesses were burned up like someone put twenty thousand volts through them.

The only thing Chief Taylor wasn't surprised about in the past week was the increase in UFO sightings in the town. Usually two objects had been reported, and usually accompanied by strange and other-worldly noises that a lot of witnesses had said sounded almost like laughter. Twenty years earlier, Taylor might have thought that the hippies had done something to the town's water supply. But today, there were so many groups he could suspect of such a thing that he didn't know where to start. Life had become very complex for Chief Taylor in the last two decades, and the past week wasn't helping matters at all.

It had been a hard week for thirteen-year-old Jason Coyle, too. In more ways than one. Every evening he had gone up to his bedroom at the agreed-upon time and waited for J.D. to appear at his window like something out of the Saturday Night Creature Feature on channel eight. The rest of it was like a dream. Come sunrise, he had difficulty believing that it had actually been real.

In seven short days he had already seen half of the girls in his class naked, or mostly naked, in their bedrooms and bathrooms. The bathroom stuff had been really cool. He had seen some of his teachers, too. Including Mrs. Sneddon actually doing it with her husband while *he* was wearing *her* underwear. When J.D. had started pounding and screaming at the Sneddons' bedroom window, Jason had thought he would wet his pants with laughter. The next best thing to being a mutant, he supposed, was being a mutant's best friend.

In fact, during the daytime, he and J.D. had had long talks about whether or not Professor Xavier's School for Gifted Youngsters might be based on a real place. J.D. said it might be worth a call to Marvel Comics in New York just to ask a few questions.

Of course, there were a couple of drawbacks to the whole thing, Jason knew. J.D. had been spending most of his allowance on dates and stuff the last few months so the money for the spray paint had had to come from Jason's bank account, along with the money for the bus trips to Windford so they could buy the paint in stores Chief Taylor wouldn't be visiting. He knew his mother would shit if she found out he was making withdrawals from the money that he was supposed to use to visit his dad in August, but J.D. had figured they would have the money made up with their earnings from Lucasfilm by then. Whenever Jason got too worried about what was happening, a few words from J.D. seemed to make things better.

Then there was the loss of sleep. Between staying up half the night as the Larkin's Mill X-Men and staying up the other half of the night thinking about Mrs. Sneddon and the girls in his class, Jason doubted he was getting more than an hour or two of sleep each night. But all that would end soon, he thought as he walked down the tree-covered street to J.D.'s house. This weekend it was off to California, George Lucas, and fame, fortune, and women! Not girls, J.D. had to keep reminding him, but women. Jason thought that the women part of it would be easier now that J.D. had made his pimples go away.

Jason was five oak trees down from the Danylkiw house when he had his first warning of impending doom. There was a silver Audi parked in the driveway.

Jason cut up a neighbor's yard and walked crouched over in front of the old wooden porch that most of the houses on the street had. That way he was able to check out the Audi without being seen from the Danylkiws' front window. There was a small dent on the Audi's hood, not enough to break the paint but just about the size of a Nike jogging shoe. It was Lori Daniels's father's car. This was not impending doom, Jason thought, this was the Grand Canyon of deep shit.

The thirteen-year-old decided it was not the proper time to ring the Danylkiws' doorbell and instead made his way across the street and down two more overreaching oak trees to the mailbox at the corner. There was a black Ford Aerostar parked by it which would give him the cover he needed. He could sit on the curb until the Audi left and then head in to check out the damage. Part of Jason wished that he was the one who was being bawled out for messing around with a girl. The other part hoped that J.D. would go easy on them all.

Inside the Danylkiw house, things were a lot quieter than they normally were. In the Danish Modern living room, Tom Danylkiw stood by the teak and black leather chair his wife, Carol, sat in. Across from them, Elliot Daniels sat at one end of the sofa and his daughter Lori sat at the other, staring at the floor with her hands folded in her lap. John Danylkiw, at least as red-cheeked as Lori, sat alone in another chair. For the moment, fortunately, he was being ignored. Unfortunately, the reason he was being ignored was because Mr. Daniels had just deposited onto the coffee table what John had left behind in Lori's bedroom and everyone in the living room was staring at John Danylkiw's Fruit of the Looms. Whatever else he was, he was fourteen years old and he wanted to die.

"Ah, well," Carol Danylkiw said to break the silence, "they might be John's . . ." She stopped and looked at John as if she had no idea what else Mr. Daniels wanted her to say. Her green eyes narrowed in her freckled face, silently asking her husband or her son for some help.

John looked at his father. For some reason, his father had the megaserious expression he wore when he was trying not to laugh. What was funny about Mr. Daniels practically torturing his daughter into confessing that it was John who had jumped out of her bedroom window last Friday night? John wanted to know.

"Of course they're his!" Elliot Daniels said indignantly. He was a short, prissy-looking man with a small black moustache and, at the moment, his cheeks were even brighter than John's and Lori's. "My Lori says they're his, so of course they are!"

"I don't think that's the point here, Mr. Daniels," John's father said, trying to diffuse the man's anger. Tom Danylkiw was the opposite of his wife: coffee skin, wavy brown hair, and penetrating black eyes. A fascinating history of globe-circling ancestral heritage was spoken of in his features. None of his friends or neighbors thought twice about John's darker appearance.

"What do you think the point is, then?" Daniels demanded. His voice was becoming shrill. It had been growing more and more high-pitched each time Mr. Daniels realized that John's parents weren't taking this matter quite as seriously as he was.

"The point is, Mr. Daniels, that our kids appear to have gotten carried away in something which we should discuss with them, as parents, and in private. I don't think a confrontational app—"

"*Carried away!*" Mr. Daniels sputtered. "My daughter didn't get carried away! She doesn't get involved in such sordid things. She was forced! Your . . . your . . . filthy urchin rap—"

"*Daddy!*" shrieked Lori. "John didn't *force* me and we didn't *do* anything!"

"Of course he forced you, sweetheart," Daniels said, voice trembling. "Filthy boys like him always—"

"That's quite enough!" It was Tom Danylkiw's turn to raise his voice. "This conversation is getting completely out of hand. I will not stand by and let you keep insulting my son when it's clear that Lori is older than—"

"You leave my daughter out of this!"

"You were the asshole who brought her *into* this!"

"How dare—"

"Daddy!"

And then John took over.

"Shut up," he said, barely loudly enough to be clearly heard over the adults' ranting, but it did its job. Everyone stopped talking instantly.

There was a moment's silence, as if they were trying to remember why they had fallen silent, and then the three adults and Lori opened their mouths to continue.

Nothing came out.

Not only had they stopped talking, they were no longer capable of speech at all.

John sat back for a moment, feeling peace return to him. It had taken a while for the idea To come to him, but this approach was better than floating in front of them or putting his hands under the hood of Mr. Daniels's Audi and burning out its ignition system. Yeah, this was the absolute best. Then he noticed that Lori was rubbing at her throat the way the adults were, opening and closing her mouth like a suffocating fish.

"You can talk, Lori," he said to her softly.

"Acck," she croaked. "What happened?"

John stood up and walked over to her side of the couch. "It's okay. I'm just making them be quiet for a while." He held out his hand to her.

"What?" she said. "How . . . ?" She took his hand and stood up beside him.

"Shhh," he smiled at her. Then he looked at Mr. Daniels, who clutched with both hands at his suddenly shut-down vocal cords. "There are a few things I want to say to your father," John said. He only wished Jase had been there to witness this, the greatest triumph yet of the Larkin's Mill X-Men!

Across the street, Jason Coyle was having a hard time keeping track of what was happening over at J.D.'s house. At one point, he was certain he had heard voices coming from the house, and if he could hear them from where he was sitting then they sure had to have been loud. It was at just about that time that another black Aerostar pulled up in front of the first. Two men got out of the second van. One was bald and the other had a beard. They wore windbreakers and jeans and Jason didn't recognize them as being from the neighborhood. Then two more men got out of the first van. Both had blond hair and they looked related, like brothers.

Since the second van was blocking his view of the Danylkiws' driveway, Jason got up from the curb beside the mailbox. The man with the beard noticed him and tapped the arm of one of the blond men. Both checked what looked to be an instant photograph of something and then stared at him for a few seconds longer. Then they wiggled their fingers at each other and turned away. They looked as if they were trying to watch J.D.'s house, too.

The thousands of hours of television he had watched in his thirteen short years were paying off for Jason. He clearly recognized that he was witnessing what Officer MacGruff called "suspicious behavior." Jason had an almost Pavlovian desire to find a grown-up to tell about the four men in the two black vans. He started to walk away from the vans, scanning the windows on the street for the familiar red sign of a Block Parent house. But the only sign he could see was in the Danylkiws' window and he couldn't go there because he didn't want to tip off the bad guys.

Jason saw the men were busy at the back of one of the vans so he crossed the narrow residential street and went up to the door of the house two down from J.D.'s house. He seemed to remember J.D. waving hello to the people who lived here last summer so maybe they'd be partially intelligent. He rang the doorbell three different times. The blond men by the vans were carrying small dark cases. All four men were waving their hands around and looking at J.D.'s house. Jason started to feel panicky.

He walked quickly over to the house next door to the Danylkiws'. He rang the doorbell and knocked on the screen door. The men were crossing the street. Baldy was looking at Jason.

The front door opened. A man who, to Jason, was at least two hundred years old stood there.

"What do you want?" the old man said, clearly annoyed and smacking his gums.

Jason looked over at the men again. They were going up the Danylkiws' front walk.

Jason opened the screen door and tried to step into the old man's house. The old man pushed Jason back.

"You're not going to rob me, you little thief!" the old man snarled gleefully.

Jason struggled to stay within the door. "Call the police," he whispered.

"That's just what I'm going to do if you don't go away!" the old man cackled. He shoved Jason out the door and slammed it.

Jason pounded on the screen door again. "Please! Please!" he cried. Then he looked over to the Danylkiws' front porch. The screen door over there hung down at an angle. The men were gone.

Once again, Jason didn't hesitate. It didn't matter to him if the men were Russian spies after the secret of J.D.'s powers, or even emissaries from Magneto's Brotherhood of Evil Mutants, just like in the comics. All he knew was, if it was J.D. they wanted, first they must deal with Jason Coyle, a Larkin's Mill X-Man, and J.D.'s best friend.

The tears were rolling freely down John Danylkiw's face as he watched Lori's father take the underwear from the coffee table and put it on his head, just as John had suggested. Even Lori was laughing, though she was trying hard not to. John's parents, still speechless, wore more serious expressions, but John figured that could be dealt with later. Then the front door burst open.

Four men rushed in, two carrying small black cases. The first one through the front door saw John standing in the living room and led the others in.

John's parents and Lori's father struggled to stand up but John's suggestion that they not be able to leave their seats held firm. The four men rushed into the living room, hesitating when they saw the three adults sitting there, but quickly realized that, for some reason, the adults weren't going to try to stop them.

John and Lori stood by the couch and ineffectually shouted

at the men to go away. The reality of the men's presence hadn't sunk in and the children made no move to escape.

Their inaction was broken when the first man reached them and slammed his forearm into Lori's head, sending her tumbling over the coffee table. John swung his fist reflexively at the man's bearded face but he ducked easily and came up after the swing to catch John's arm. John tried to pull away but a second man, the bald one, came up from behind and lifted him, immobilizing him in a bear hug.

One of the blond men opened his small case on the coffee table. John peered in. It looked like the inside of a doctor's bag. Reality finally clicked in.

"Move! Move!" he shouted at the adults. "You can speak!"

Instantly Tom Danylkiw threw himself on the back of the man at the case. Elliot Daniels ignored the two other men holding John and jumped over to his daughter, groggily sitting in the middle of the floor. The second blond man swung his case against Daniels's head and sent him down to join Lori. Carol Danylkiw kicked viciously at the man who had struck Daniels, hobbling him but getting the case across her jaw as a counterblow.

John couldn't move against the pressure of the bear hug. He felt he was being suffocated. He winced as he saw his father flipped onto his back and kicked in the head.

The man who had kicked John's father went back to the case on the coffee table. John could see blood trickling from his mother's mouth. He began to tremble all over. He couldn't breathe but, it seemed, he no longer had to breathe.

Jason appeared in the front hallway. He stared into the living room with his beady eyes so wide they almost looked normal. He saw John being held by two men from the vans and sprang forward like a championship sprinter, his mouth opening into a deafening yowl of attack.

John knew that his friend was intending to shout, "X-Men assemble!" and in the back of his mind, he thanked Jason for that. Then he killed the bald man holding him in the bear hug the same way he had burned out the ignition systems in all those cars. Twenty thousand volts.

The man didn't even have time to scream. He crumpled backward and John dropped to the floor. His arm was still held by the bearded man but John stared him in the eyes. The man let go and began cautiously to back away.

Jason was hollering and flailing his arms like propellors at the man who had kicked John's father. The man was trying to connect with his case but Jason's rotund body kept weaving out of the way with the light-footed grace of a dancer. The boy was inspired and capable of great things. But the other blond man was coming up from behind.

John flew.

He pushed off from the corner of the coffee table and arced over to Jason. The three men who were left fell back at the sight of John grabbing Jason's arm and pulling the fat boy up into the air to float beside him.

"Don't move," John commanded from against the living room ceiling. Beside him, Jason bobbed back and forth with each puffing breath. His fists were bloodied.

The three men exchanged glances.

"Come down now or I will kill these people with this," the bearded man said. His words sounded sloppy and illformed. He held up a hypodermic needle from the open case.

"Don't speak!" John shouted at him.

The man knelt down beside John's mother and roughly pulled up on her right arm. She moaned.

"STOP IT!" John shrieked, but the man was unaffected, as if he couldn't hear John's commands.

"Come down or she dies," the man said and held the needle against Carol Danylkiw's forearm. John could see the man's fingers digging into his mother's flesh.

"All right," John said. "All right, I'll come down."

He and Jason descended slowly. Lori and John's father were conscious and watched without understanding what they saw. Elliot Daniels groaned softly into the carpet.

"Don't try anything," the man with the hypodermic needle warned.

Then John felt a sharp stab in his right buttock and cried out.

"Nothing!" the bearded man shouted as he pressed the needle against John's mother.

John trembled with ferocious anger but the threat to his mother made him unable to act. The men would not respond to his commands. He could feel numbness spreading up his back. He heard Jason squeal beside him.

The drug worked quickly. Jason fell flat on his face. John slumped to his knees. From the corner of his rapidly blurring vision, John saw the body of the man he had killed being carried away.

I wonder if I'll go to hell? he thought. And then the numbness spread all the way.

As Lori, her father, and the Danylkiws waited for Chief Taylor to arrive, they wondered what they could possibly say. Surely the things they had seen had not been real.

"The boy's a demon," Mr. Daniels said. "He's not human." The side of his face was swollen blue and yellow. He spat blood from his mouth onto the living room carpet.

"Shut up, Daniels," Tom Danylkiw said tightly as he pressed an ice-filled washcloth against his wife's face.

"I will not shut up," Daniels said. "First your boy *flies* from my daughter's bedroom window. Then he *hypnotizes* me. And then he floats around the room as if he was a witch or something . . ."

Tom Danylkiw stood up from his wife's side and walked over to Elliot Daniels.

"Mr. Daniels," he said, and it was in a voice that demanded attention, "I don't know what went on here just now, but I do know that it involved a great deal of violence and certainly those men had cases full of drugs. What we saw was probably something that minds do when they get beaten silly and are exposed to drugs. What we saw probably never happened. But what did happen is that my son has been taken by people and we don't know who they are or why they did it." It was hard to tell if Danylkiw was about to scream or about to cry. "So you just shut your filthy goddamn fucking mouth up before I do it for you."

Elliot Daniels clenched his teeth. There was something in there aching to come out.

"Mr. Danylkiw," Lori said in a fragile voice. The blood on her head came from her scalp. "I saw part of the license numbers on the vans they were driving. I memorized them. I did."

Tom Danylkiw's face softened instantly.

"Oh, dear God, child," he said to her, a look of enormous relief spreading across his face. "Thank you, oh thank you." He went to hug her.

"Keep your hands off her!" Daniels shouted.

Danylkiw spun, face contorting with fury. "For God's sake, Daniels! My son has just been kidnapped!"

Daniels sputtered and snorted and came out with, "Well . . . well . . . it serves him right!"

Tom Danylkiw was glad the man had said it. The sound of his fist smacking Daniels' jaw helped take some of the pain away from the day. Not a lot of it, but enough.

EIGHTEEN

It was a bad day for Jim Hyams. It had been a bad week. In fact, he thought, the whole year deserved to be shucked out into the trash and hauled away on a barge. Here he was, no longer a special detective, not even an Academy rookie, and he was doing surveillance duty to break the suspected murder of Detective Julian Burch, a man he had detested.

If he thought he had a choice in the matter, Hyams would have cut bait days ago. The ten thousand a year he had from his parents' trust fund would go far in Mexico, he knew. But Detective Ioannou had him by the pink, round, and hairy ones. One step out of the city, Hyams had been told, and he was an accessory to Burch's murder. It wasn't supposed to be fair. It was the system. At least Ioannou's version of it.

Surveillance of Paul Almagro's old apartment building was tedious and, Hyams concluded, that was why Ioannou had assigned him to it. Technically, he was supposed to keep track of all those who appeared to have regular business in the building and watch for any indications that *El Niño* was trying to get some of the things out of his apartment. But Hyams felt he was simply being put on a shelf until Ioannou figured an angle on the case. Detectives like Burch just did not murder apartment landlords so they could commit suicide in a room from which another body disappeared. If Ioannou's waiting to make sense out of that situation, Hyams thought, I'll be stuck on this duty till the end of the century.

Hyams settled back in the front seat of the beat-up Maverick he had been assigned from the motor pool. The car looked so shoddy and rusted out that if he had to leave it for any reason, it should be safe from the street vultures for at least an hour. He lit another Marlboro Light and stared down the tenement street, thinking of Mexican sunlight.

About a half a pack later, someone who was not a regular of the street walked past Hyams's Maverick. Hyams dutifully marked the time of her appearance on the police-issue black notebook open beside him and shook his head. The street was high welfare, high crime, high drugs, and low everything else. The woman was about as out of place as she could get and still be on the same planet. She stopped in front of Paul Almagro's apartment building. Hyams stubbed out his cigarette.

As one of his courses had taught him, he began to assemble a description of her as she stood looking up the stone steps to the plywood-covered main doors of the building. Female, cauc. Five ten. A hundred and thirty. Short, dark hair. He'd put her in her late twenties, maybe early thirties. He guessed that the simple slacks, jacket, and blouse she wore cost as much as a first-year officer would make in a month. Her shoulder bag might as well have had a big sign on it that said "Steal me." Whatever she thought she was doing, he thought, she sure shouldn't be doing it in this neighborhood.

The woman walked up the steps and pulled open the door. Hyams was positive she wasn't a hooker making a phone date so he got out of the car and headed over to the building. Time for his good deed of the day.

When Hyams stepped into the dimly lit lobby, the woman wasn't there. He passed the taped outline of the landlord's body and headed to the staircase. Already she was at least a floor above him.

Hyams was breathing a bit more forcefully by the time he reached the floor on which she had turned off—the seventh. Now he really was curious. It was Almagro's floor. She was standing halfway down the corridor, one hand in her shoulder bag. Hyams walked down to her, slowly and smiling. He knew she was in the wrong neighborhood because she didn't even appear to be nervous at his approach.

"Hello there," he said. "Can I help you?" Seeing her up close like that, he decided to add attractive to his description.

The woman didn't say anything. But she moved her feet as if she were bracing herself.

"It's all right," Hyams said, trying to reassure her. "I'm a police officer."

"Then let's see the badge," the woman said coolly.

Hyams stopped about six feet from her. Oops, he thought.

"I, ah, I don't exactly have one," he said sheepishly.

The woman removed a cylinder from her purse and held it in front of her. "Then I'd back off nice and slow," she suggested.

"Ah, did you know Mace was an offense now?" Hyams said. No wonder she wasn't nervous. He backed away a step.

The woman stepped forward. "When you find your badge, you can write me a ticket," she said.

Hyams held up one hand and reached into his back pocket with the other. "Just a second. I've got my ID from the Academy." He pulled out his wallet and held it open to his trainee photo card.

"Academy?" the woman repeated.

"Almost a police officer," Hyams said. He held out his wallet at arm's length. The woman's free hand shot out and snapped it from his loose grip. For an awful moment, Hyams thought he was going to be ripped off.

The woman examined the photo card and Hyams. Then flipped through the rest of the wallet. When she came to the driver's license she looked up at him with raised eyebrows.

"James *Kirk* Hyams?" she asked.

"My parents claim they never saw the show," Hyams explained. He was used to it by now. He hoped she wouldn't make the joke about him making captain. She didn't.

She handed back the wallet. "I'm Susan Foster," she said. "Is it too much to ask why you were following me in here?"

She eased the aerosol can of Mace to her side but made no move to put it back in her bag.

"I was going to ask you the same thing," Hyams said, replacing his wallet. "Not following me, I mean, I wasn't following you, I mean, just what you were doing here."

Foster smiled at the three sentences in one. A nice smile, too, Hyams noticed.

"Is there a problem with me being here?" Foster asked. "I saw the outline down in the lobby. You're helping out with some sort of investigation as a class project?"

"Not a class project," Hyams said. He kept his distance, she kept her Mace ready. "I was out of class on a special assignment for a couple of months and the detective I was teamed with . . . ah . . . was killed here last week."

"Sorry to hear that," she said without sounding as if she meant it. "So?"

This wasn't going like any interrogation for which Hyams had ever been trained. The suspect was the one who was supposed to feel off guard.

"So," Hyams said uneasily, "you're standing in front of the apartment of the guy who's suspected of being involved with the murder." And she was.

"Almagro?"

Hyams nodded. This was getting interesting. What was her connection to him?

"The son?" Foster asked for clarification. "Paul Almagro the fourteen-year-old boy?"

"That's the one," Hyams said. "*El Niño*. Leader of all the gangs."

They watched each other with half-smiles of surprise.

"Paul Almagro is a gang leader?" Foster asked.

"Not *a* gang leader. *The* gang leader. My partner was investigating him. He said that by August, *El Niño* would have almost all the gangs in the city under central control."

Foster whistled silently. Hyams couldn't help but notice her lips. This is ridiculous, he thought.

"What's your interest in Paul?" he asked her.

Foster's eyes narrowed. "It's his mother actually. Constance. I'm a science reporter. She took part in a . . . a special medical study about fifteen years ago and I'm following it up for an article I'm working on."

Hyams was impressed. She was smart, too. "What kind of medical study?" he asked.

"Use of radioactive iodine in the treatment of thyroid conditions," Foster said quickly. "*Is* the mother still around?"

"No information on any family or relatives," Hyams said. He felt as if he were apologizing to her.

"You wouldn't happen to have a photograph of him by any chance?" Foster suddenly asked as if she just had a brilliant idea.

Hyams looked at her questioning expression and decided it was a good thing Susan Foster was too smart, too successful, and too good-looking for him. Realizing that at this stage was going to save him a lot of grief.

"Would it help your follow-up?" he asked.

"Sure would," Foster agreed. "She had the treatment before her son was born and the effects of it on children are what I'm concentrating on. A photograph of Paul might reveal characteristics related to the treatment."

"Sort of like thalidomide?"

"Not as drastic as that. *Do* you have a photograph?"

"Not exactly," Hyams said, wondering if he should proceed. "But there are police photos of him in his file. He's a juvenile so I couldn't let you take them or use them in a magazine or whatever, but if you think looking at them would help . . . ?"

"A tremendous help," Foster said with a smile. "When can I see his file?"

Hyams felt as awkward as if he were asking her out on a first date. He checked his watch. "I have duty for another three hours. After that we could go to the station. If anyone asks any questions, just say you're in to identify some kid who tried to take your purse. Okay?"

"Okay," she said. Then she looked at the apartment door. "I suppose everything's been cleared out of there?"

"No pictures, if that's what you mean," Hyams apologized again. "And I couldn't let you in, anyway."

"That's all right." Foster shrugged and she reached out to touch his arm. "Where shall we meet when you get off?"

They set a time and a place and Hyams escorted her from the building and over to Fifth where she'd have a better chance of getting a cab. Foster had a car, she told him, but she knew better than to try street parking up here. Hyams waited with her until she flagged a cab and then he walked back to the Maverick, already the subject of intense interest to a group of kids.

For the rest of the afternoon, Hyams and his cigarettes kept watch on the apartment building and he didn't once think of Mexican sunlight. Instead, and much to his embarrassment, he thought of the way she had touched his arm.

NINETEEN

The room was stifling hot. Juan knew that meant the sun was shining out in the barrio, sparkling in the chrome of the low-riders, burning in a yellow ball too bright to look at, but able to be blocked out by a single hand. Juan held out his hand before his face. He could see nothing. Those dreams had stopped.

"Juan? Do you want something?"

Juan felt his cousin's hands enwrap his own. Marguerite was always there, always his strength and his support.

"No, dear one. I was just trying to touch the sun." He did not need eyes to know the wistful expression on her face.

"The dreams again?" she asked.

"Not like before," Juan said. "Different dreams. Nighttime dreams." He squeezed Marguerite's hands. "In them, I'm flying."

"In an airplane?" Marguerite asked in a voice full of wonder.

"No, just by myself. Someone else is there with me but we fly on our own. Like birds." Marguerite said nothing. "That is not the dream you want to hear, is it? You want other dreams. The dreams you always talk to me about. The future. And freedom."

"Your dreams are miracles, Juan. Like your touch. But why should God send you just ordinary dreams that mean so little? Why can he not send the dreams like in the Bible?"

"And why can I not heal myself?" Juan took his hand away from hers. He pushed against the arms of his chair to make himself more comfortable.

"Is it time for . . . ?" Marguerite asked gently.

"Not yet," Juan interrupted. He had never minded being changed and cleaned by Marguerite. One handicap among many which he had learned to accept. But with the new dreams, the nighttime dreams, had come visions of girls and women as he had never known they could be. He found them disturbing. He felt uncomfortable now, when Marguerite attended to him.

"Perhaps the dreams aren't ordinary," he said to change the subject. "Perhaps they only seem ordinary because I have not yet learned to interpret them in the way they were intended." He shifted again.

"Do you think so?" Marguerite asked. There was an aching plea to her voice.

"I don't know, dear cousin. There is so much I don't understand. I wish . . . I wish . . ."

"Yes?" Marguerite said. Juan did not reply.

"Perhaps it is time I changed you," Marguerite said after a few moments. Juan's embarrassment was echoed in her voice. "Esperanza's visitors will be coming soon and—"

"No!" Juan said. "Not again. I will . . . I will . . . like the dream." He pushed both hands as hard as he could against the arms of his chair.

"Juan don't!" Marguerite cried. "You shall fall again and Esperanza will beat us!"

"Don't touch me," Juan commanded.

Marguerite stood still in the dark room, her hands useless at her sides. Only the one candle they were permitted when there were no visitors was lit and the wooden face of the Savior hid in its dark shadows. She bit her lip as she watched her cousin rise in his chair, legs stiff and unmoving beneath the shawl he wore over them. He had tried this many times. And he had failed many times. But this time, his hands left the chair and he continued to rise.

"Juan . . ." she breathed in amazement. "You have done it."

For the first time in her life, she saw her cousin stand upright, head erect and proud. After all these years, the miracles he had brought to so many others were now being repaid to him.

"You can walk," she said. "You can walk." Maybe God would restore Juan's vision, too, give him normal irises and pupils instead of the solid white eyes he had had since birth. "Perhaps now," she said recklessly, "we can leave this place. Escape from Esperanza."

"Not yet," Juan said.

"Why? You can walk now. We can get away."

"We must wait."

"Wait? For what?"

"For . . . for a . . . friend," Juan finally said.

"What friend?" Marguerite asked in confusion.

Juan twisted his head around the room as if his blind eyes were trying to catch sight of something elusive. "A dream friend," he said as if it made sense.

"When is the friend coming?" Marguerite asked.

Again Juan twisted his head. "Soon," he said. "Soon, and then I will go with him."

"What about me?" Marguerite said in surprise. "Will I not go with you?"

Juan moved his head to face the floor and then raised it again. "Take me to the bathroom," he said and held out his arm to be guided.

"But what about—"

"Please, Marguerite, now," Juan said. "For the first time in my life, let me do this by myself." He moved smoothly, assuredly forward.

Marguerite bowed her head. "Very well," she said and directed him to the door.

When he was in the hall, she turned him in the direction of the bathroom and he set off on his own. She marveled at the strength and grace of his footsteps. And then his shawl fell away from him and she saw that as he moved down the hall, his legs hung motionless, his feet dangling inches above the floor.

She crossed herself and fought to hold back the scream struggling within her. Send that friend soon, she prayed to the Savior, send him soon.

TWENTY

"So what science magazines do you write for?" Jim Hyams asked as Foster aimed her Prelude toward illusory gaps in the rush hour traffic. "*Omni?*" he suggested.

"I said *science* magazines," Foster grimaced. "*Discover, The Sciences*, industrial specialty magazines. A few features in the *Times*." She looked over at Hyams to make sure he hadn't felt insulted by her comment. He was smiling at her.

"Well, I only read *Omni* for the pictures anyway," he said.

A good sport, she thought. Cute, too, as if it meant anything. She didn't think she was quite old enough to be his mother but she might as well be.

"So, if Paul Almagro is wanted by the police," she said, swerving in front of a taxi and shooting through an amber light, "shouldn't there be a photo of him put out into general circulation? Like a wanted poster or something?"

"Of course," Hyams said and tapped at his forehead. "I'm too used to thinking it's an undercover operation. I can get you one of the bulletin notices with Paul's picture on it. Turn right up at the lights."

Foster decided she couldn't pass the bus beside her so she suddenly braked and slid in behind it. The cab she had cut off earlier, and which had been manfully striving to pass her ever since, barely avoiding smashing into her from behind. She smiled and waved as the cabbie screeched by, leaning on his horn. If she had been alone, she would have said something to him, too.

"Is it common for rookies to be taken out of the Academy for special assignment?" she asked.

"It happens from time to time," Hyams said. "Usually when they need a fresh young face in an undercover operation. Most cops don't make detective till they're in their thirties." Foster cringed. He made "thirties" sound ancient. "In Operation Superbowl, the average age of the gang members was between twelve and eighteen years old."

"You're not eighteen, are you?" Foster asked, trying to be funny about it.

"A bit older than that," he said. From the corner of her eye, she could tell he was watching her. For a reaction? "Twenty-four," he told her.

Twelve years difference, Foster thought. The phrase that came to mind was San Quentin quail. Oh well, even if he were ninety he'd still outlive me.

Hyams pointed out the entrance to the police lot and, with a squeal of brakes, Foster landed them safely.

Hyams still had a desk on the fourth floor—a place where Ioannou could leave messages. It was beside the bathrooms, as far as it could be from a window, and had no phone, but it was a spot where Foster could sit while Hyams brought her *El Niño*'s file. As she waited, she looked around at the other desks crammed into the open area and watched the detectives at work. She couldn't tell how any of them knew what they were doing. It was even louder, messier, and more confused than the first newsroom in which she had worked in Detroit.

A bulletin board on a wall about ten feet from the desk, no doubt placed there to intercept the bathroom traffic, reflected the confusion of the room. Foster estimated an archaeologist could find at least three levels of earlier civilizations beneath the outer layers of multicolored notices and announcements pinned, taped, and stapled to the board. The most prominent among them featured items for sale: time-share condos, furniture, and guns. A few other notices mentioned PAL events and dances. Departmental stationery displayed neatly typed lists that Foster couldn't read and, as if in token gesture to the work being done there, a few wanted posters hung in the topmost corner. She had just noticed them when Hyams came back.

"Any of those pictures of Paul?" Foster asked as Hyams placed a thick file case on the desk. He squinted at the board.

"Oh, yeah," he said. "Good eyes." He went over to the bulletin board, stood there a moment reading the fine print on one of the posters, then came back shaking his head.

"Thought it was but it wasn't," he told her. "Some poor kid

who was kidnapped in Pennsylvania." He started to pull up a second chair.

"Was there a name on the notice?" Foster asked. She didn't like coincidences.

Hyams froze in the middle of sitting down. "I'll get it for you," he said with an accommodating smile.

She saw him pull one notice from the board, look at it, then remove a second. He handed her both notices. "Double kidnapping," he said.

Foster stared at the fat child's face on the top notice. The last name was Coyle.

"The bottom one's the guy I thought looked like *El Niño*," Hyams said.

Foster examined the second notice. She saw the soft, undistinguished face of a fourteen-year-old boy with dark, brooding eyes and, though it was hard to tell from a black-and-white picture, a dark complexion. She checked the name. Danylkiw. It was on her list.

"Show me a photograph of Paul," she snapped. "Quickly."

Hyams slipped the elastic cord from the file case on the desk and slid out the contents. He pulled out a recent copy of *El Niño*'s rap sheet. Police photos were stapled to it. He looked at them appraisingly until Foster pulled them down to the desk.

"That's odd," he said. "They could almost be twins."

Foster felt her chest constrict. Paul Almagro and John Danylkiw *could* almost be twins. Paul had a thinner face, leaner perhaps, more intent. John's was rounder, lighter, almost spoiled-looking. But both shared the same dark eyes, the same long nose. And Paul's mother and a woman named Danylkiw had been artificially inseminated at Wyndham's clinic.

"Are you all right?" she heard Hyams ask her.

"Fine," she said. "Fine. *When* was the Danylkiw boy kidnapped?"

Hyams pointed out the on-or-about date at the bottom of the notice: one week after the trunks were stolen from Wyndham's apartment building.

"And when did Paul go missing?"

"Two weeks before the kidnapping," Hyams said, a look of concern on his face. "Are you thinking there's a connection between these kids?" He looked at the photographs again. If John had been brought up on the streets of New York, he might have had that lean intent look. If Paul had lived all his life in the middle-class security of a small Pennsylvania town, perhaps he would have had a chance to put on some extra weight. "*Is* there a connection between these kids?"

Foster tried to remain calm. "Are there any more kidnapping reports?" she asked. There was too much concern in her voice for Hyams not to be alerted.

"Couple of hundred kids go missing every day," he said. "What's the connection here, Ms. Foster?"

"Then why aren't there a couple of hundred notices up on that board?" Foster countered. "I said 'kidnapping reports.' Like this one." She read from the notice. "Four kidnappers. Drugging the kids before they take them. Vans rented with stolen credit cards. This doesn't happen every day. Is there a central data base or something you can search through?"

"Search for what?" Hyams sounded exasperated.

Foster pulled a four-by-five notebook from her bag, flipped through it, and ripped out a page of handwriting.

"Fifteen names," she said, handing the page to Hyams. "Check to see if any child kidnapped or reported missing in the last two weeks has one of these names."

Hyams took the page but didn't look at it. "Why?" he asked.

Foster tried to remember the lie she had told him back at Paul's apartment building. She decided to try something new, more startling. "All the mothers of the children on that list were given an experimental drug during their pregnancies," she began, hoping that if she talked fast enough he'd accept her intent if not her details. "There were side effects for the children. That's what I'm writing about. But the drug company behind it may be attempting to get rid of the of the children to keep the story hidden." She looked at him, willing him to believe what she said.

"Do you have any proof?" he asked.

She couldn't read the expression on his face. She shook her head. "That's why I'm trying to find the mothers."

Hyams read the page from her notebook and took a deep breath. "Okay," he said. "But then you're going to have to fill me in on what's really going on here. I have an uncle who had radioactive iodine treatments in the fifties and as far as I know, they haven't been used since then. And I'm not prepared to think that drug companies go around kidnapping people so they can hide side effects. If they did that, a lot more people would be disappearing each year." He paused for a moment. Foster felt he was giving her an opportunity to come clean. She said nothing.

"If there's a connection between these two kids and any of what you've been telling me," Hyams continued, "then I'll introduce you to some detectives who can help you. But if there's a connection between all this and what happened to my partner, then you're going to have to tell *me* everything. My ass is on the line here and getting Records to run these names through isn't going to help me any. Is that a deal?"

"Deal," Foster nodded. Hyams walked off through the maze of desks and she tried to create a new story to tell him. If he didn't believe the one about a drug company conspiracy, then he definitely wasn't going to believe the truth.

Hyams was back within half an hour. He had a serious expression on his face, about a foot of computer printout in one hand, and another piece of paper in his other. He put the printout down in front of Foster.

"Ahmed Shamir," he said without inflection. "Thirteen-year-old boy in Montreal, Canada."

Foster could understand enough of the cryptic abbreviations on the police printout to read the details.

"Killed," she said softly. "During what might have been a kidnapping attempt."

"He was on your list," Hyams said accusingly. He threw down the other sheet of paper. It was a wire photo. It might have been of John Danylkiw, or of Paul Almagro. The resemblance was that strong. But, instead, it showed the empty staring face of a boy who had been cruelly thrown from a twelfth-floor balcony during a fight with three assailants who had broken into his parent's apartment.

"What's the story, Ms. Foster?" Hyams asked. He made it sound official.

Foster spread the three photographs in front of her. No longer twins, they could be triplets. And there were twelve more names on her list, perhaps another fifteen in the missing trunks.

She stared up at Hyams, assessing his resolve. It seemed solid. She couldn't think of a convincing way to back down.

"The most important thing for you to understand right now," she began, "is that I'm only trying to *locate* these boys. It seems there're some others who are trying to *kill* them. And I don't know who those others are."

Hyams sat on the edge of the desk and waited expectantly for Foster to continue. She didn't let him down.

THE POWER

JULY/AUGUST

ONE

Jason Coyle had decided there was a pretty good chance he was dead. He couldn't see anything. He couldn't hear anything, and about the only thing he could feel was a tightness that pulled at all the parts of his body. The evil mutants killed me, he thought, and now I'm being buried in a coffin. He wondered if J.D. had been killed, too. He wondered if his mother was feeling bad for not increasing his allowance. He wondered if corpses could feel they had to use the bathroom.

Jason heard something. It sounded far away, or maybe just muffled. Then he saw something. It was like seeing sunlight through his eyelids. That's an idea, he thought. He opened his eyes.

He was in a white room with lots of different colored wires hanging from dark holes in the walls. The holes had the shape and size of TV screens and panels with hundreds of switches ran below them. He tried to turn his head to see more of it and realized that the tightness he felt was because he was tied down to something. And his mouth was gagged.

"The fat one's coming round there, Bobby Jay," he heard a voice behind him say.

"He don't look much like the other one, brother Randolph," another voice replied. "Thought these here clones were supposed to be identical."

"Not rightly sure which is which," Randolph answered.

"Brother Malcolm said it was the skinny one who killed brother Eric. But both of them ended up floating by the ceiling."

Jason strained to look at something to his left. It was J.D., tied up on top of a long table the same way Jason was. Just past his friend were some more tables with shiny, fake wood-grain tops. They were empty, but straps were piled on top of them as if more kids were expected to be tied to them. The two men walked around in front of him. Jason felt relieved. He recognized one of them as someone from television, one of the religious shows from early Saturday morning.

"Hi there, son," Bobby Jay said as he leaned over Jason's bound form "Know who I am?"

Jason tried to say yes but all he could do was gurgle. He settled for moving his head up and down about an inch. Those straps were tight.

"Of course you do, son, of course you do. Satan must know his enemies just as the Lord must know his flock. Isn't that right, son?"

What? Jason thought.

Bobby Jay turned to Randolph. "I can see the devil in this one's eyes. Full of confusion and spite. They were wise to take him." He walked over to J.D.

"Anyone home in there?" he said happily to J.D.'s unmoving body.

Jason gurgled again when he saw Bobby Jay slap J.D. across his face. Bobby Jay smiled over at Jason.

"Don't like to see your friend get hurt, son?"

Jason shook his head. A half inch one way and a half inch the other.

"Like to help him out?"

Up an inch. Down an inch.

"All you have to do is confess."

Blink. Blink.

"Your sins, son," Bobby Jay said with a great big smile. "Confess your sins and you'll be free to go."

Jason looked at the reverend without comprehension.

"You know what sins are, don't you, son?"

Jason nodded yes.

"Of course you do. Your master is the Lord of Sins, isn't he?"

No.

"You just proved it by telling another lie there, son." Bobby Jay lifted his hands as if to surrender. "Might as well check them out for the mark of the beast, Randolph."

Jason didn't like the sound of that. He tried to struggle against the straps holding him down.

Bobby Jay smiled again. "Afraid we're going to find something?" he said to Jason.

Randolph walked into Jason's field of vision. He wore stiff and shiny black rubber gloves and carried a large knife. Jason squealed through his gag. The kids at school had told stories about stuff like this. He had even seen it on the news. These crazy grown-ups were going to chop him up into little pieces and then stick him in their freezer. He squealed again and started to shiver with fear.

Randolph stuck the blade of the knife up Jason's pants leg and began to slice the boy's jeans open. Jason couldn't breathe or focus his eyes. He couldn't wait to use the bathroom any longer, either.

Randolph moaned and stepped back.

"The devil will use all the tricks at his disposal, brother Randolph," Bobby Jay said from a safe distance. "Don't give in now."

With a look of great displeasure, Randolph finished cutting off Jason's jeans and sodden underwear. Jason was crying hysterically. His nose was stuffing up and he felt the gag was going to choke him. Randolph wrenched off Jason's sneakers and socks and then began cutting away at his shirt and jacket.

J.D. woke up. He saw a strange man take a knife to his best friend. His scream of terror was loud even through his gag. Jason turned at the sound. So did Bobby Jay.

"So you've decided to come back from the pit, have you?" Bobby Jay said. J.D. struggled uselessly against his straps.

"Less you can change yourself into a gorilla there, son, I'd advise you to ease up a might. Enough straps on you to keep a dozen grown men held down."

J.D. stopped. It was evident from his expression that he also recognized Bobby Jay.

"I can see the devil in your eyes, too," the reverend said to J.D. He returned to Jason. All the boy's clothes had been cut away. Bobby Jay slapped him hard across the face and watched J.D. for a reaction.

It was murderous in its intensity.

"You don't like seeing your friend hurt either, do you son?" Bobby Jay said. "Good. Very good." He strutted over to J.D. "Don't suppose you'd like to confess *your* sins, now, would you?"

J.D.'s face stared up in confusion.

"Didn't think so," Bobby Jay said and winked at him. "Randolph, better check this one out, too."

Randolph left the quaking, wheezing body of Jason and approached J.D. with the knife. J.D. screamed at the sight of it. His whole body strained up against the straps. Bobby Jay bent over, hands on his knees, and stared in earnest concentration at the gap that had appeared between J.D.'s body and the surface of the table. The table legs started shifting against the floor.

Bobby Jay stood up and brought his clenched fist down as hard as he could into J.D.'s stomach. A terrible explosive gasp burst through J.D.'s nose and his eyes crossed. Instantly, the table was motionless and J.D.'s face showed the panic of someone who couldn't breathe.

Bobby Jay turned to Randolph, who was taking advantage of J.D.'s abrupt paralysis by slicing open J.D.'s jeans. "I think we got ourselves an Antichrist here, brother Randolph. Did you see how that table was hopping around? Oooo-eeee. Praise the Lord."

Left alone for the moment, Jason fought to clear his nose and catch his breath. When he forced his eyes as far to the left as they could go, he could see the man with the knife examining J.D.'s naked body as if he were looking for something written upon it. The television guy was fiddling with some of the wires hanging out from the wall.

"Nothing here," Randolph said to Bobby Jay. "If they do have the mark of the beast, then maybe they're lying on it."

Bobby Jay came back from the wall holding something like a fat pen in his hand. An electrical cord ran out from behind it and snaked back to the wall. "Well," he said, "I don't think it's wise to take a chance on unfastening them quite yet so we can have a look-see. Have to wait until we fix up the old studio in the Bible college as a holding cell and move them out of this control room.'' He tapped his finger against the thing in his hand. ''Guess we'll have to give them a mark of our own. Let the devil know who he's dealing with.''

Bobby Jay stood by J.D.'s head. Jason could see that J.D. was paying attention to what was happening again. He saw Bobby Jay lift the thing in his hand. His mother had one just like it on her workbench. It was a soldering iron.

Bobby Jay held the iron over J.D.'s forehead. ''Mark of the beast, son,'' he said with a smile. ''Mr. President can't tell the players without a scorecard.''

He brought the soldering iron down. For an instant, just before J.D.'s muffled scream, Jason heard the sizzle of his friend's flesh. The screaming took a long time.

Then Bobby Jay came over to Jason. He was still smiling the same smile that Jason recognized from TV, a saved—truly *saved*—smile.

''Well, son,'' the reverend said with a friendly wink. ''You're next.''

TWO

Father Panati's mouth dropped open. ''*How* much did you tell him?'' he asked in amazement.

Susan Foster had no time for games anymore. This was serious. She looked grimly across Panati's office desk and told him the truth.

''*All* of it,'' she said.

Panati rocked his head back and forth. ''Oh, Susan, how could you? If this hits the papers and the television—*and* the Vatican!—and we're all running around like headless chickens . . .'' He was speechless.

''Hold on,'' Foster said, trying to calm the priest down. ''I only said I *told* him about it. I didn't say he believed me.''

''You mean you told him everything and he decided not to do anything about it?'' Hope sprang into Panati's eyes.

"I didn't say that, either," Foster backtracked. "He's checking into it."

"Oh, wonderful," Panati moaned. "Commission of inquiry at the police board? Special meetings with the mayor?"

"Francis, calm down!" Foster said sharply. "It's going to be all right. First of all, the kid's not a police officer. He's not even a rookie yet. So it's not as if he has to report to anyone. And if it weren't for him, we'd still be stuck with tracking down the . . . children . . . with just the information in what we have of Wyndham's files. The kid's got access to police data banks. That's how he came up with the connection between Paul Almagro, the kidnapped Danylkiw boy, and the murdered boy in Montreal. That's why I had to tell him the truth."

Panati swiveled on his chair to stare out through the filmy, small-paned windows of his office. "I'm sorry, Susan," he apologized. Somewhat reluctantly, she thought. "I asked you to become involved in this matter because I knew you'd have a lot to offer, so I shouldn't complain when you do offer us something."

"I understand what you're concerned about, Francis." She tried to bring the conversation back to something friendly and useful. "And I believe this Jim Hyams wants to avoid any sensationalism, too. He's in an awkward political position in the police force right now."

"What *was* his reaction?"

Foster laughed in recollection. "Well, I had already tried to snow him with a couple of other bizarre stories, which he wisely didn't fall for, so when I told him about Dr. Wyndham claiming to have made clones from the blood on the Shroud of Turin, he didn't believe that either."

"Then why is he cooperating?"

"The photographs," Foster explained. "There are differences among the boys. Different hairstyles, of course, slightly different features, maybe because of different diet or small differences in their ages, but they are close enough to be twins. Or, in this case, triplets. That was the clincher as far as Hyams was concerned. And for me, too. I don't think he believes everything I told him, but the boys indicate that something common is involved and, maybe, it extends to what he's most concerned with: the murder of the detective who used to be his partner. The evidence doesn't convince him but he feels there's enough to justify a bit more digging."

Panati turned back to face Foster. He looked more at ease. "What's he checking out for us then?"

"He'll keep in touch with a friend he says he has in the police records department who's watching for any of the names on our list to come up."

"Shouldn't we track those children down and warn them that someone might be after them?"

"We should," Foster agreed, "but Jim said he couldn't think of a way to do that without alerting the police. And that would mean too many explanations. For now, he's having their parents searched for through motor vehicle registrations and he's looking into the official reports on Father Montgomery's murder and the theft of Wyndham's records."

"Because whoever has those knows where to find the rest of the children?"

Foster nodded. "There must have been more complete records in the stolen trunks for them to have tracked down some of the children whose names I got from their mother's medical records. One of the trunks probably had a master list of all of them."

Father Panati slammed his fist on his desk. "But *who*!" he said. Then blinked as if his outburst had taken him by surprise as much as it had Foster. "Sorry," he muttered again. Foster shrugged and smiled.

There was a knock on the office door. Panati told whoever it was to come in and Jim Hyams entered. He carried an old Zabar's cloth shopping bag. Foster made the introduction.

"We were just talking about you," she said as Hyams pulled a second chair up to Panati's desk. "I wasn't sure if you'd manage to catch up with me here."

"And miss out on all the new stories you're dreaming up to tell me?" he said with a crooked smile. He rummaged through his bag.

"I've been poking around the basement in Wyndham's apartment building," he began. "Since the priest and the fellow with him were stabbed in the area around the service entrance, Forensics didn't spend much time down by the lockers." He dropped his voice. "And I'm afraid the officers involved in the investigation feel it's just another one to mark down to juveniles.

They'll stick with it for another week or so but they're not expecting to get very far."

"No clues at all?" Panati asked.

"They don't really call them clues anymore, sir. About the only thing they have to go on is that the superintendent's wife said she saw a black van down in the alley and was going to go down to tell it to move about the time the murders occurred. But she couldn't give a license or a make." He shrugged. "Anyway, I did find these in the piles of trash in the lockers adjacent to Wyndham's. You said the trunks looked as if they'd been broken into a few times so I'd assume some of the papers from them got shoved in the trash piles instead of back in the trunks."

Hyams spread some wads of crumpled papers over Panati's desk. Then he handed a dust-covered black binder to Foster. "This looks like something you'd be interested in," he said. "I think there're chemical notations in it."

Both Panati and Hyams watched as Foster began skimming through the handwritten pages in the binder.

"It's Wyndham's handwriting," she said. "I recognize the scrawl and the nonsense abbreviations he used." For a few moments there was only the sound of rustling paper in the cluttered office. Then Foster said, "Bingo."

She looked up smiling. "This is his reconstruction log," she said.

"Which is?" Panati asked.

"The records of his technique for reconstructing a complete human genetic sequence from the organic material on the shroud."

"Excuse me," Hyams said, "but don't you already believe that the three boys are proof that he did it?"

"Not at all," Foster replied. "Cloning doesn't take a great leap of the imagination so we're probably safe in assuming that the three children are clones that Wyndham implanted in women who were expecting to be artificially inseminated. But that doesn't prove anything about the *source* of the genetic material. There's still a chance that Wyndham simply prepared the clones from a living human being and made up the story about the shroud."

"Why would he do that?" Hyams asked.

"Why do people say they're abducted by flying saucers?"

Foster answered. "There's no law that says brilliant scientists can't be as loony as anyone else. Trust me, I've interviewed them."

"But you don't really think Wyndham was 'loony,' do you?" Hyams observed. Panati waited for the answer to that one, too.

"No, it just doesn't show through in his records or his intent. Not yet, at least."

"So it *is* possible that he could have cloned Jesus from the blood on the shroud?" This was the sticking point for Hyams.

Foster sighed. "A few years ago, scientists at Berkeley were able to extract DNA from the hide of a South African animal called a quagga. It resembled a zebra but the species had been extinct for almost a hundred years so zoologists weren't able to say whether the thing had been more closely related to zebras or to horses. It was a minor question as far as the rest of the world was concerned, but by examining cloned portions of the quagga's reconstructed genetic code, the scientists were able to prove that it was most closely related to zebras. Or had been."

"But that was from something less than a hundred years old," Hyams protested. "What kind of shape is DNA in after two thousand years?"

"Again, that's not an insurmountable problem. It's common practice for the blood relations among the royal mummies of Egypt to be mapped by examination of their genetic structure. A lot of that DNA is coming from organic matter that is more than *three* thousand years old. And the Berkeley scientists who worked on the quagga are going ahead with plans to clone mammoth DNA, which is ten thousand years old. They're even developing techniques to extract DNA from the collagen found in million-year-old Neanderthal bones."

"But isn't it quite a jump from examining genetic material to actually reproducing it?" Hyams asked.

Foster realized she was enjoying this. The kid was sharp, she thought.

"Yes and no. For one thing, most of the big drug companies manufacture some of their products by cloning techniques. There are automated machines the size of big photocopiers that automatically break down, rearrange, and reproduce DNA chains. For another, there's almost no doubt in the scientific community that the—forgive the term, please—resurrection of extinct animal species will eventually be possible. If not now, then someday soon.'' Foster assessed the skeptical looks she was getting.

''Right now,'' she continued, ''in special containers all over the world, collections of prehistoric insects trapped in amber—that's fossilized tree sap—are being prepared for an incredible experiment.''

''Which is?'' Panati prompted.

''Some of those insects have been identified as blood feeders.'' Foster really was excited. She hadn't felt this way since before she had gone into the hospital. ''Like mosquitos,'' she added. ''And, there's a chance that some of the insects in the amber were trapped just after feeding so that some of them may actually contain dinosaur blood in their digestive organs. Work is now going on to develop techniques of breaking open the amber without destroying the millions-of-years-old organic material within it.''

''You're saying they're going to bring back the dinosaurs?'' Hyams asked about as skeptically as he could while remaining polite.

''All I'm saying is that it is a possibility. But I will say that within twenty years, we're going to have passenger pigeons and dodo birds in our zoos. We're going to have marsupial dogs and marsupial tigers and all sorts of other recently extinct animals brought back to life. The organic material is there. The technology is developing. *And*, though it might not be in our lifetimes, there's a strong possibility that someday people will be going to their zoos to see dinosaurs.''

Foster realized her voice was trembling with enthusiasm. This was the feeling that had been lost to her for so long. This was the feeling that used to make it so easy to get up in the mornings. What wonders will I experience today? she had thought in those days. What new things will I learn? What new discoveries will be announced? How could life ever seem boring or useless when there was so much still to learn? Her hands felt sweaty.

''Well,'' said Father Panati, ''that was the best sermon I've heard in a long time.''

Foster felt embarrassed. She hadn't intended to get so carried away.

Hyams smiled at her, trying to put her at ease, she thought.

"So, in ten words or less," he said, "what Wyndham claimed to have done is possible?"

"As I said to Francis," Foster replied, "in ten words or less, it's inevitable."

THREE

Despite the crowds of summertime tourists, Dean Fuller felt glad to be back in Washington. Bermuda had been pleasant, but the days without a standard routine had forced him to confront the fact that Barbara-Jane was convinced her vision of the end of the world was true. Each time Fuller had brought up the topic, his wife had resolutely refused to discuss it.

"Perhaps you were mistaken," he had said.

"Haven't been yet," she had replied.

"Think of the panic you might cause," he had tried again.

"The people need a chance to get their spiritual lives in order."

That had been the extent of their conversations.

At the door to their Georgetown house, they were greeted by Rose, stooped and plump, with a disturbing scowl that hid a more or less pleasant disposition. Fuller had offered their housekeeper a vacation at the same time he and Barbara-Jane were away, but, as always, Rose had declined. She seemed to have no other purpose than to serve the Fuller family. She had no need for anything else, either, she had told him many times. Dean Fuller had stopped trying to persuade her to change her mind years ago.

"You look fit and rested," Rose said as she bustled about the black-and-white tiled foyer. Fuller had to be firm about insisting that *he* would take the suitcases upstairs. Barbara-Jane, atypically, did not join in the commotion of returning home. She continued the resigned silence that she had maintained almost constantly since her final vision.

Rose took Barbara-Jane into the kitchen for some tea while

Fuller went into his study to see what his secretary had dropped off for him. The investment firm practically ran itself these days so he wasn't expecting much, even after a three-week absence.

As he expected, the file was slim. There were two letters for him to sign, evidently not important enough that holding them for three weeks had caused any trouble. But the phone messages concerned him.

Five were from Tom Jefferson. One was from the office of the President. Something's hit the fan, Fuller thought as he sat down behind his mahogany desk and dialed the direct White House inner office number.

He smiled as the receiver clicked. Unlike the Moscow-Washington hotline, this line was always answered on the first ring.

Fuller asked for Tom Jefferson. He was informed that Mr. Jefferson was no longer employed by that office. He had resigned from the White House staff and was believed to be on vacation with his family at this time.

Fuller thanked the voice on the phone and examined the message slips from Jefferson. Sure enough, the last two listed a different call-back number. He dialed again. Jefferson answered. His voice sounded tired. After saying hello, Fuller wasted no time.

"How could you resign, Tom? After all you went through to get that job." Fuller was shocked. Jefferson was a bright young man on the move in D.C. Nobody gave that up without a monumentally good reason. Usually his or her own death.

"Simple," Jefferson said bitterly. "Number One just filled in the date on my standard letter of resignation; the one everyone turns in on the first day on the job."

So, he was fired, Fuller thought. That made a bit more sense. But not much more.

"What happened? Policy difference?"

"You got it."

"But over what? I never heard you say a word remotely against the President. Or anyone else in the administration, for that matter."

"Things have been changing rapidly, Dean." He spoke with exaggerated precision.

"In the White House? Since when?" Fuller asked incredulously. Fast change there was unheard of.

"Since the Reverend Bobby Jay had a long cozy ride in Air Force One." Fuller heard a familiar clinking sound in the background. Jefferson was drinking, had been drinking by the sound of it.

"I don't understand," Fuller said truthfully.

"You know what the President asked me, Dean? He asked me, 'Tom, when were you last in church?' "

"What's that got to do with anything?" This is beginning to sound foolish, Fuller thought.

"It has everything to do with everything, now," Jefferson slurred back. "I said, 'Well, Mr. President, I believe I was last in church for Christmas services at my wife's parents' church.' And you know what he said? He said, 'That's six months ago, Tom.' He said, 'That's not good enough, Tom.' And then he said, 'I'm afraid I'm going to have to ask you to resign, Tom. Ask you to do the right thing so that caring people—*caring* people,' he said, 'who know where their priorities lie can come and work for their country where it counts.' That's what he said."

Fuller couldn't believe what he had just heard. "Are you telling me that the President told you to resign because your church attendance didn't meet with his pleasure?"

"Praise the Lord, as Bobby Jay would say." Jefferson had been drinking for a long time.

"Tom," Fuller said angrily, "that's unconstitutional, that's illegal, that's morally repugnant, that's just insane. I could give you the names of a dozen lawyers who could get this into the Supreme Court by fall *and* do it for free. *And* win it in their sleep."

"He's the President," Jefferson mumbled.

"All the more reason he should uphold the First Amendment, Tom. How could you go along with that decision without putting up a fight?" Fuller could feel his face turn crimson.

"Always been a team player," Jefferson said softly. "Couldn't move against Number One. He's a great man, Dean. One of the best presidents this country's ever had."

"Tom, you're not on the team anymore. He kicked you off. Fight back, for Christ's sake."

"It's for Christ's sake that I'm off," Jefferson said and started to laugh. "I was replaced by one of Bobby Jay's holy rollers."

"*What!*" Fuller undid two buttons on his shirt, even though the collar was already unfastened. Leave town for three weeks and the whole country goes back to the middle ages, he thought. What's coming next, a new inquisition?

"That's right," Jefferson continued. "The President's new assistant chief of staff is Chuck Longsworth, former chief administrator of the Bible college at America's Glory. 'Part of a new revival of old-fashioned patriotism and morality that is going to sweep this great nation of ours.' Want to guess who said that?"

Fuller was afraid to ask the next question, but he had to. "Anyone else affected by this, Tom?"

"Three," Jefferson said bluntly. "So far."

"And the *Post* hasn't got hold of it? Nobody's leaking this to anyone?"

"Maybe here and there, Dean. But he *is* the President and, I don't know, maybe the people do want a moral revolution." There was no energy left in Jefferson's voice. He sounded like a man drained of everything he had once cherished. "Guess we really should have tried harder to keep Barbara-Jane from telling Number One about her vision, huh?"

Fuller shut his eyes to reflect. "Barbara-Jane hasn't told the President anything," he said with surprise. "The President was in California when she had the vision and then we left for Bermuda before he came back. I'm sure she couldn't have called the White House while we were down there. I know there were no long distance calls on our hotel bill. She hasn't said a word to the President. I'm certain."

There was silence on the other end while Jefferson digested what Fuller had said. "Well," he replied finally, "then the good Lord must be handing visions out a dime a dozen because I'm sure Number One knows about it."

"Knows about what?"

"The holy battle of Armageddon on the Labor Day weekend," Jefferson snorted. "In my last two days at the office, he sure was excited about something that was going to happen then."

"The campaign kickoff," Fuller suggested nervously.

"This wasn't election fever, Dean. In fact, he's almost gone as far as to tell people not to keep working on it. Do you believe it? I don't think the President believes there *will* be an election this fall."

"Say you're joking," Fuller said. "Please say this is a joke."

"No joke, Dean. I do believe the President of these great United States of ours has, as Bobby Jay would say, seen the light."

FOUR

Jim Hyams fought to keep a serious expression on his face. Sitting in the meeting room with Father Panati's planning committee, he felt there was a distinct possibility that he had somehow been trapped in a Marx Brothers revival.

Susan Foster he could take. In the weeks they had been working together, he had become quite fond of her. Fond was a different sort of word for him to use when it came to a woman, but he didn't know of any other that fit as well. He certainly found her attractive and pleasant to be with, but there was a distance to her, something he felt couldn't be bridged. At times he thought it might be the difference in their ages—he wasn't sure what the difference was but he felt she had to be at least five years older. Other times, he thought it was just in their different backgrounds—she a college-educated writer, he a coupon-clipping brat who thought he wanted to be a cop. In any event, he usually concluded that it didn't bear much thinking about. He was happy enough to leave it at being fond of her.

Father Panati was a different matter. Hyams found the idea of someone being celibate for his whole life to be fascinating in the same awful sort of way that observing his first autopsies had been. The priest seemed normal enough, but Hyams found it difficult to understand why. He realized, however, that coming from an undemanding Episcopal background, his knowledge of the Catholic Church had been limited to listening to relatives talk about John Kennedy's days, seeing the Pope on the news, and a few Bing Crosby movies. That was about all he felt compelled to know about it, too.

The others on the planning committee were like characters from old movies to him. Thorkel might have passed as Daddy Warbucks if he could ever manage to speak without sounding as if he were about to cough up his lungs at any moment. Father Carey could qualify as the shyest man in the world for the way he habitually sat with his head bowed, as if trying to shrink from view. And Andre Delambre, the student about whom Foster had warned him, really did resemble an extra from *Star Wars*.

Looking at the others sitting around the table, while Panati fussed with a kettle and instant coffee at the end of the room, Hyams had no trouble understanding why these people believed in clones created from the Shroud of Turin. The idea was as bizarre as they were. With the exception of Susan Foster.

Panati began passing around Styrofoam cups. Hyams sipped at the one he was given and smiled the polite way his mother had taught him. He might as well have been drinking something thick warmed up from the Hudson.

"There's not much to report this evening," Panati said to begin the meeting. "Our new member, Jim, says that the investigation into Father Montgomery's murder is still open but with no new leads. Susan tells me that she has arranged for a medical friend of hers to go over the files from Dr. Wyndham's trunk but that so far no evidence has come up to suggest there is anything to support Wyndham's claims." Panati looked around the table. So did Hyams.

Everything he and Foster and Panati had put together about the children, including Foster's analysis of Wyndham's reconstruction log, was being kept from the other three people. Foster was more convinced than ever that one of them was reporting back to whoever had stolen the other trunks and set out after the children. The charade of these planning meetings was to keep those mysterious others off guard. It had become Hyams's job to identify the leak.

"Well, then," Panati said, "I suppose it's time for Andre to begin."

Delambre opened and closed his eyes a few times, as if making sure they still worked. Then he passed around to everyone copies of three thick reports. The dark green covers were stamped with the silver initials S.T.R.P.

"It stands for the Shroud of Turin Research Project," Delambre said without being asked. "Begun in 1978 and meeting almost every year since then."

Hyams flipped through the first volume he had been passed. He stopped at a photograph of the shroud in its entirety: a long strip of linen—fourteen feet by five feet the caption said—with two full-length images of a man imprinted upon it. The images were arranged head-to-head, one of them a front view and the other a back view.

Thorkel contemplatively weighed the three volumes of the report in one meaty hand. A cigarette was in the other. "Do we have to read these or is there a consensus?" he coughed.

"Two consensuses, actually," Delambre said in a snotty way. "The first is that the Shroud of Turin is the burial cloth of Jesus. The second is that it is a fraud."

Thorkel let the reports thud onto the desk. "How many years have they been studying it?" he asked.

"Scientifically," Delambre qualified, "since 1898. That was when an Italian took the first photographs of the shroud. When he developed them, he found a positive image on his negatives. That meant the image of the figure on the shroud was a negative to begin with."

"Is that important?" Panati asked. Delambre's tone had seemed to indicate it was.

"The concept of negative images didn't really exist in art until the advent of photography. The Shroud of Turin has had its"—Delambre grimaced at Hyams—"*continuity* I believe you police people call it, documented from about 1357. Proponents of the shroud's authenticity claim that if someone back then were to have created a fraudulent shroud, they would have painted a positive image because they would not have known about negatives."

"What do you mean by 'continuity'?" Panati asked.

"In this case, it means that the shroud that exists today in Turin, Italy, has had its whereabouts rigorously documented since 1357. Strong circumstantial evidence, however, links the shroud to the Mandylion—a sacred portrait of Christ that was discovered hidden in a wall in Edessa in 525 A.D. Some people believe they are one and the same.''

Hyams pointed to the photographs in the report showing the full extent of the image on the shroud. ''How could something like this be considered just a portrait?'' he asked.

''A burial cloth was considered to be unclean. Supporters of the shroud consider it likely that the disciple Addai folded the shroud so that only the face imprint was visible. Addai is reported to have traveled to Edessa in A.D. 30, bearing such a portrait. The portrait was credited with the miraculous cure of Abgar the Fifth, and his subsequent conversion to Christianity. In any event, it appears the Mandylion was finally unfolded around A.D. 1025, revealing there was far more to it than anyone suspected.

''Eventually, it was taken to Constantinople, where it disappeared in the sacking of 1204. Unconfirmed rumors suggest that the Knights Templar began worshipping a strange idol of a red-bearded man's head at that time, but the story's never been authenticated. The connecting jump from this point is that the Knights Templar's master of Normandy was a Geoffrey de Charny. He was burned at the stake in 1314 as a heretic, but in 1357, the Shroud of Turin as we know it today was first exhibited by the family of another Geoffrey de Charny in Liroy, France. Whether the two de Charnys were related has never been proven or disproven, and the controversy surrounding the shroud's authenticity has continued ever since.''

Panati tapped the volumes before him and asked, ''Where does the controversy stand today?''

Delambre smiled smugly. ''On the negative side, that is, the position of those who believe the Shroud of Turin is a fraud, the most common explanation is that the image on the shroud is a painting that was made in the 1300s.''

''Even if it's in negative?'' Panati asked.

''The critics offer two explanations for that. One: the medium used to create the image has been chemically altered by aging, changing from a positive to a negative. Two: any artist who made engravings would understand the concept of negative images, even in the fourteenth century.''

''If it were a painting,'' Foster asked as she glanced through the reports, ''wouldn't scientific testing reveal the presence of paint pigments?''

"It's been tried," Delambre said, obviously enjoying his position as the focus of that evening's meeting. "It's also one of the most controversial areas of shroud research. The critics say pigment has been found. The supporters say the evidence is flimsy and has been misinterpreted. A middle ground is willing to accept that, though the shroud is genuine, its image was retouched by an artist a few centuries ago. This was a common practice for religious paintings. Even the works of Michelangelo have been retouched."

"But surely pigment is pigment," Foster said. "It's there or it isn't."

"The substance in question is a form of iron. Might be from paint or it might be from blood," Delambre said.

"That's an important question," Panati interrupted. "*Is* there blood on the Shroud of Turin?"

"There are what appear to be bloodstains on the shroud. In fact, they're one of the more compelling reasons to believe the shroud is genuine." Delambre didn't even need a question to know he should continue. "The patterns of the staining reveal wounds that match the accounts of Christ's crucifixion in the Gospels."

"But wouldn't any artist refer to those accounts in order to produce a believable fake?" Hyams asked. The answer seemed evident to him.

"Of course any artist would," Delambre replied, "as far as the Gospels went in their descriptions. However, common practice in the fourteenth century was to depict the crucifixion with Christ being attached to the arms of the cross by nails through his palms. In actual fact, the flesh and bones of the palms are not strong enough to support a person's weight in that manner. From studying skeletal remains, we know today that Roman crucifixion was carried out by nailing victims through the wrist. And that's where the nail wounds of the figure in the shroud appear. A detail unlikely to have been known by a fourteenth-century artist." Delambre acknowledged the impressed reactions of the people around the table. He continued.

"The blood flow issuing from those nail wounds show two different paths taken by the blood as it ran down the figure's arms. This is consistent with death by crucifixion, which is essentially death by asphyxiation. Asphyxiation occurred when the victim hung loosely by his arms, a position that cramps chest muscles and can lead to unconsciousness in about twelve minutes. A victim could prolong his ordeal by straightening his legs to relieve the pressure on his chest. This would have been very painful, because his feet would have been fastened to the cross by a spike, but possible. That's why it was common for the Romans to eventually break the legs or ankles of their victims. So they couldn't stand up. Because a victim would alternately stand and slump, the blood trickling down the victim's arms would take the two different paths shown on the shroud, corresponding to the two different positions of the arms."

Father Carey quietly crossed himself in response to the details of Jesus' death.

"Other details abound," Delambre went on. "the Bible tells that Jesus was scourged or flogged. The dorsal view of the figure on the shroud also shows these wounds as tiny, dumbbell-shaped marks. The shape and size of the wounds are consistent with the Roman *flagra*, whips with small, twin metal pellets tied to their thongs. Bloodstains on the figure's head resemble those which might occur from a crown of thorns. A major wound on the chest is consistent with the Gospel account of a Roman soldier thrusting a lance into Christ's side after death. And the stain from that wound is consistent with posthumous infliction—very little blood flow but a great deal of clear fluid, presumably lymph or water that had accumulated as a result of asphyxiation."

"John nineteen, thirty-two to thirty-four," Panati murmured, nodding.

"Any details not associated with the bloodstains?" Thorkel asked.

Delambre shut his eyes for a moment, as if considering whether or not he should nap. Evidently, he decided not to. "The figure has a long pigtail of hair down his back, consistent with Jewish custom of the time, and again, something a fourteenth-century artist would be unlikely to know."

"Let's get back to the blood for a moment," Panati interrupted again. "You said the markings 'appeared' to be bloodstains. Are they or aren't they?"

"The bloodstained areas of the shroud contain a blood component called porphyrin and, at their edges, show evidence of separation between whole blood and blood serum." Delambre looked straight at Foster. "And they are the only portions of the shroud to contain protein residue."

"The stuff that genes are made of," Foster commented. No one laughed.

"Other details not related to blood include image-enhancement studies run by computer, which show that the density gradations on the image on the shroud contain three-dimensional information. A painting, or even a photograph enhanced in the same way, clearly shows distorted two-dimensional flattening. Other computer studies indicate that there is no 'directionality' to the image on the shroud. That is, there is no indication of brushstrokes or any other artificial application of a coloring medium to the cloth, which is, incidentally, consistent in weave and composition to known examples of two-thousand-year-old Middle Eastern burial cloths."

"What do you believe?" Thorkel said abruptly. From the way he was disdainfully eyeing the three thick volumes, Hyams thought that the businessman had never read anything longer than a balance sheet in his life.

Delambre was being far too smug about his place in center stage. "I'm afraid I have to remain neutral," he said imperiously.

"Why?" Panati asked. He placed his hands on the volumes before him. "Surely the answer is found somewhere in all this."

"Not yet," Delambre said. "One test still has not been conclusively performed. And until it is, speculation is unproductive."

"What's the test?" Panati asked.

"Carbon-fourteen dating."

"Hold it," Foster said, suddenly remembering. "I thought that the shroud *was* carbon-dated a couple of years back."

Delambre looked totally disinterested in her. "A carbon-dating test of sorts was performed on samples of the shroud in 1988, but the results were terribly inconclusive."

"Is that what it says in here?" Thorkel asked, tapping the reports.

"It's one opinion of many," Delambre answered with a sigh. "You see, carbon dating is a method of measuring two different types of carbon atoms—stable and radioactive. All living things continually ingest both types of carbon every day in a precise ratio. However, when a living thing dies, then the total amount of carbon in it is fixed and the ratio changes as the radioactive carbon decays into a stable form. By measuring the carbon ratios that exist in something made from once-living matter, we can calculate how much time has passed since the living matter died and stopped ingesting radioactive carbon. In the case of the shroud, that would be how long it's been since the flax plants were picked to make the linen it's composed of."

Delambre looked around the table but nobody was prepared to interrupt him.

"To continue," he said, "the thinking behind carbon-dating the shroud was that if it could be found to be only seven hundred or so years old, then quite obviously it would be a fraud. However, if it was found to be about two thousand years old, then it could very well be the burial shroud of *a* man who died by crucifixion. Whether or not it is the shroud of Jesus or the shroud of one of the thousands of others the Romans crucified in that period is something, I'm afraid, that the test couldn't prove. Although the degree of correspondence between the wounds described in the Gospels and the wounds on the shroud is fairly exact."

"So how accurate was this test supposed to be?" Thorkel asked.

"With something two thousand years old," Foster offered when Delambre uncharacteristically hesitated, "carbon dating is accurate to within seventy years, plus or minus."

Panati pursed his lips. "What does the report say was the result of that test, Andre?"

"All three testing centers—Oxford University, the University of Arizona, and Federal Institute of Technology in Zurich—reported that their tests indicated the cloth of the shroud was created somewhere between 1260 and 1390."

"So that's that," Thorkel announced, pleased that there was finally a direct answer.

"Actually, it's not," Delambre said imperiously. "For one, the Church did not accept the results as being conclusive."

"Why not?" Thorkel asked. It had become a personal discussion as far as he was concerned.

"On the one hand, there were several technical problems with the test. The hundred-and-thirty-year range of dates, for example, was far greater than should have been found. And several of the institutions that had agreed to be part of the test dropped out before receiving their samples for reasons which were never made clear, though which might have had something to do with rumors about the amount of contamination the shroud samples had been exposed to. For instance, it is well documented that the shroud has been washed on a number of occasions and any residue from soap made from animal fat would hopelessly throw off any carbon-dating test. Even smoke from the candles used to light the shroud before electricity could be enough to give a false age."

"So what's on the other hand?"

"Politics," Father Carey said quietly. It was the first time he had spoken during the meeting. "The shroud is an enigma and has served as a focusing point for many people. For some, it has been the pathway into the Church, a means by which they can first think of Jesus as a living human being and then come to know him as the Son of God. For others already within the Church, it serves as a reminder, like an icon or a crucifix attached to a rosary. After all these years of expositions of the shroud, after all the miracles attributed to it, why should science intrude? Far better it remain a mystery—from the Church's point of view, of course."

"So for all that's written in these volumes," Panati concluded—perhaps with a touch of bitterness, Hyams thought, "there is no answer, yes or no?"

Delambre shook his head.

Hyams had an idea. "But if Dr. Wyndham really did manage to extract human genetic material from the blood-stained areas of the shroud, wouldn't that be the proof that the shroud was real?"

"Not necessarily," Delambre said condescendingly. "Any artist clever enough to have created a fraudulent relic like the shroud would almost certainly use human blood to create the bloodstained areas."

"So Dr. Wyndham may have cloned reproductions of a fourteenth-century forger instead of Jesus?" Hyams followed through.

This time Delambre nodded.

"In other words," Panati sighed, "no answer."

"But one more question, please," Hyams said as the meeting

seemed to be winding down. "If there's really so little that can be known about the shroud, even after all this investigation, why is it such a controversial subject?"

"The image," said Father Carey, surprising Hyams with his forcefulness. "Even if you unquestioningly accept the evidence that the shroud is the burial cloth of Jesus, there is absolutely no explanation for how the image was formed on it."

"Chemical reaction," Foster suggested. She acted as if that were the only obvious explanation.

"No known reaction could produce it," Carey countered. "Every mixture of spices and oils used to anoint the dead at the time, combined with all the chemical reactions of a sweat-covered, bloodstained body have been experimented with. None has produced anything remotely resembling the resolution and focus of the image on the shroud."

"Hold on," Foster said. "The photographs in these reports show that fabric samples from the image area were removed for electron microscope study. Even if the shroud's examiners don't know the exact process by which the image was created, they have to know what the image is composed of. They'd be able to see whatever substance makes up the image in the photographs taken by the electron microscope."

Both Delambre and Carey shook their heads.

"That's just it," Delambre said. "The image exists only within the surface molecules of the cloth fibers. It's not composed of a foreign substance. It hasn't soaked in like a chemical film or paint, and it hasn't corroded the fibers like a chemical reaction. In fact, there is only one physical phenomenon that can reproduce anything like the image on the shroud."

"Well?" Thorkel, Hyams, and Panati said together.

"A scorch," Delambre said, then paused for effect. "A very brief, very high-intensity exposure to heat. Researchers have likened the amount of energy required to that which imprinted the shadows of the people of Hiroshima upon the walls and sidewalks of their city when the atomic bomb exploded. And, of course, if the shroud *has* been exposed to any type of radioactivity, then whatever stable carbon which existed in the cloth could have been transformed into radioactive carbon. Even if the shroud is two thousand years old, just an eighteen percent increase in radioactive carbon would yield carbon-dating results showing it only to be about 650 to 700 years old—just as was found in the actual tests."

Foster's eyes widened in disbelief. "Are you suggesting that while whoever it is who's depicted on the shroud was wrapped within it, he emitted some sort of energy similar to nuclear fission!"

"I'm not," Delambre said. "But a number of scientists in those volumes are. It's called flash photolysis."

"A dead body couldn't possibly do that," Foster protested.

"If one believes the Gospels," Father Carey explained gently, leaving no doubt as to what he believed, "the man in the shroud did not remain dead."

"Well, no *living* human body could generate that type of energy, either," Foster said.

"If one believes the Gospels," Father Carey repeated kindly, "the man in the shroud was more than human."

FIVE

Outside the room was summer. Marguerite could smell the flowers on the breeze that stole through the gaps in the dilapidated walls. She could feel the warmth in the shafts of sunlight that shone through the cracks in the boarded-up windows. She could tell by the fancy summer dresses that Esperanza wore. But because that was all she could know of summer, its presence made her stomach twist as if she had the flu again, and nothing Juan could do could make her feel healed. He could help Esperanza's visitors, though.

A young man with shadowed eyes was the fifth to visit that day. He walked stooped over. His backbone bent out from his neck like a step on a staircase then curved into a twisted hump. Marguerite knew his parents had paid more than eight hundred dollars for this meeting with Juan. They had sold everything. Juan was the young man's final hope.

"How long will it take before I know?" the young man asked

in the soft orange candlelight of Juan's room. Sweat beaded all over his face, from the heat and, Marguerite sensed, the fear.

"Shhh," her cousin whispered. He reached up from his chair, directing the young man to turn his back to him. Juan's hands ran up and down the deformed spine, probing its strengths, learning its weaknesses, preparing for its change.

"Hold his shoulders," Juan said to Marguerite. She moved in front of the young man and held each shoulder tightly, bracing him. The young man cringed as if he were in pain already.

"Do you believe in the Savior?" Juan asked, his voice a whisper.

"Y-yes," the young man replied, tensing beneath the pressure of Juan's hands upon his back.

"Then say a prayer to him. Say a prayer to him and do not stop."

The young man began to mumble to himself. Marguerite felt him tremble. Then she felt the struggles of the change come upon him.

A dull, wet, crunching sound filled the room. The young man screamed.

"Don't stop until I tell you!" Juan shouted. "To the Savior! To the Savior!"

The young man tried to twist from Marguerite's hands but she held him firmly. Another crunch. A long, drawn-out ripple of cracks. The young man moaned as he prayed. Juan's own prayers blended in. Then Marguerite joined. She felt upward pressure from the young man's shoulders. His back was straightening.

It took five minutes. The young man threw up. Marguerite was experienced and sidestepped just in time. Juan told Marguerite to let go. She did and the young man stood alone, and straight, in front of Juan.

For long moments the young man stretched his shoulders, leaned to the left and right, and bent his arms behind his head to feel the new flatness of his spine. He turned to Juan with tears in his eyes.

"Say nothing," Juan told him. "Remember your prayers and say them often. Now you must go and eat and drink. Drink as much water as you can over the next two days. You will feel weak and tired, but that will pass and on the third day you will be well and healthy."

The young man dropped to his knees and kissed Juan's hands. He spoke excitedly but said nothing coherent. Marguerite finally forced him back to his feet and led him to the hallway, back to his parents and Esperanza, who waited in the front room.

She returned to Juan's room and began to clean the floor. Juan slumped back in his chair, eyes closed.

"Should you do more today?" Marguerite asked. She knew it would be possible for Juan to say no to Esperanza. Their aunt had learned by experience that when Juan said he must rest, no further miracles could be expected that day. Esperanza would be angry, but she would tell the visitors that they must return another day.

"No," said Juan, "There is one more I must see. Tell Esperanza to send in the deaf one. The others will have to come back."

Marguerite did not ask how Juan could say what the afflictions of the visitors in the front room were. He had demonstrated that he knew what they were to be, over and over. She left the room and went down the hallway to the front room. At least, she thought, Esperanza won't beat me before the visitors.

Marguerite returned with Juan's final visitor, a tall, bearded man who had been deaf from birth. He wasn't like most of the other visitors who came to Juan. She didn't like him. There was no supplication in him, no excitement, and no pain. She found herself wondering what he had really come for.

When the man entered Juan's room, he acted surprised to see the wooden statue of the Savior surrounded by candles on the table. What else did he expect to see in a holy person's room? Marguerite thought. She led him before Juan. The sour smell of the young man's vomit was still in the summer hot air.

With his solid white eyes, Juan appeared to watch the man but said nothing to him.

"He stands before you," Marguerite prompted.

Juan remained silent. Marguerite could feel the man becoming tense. She tapped his shoulder so he would turn and look at her.

"Perhaps you should kneel before him so he may touch your ears," she said, exaggerating her mouth's movements.

The man punched her in the face.

Marguerite fell back onto the floor. Her head throbbed and she found she could see only from one eye. She looked up to watch the man removing a doctor's needle from his jacket. She was dimly aware of a crashing sound coming from another part of the old house, as if a door was being broken down. She screamed.

The man turned to Marguerite. She screamed again. He ran at her with the needle held ready and thrust it at her.

Marguerite felt something hot tear into her forearm. She pulled away and heard the needle snap. A gaping tear had opened in her arm. She watched the blood pulse from it. The man turned back to Juan. He was no longer in his chair.

Esperanza appeared in the doorway. Marguerite stared at her, wondering why her aunt appeared to be so different. Then she saw it was because a man with blond hair was carrying her, one arm around her waist, a hand covering her mouth.

"Give yourself up," the bearded man said with the imprecise pronunciation she had heard deaf people use. "Or the woman dies."

Marguerite didn't know to whom the man was speaking. She stared at her arm, unsure if it was still there beneath the sheet of blood. She couldn't feel it anymore. The numbness was spreading to her shoulder, her neck. Things were becoming confused.

She looked back at the men. Something was moving against the ceiling like an immense spider. It was Juan. Esperanza's going to be mad at him for doing that in front of the visitors, Marguerite thought. She smiled. Somehow everything seemed to be getting funny. The numbness was beginning to feel good.

The blond man holding Esperanza pressed a second needle to her shoulder. "She'll die if I give her the full dose," he said.

"And what do you think will happen to you after that?" Juan asked. He was flattened against the ceiling the same way he used to be flattened against the floor after a fall.

The blond man jabbed the needle into Esperanza's shoulder, gripping her tightly as she struggled. After a few seconds he pushed her away. She slammed into the table with the statue and the candles. The statue flew through the air and landed in front of Marguerite. She began laughing at that because it reminded her of Juan.

Esperanza flopped around on the floor, swearing in English and Spanish. Another blond man ran into the room. Marguerite could see he had a long silver gun. He fired it at the ceiling. Something large and dark seemed to float down from it. She thought she should know what it was.

Then there was more noise and confusion, as if a movie had been broken and the actors jumped from one position to the next without moving. Marguerite felt herself being lifted from the floor by strong hands. She could see them dig into her upper arms but felt nothing. "Juan?" she asked. But she saw it was the bearded man who pulled her along, face up to the ceiling. She watched her limp and useless feet as they dragged across the floor. Then things became even more unclear to her. The candles seemed to be hot and smoky. Or was it a cool December night? Instead of candles, was the fire burning? All those unnecessary crutches?

She was in the hallway, still being dragged by her arms. Juan was being pulled beside her. Something like a bullfighter's *banderilla* stuck out from his neck. His mouth moved but he didn't say anything. His head hung down as if he was asleep. Marguerite felt cold. It must be December, she thought.

Then she saw Juan running up the corridor after her. There were flames behind him. She turned her head and saw Juan being dragged along the hall beside her. She looked behind. Juan was closer. Two Juans, she thought. She tried to laugh again but nothing would come.

There was a crackling sound that reminded her of electricity, a bitter smell that reminded her of burning hair. Marguerite fell back from the bearded man's grip. She waited to feel the impact of the floor but it never came.

Marguerite woke with the pressure of two loving hands pressed on her wounded arm. She opened her eyes. Both saw clearly. Juan was kneeling beside her. She reached out her arms to hug him. Then she saw his eyes, black and perfect. It wasn't Juan.

"Who are you?" she asked. Perhaps he *was* Juan, she thought. Perhaps God had finally healed her cousin's eyes the way he had finally granted him the power to move.

"Paul," the second Juan said. His voice was old and tired.

"Where is my cousin?"

"Sleeping." Paul read the question in her eyes. "Don't worry. He's okay."

For the first time Marguerite looked around to see where she was. It wasn't familiar.

"You're at my place," Paul said. "At least, it's mine for a little while."

Marguerite lay on a couch in a small room. Setting sunlight poured through a large window onto white walls. Rectangles of brighter white showed where pictures had been taken down. She saw a tiny stove and refrigerator built into some cupboards in the far corner. It reminded her of a small apartment she had stayed in many years ago, when Esperanza had smuggled her across the border into America. This apartment seemed much cleaner and more modern, but it was empty of almost all furniture. It felt deserted.

"Where is Juan?" Marguerite asked after taking her bearings.

"There's a bed on the other side of that wall," Paul said. "He's resting there."

Marguerite sat up on the side of the couch. She looked at her arm. There was no trace of any damage. She dimly remembered what had happened.

"Did Juan do this?" she asked, pointing to where her wound should be.

Paul shook his head. "I did," he said. "But Juan taught me how. He's taught me a lot. And others have taught him, and I've . . ."

Marguerite reached out her hand and touched Paul's face. It was different, she knew, yet somehow the same. "Are you his . . . brother?" she asked.

"I'm not sure," Paul said. "I think so, but I'm not sure."

There was a rustling sound from around the corner. Marguerite turned to the person coming from the sleeping area. She expected Juan. It wasn't. She gasped.

"That's Johnny," Paul said. "He's my friend."

The boy who stood by the couch was about Paul's age, about his size, but looked nothing like him. His skin was pale like the blue-white tinge of milk. Marguerite felt that if she pressed upon it, it would split like the skin on sour cream and something white and curdy would run out. The boy's eyes were sunken and ringed with purple shadows. His mouth hung open and he shuffled when he walked. Beneath his plain T-shirt, his chest seemed to have caved in on itself. She could hear him breathing, dry and raspy like the old men who had come to visit Juan.

"What's wrong with him?" she whispered. He looked like *el vampiro*, the walking dead.

Paul was nervous, apologetic. He stared down at his hands. "Sometimes," he said, "it doesn't work so well." He looked at Marguerite. She didn't understand. "These," he said, holding up his hands. "Whatever it is your cousin taught me, sometimes it doesn't work so well." He looked at Johnny as if he were staring at a dead relative. His eyes were moist. "I brought him back once," he said. "I think there was too much damage the second time." He rubbed at the side of his head as if an insect had just bitten him there.

"Where is Esperanza? My aunt?" Marguerite asked. She kept her eyes warily on Johnny.

"The men killed her. When the candles started the fire, we couldn't go back for her. I'm sorry."

Marguerite made the sign of the cross but did not find it within herself to cry.

"What happened to the men?"

"They're dead, too," Paul said flatly. He didn't go into details. Then he walked over to the small sink by the refrigerator and began to run water. Johnny watched him move like an exhausted dog keeping track of his master.

"I want to see Juan," Marguerite said. She stood up, feeling woozy the way she had when Juan had taken the flu from her.

Paul returned to her with a glass of water. "Let him rest. We've got a lot of work to do later on."

"What kind of work?" Marguerite took the glass and drained it. Juan had told her that the people he helped must flush many poisons from their bodies by drinking large quantities of water.

"There are more of us. More . . . brothers, I guess." Paul said.

"Like you and Juan?" When Marguerite saw Paul nod his head, she asked wonderingly, "How many?"

Paul thought for a moment. "Hard to say. Not all of us connect. Like, I know about Juan; he's the one who teaches how to fix people. Juan knows about J.D. J.D. can float and do . . . something with electricity, I think. But I don't connect with J.D.

at all. It's like a bunch of phones all wired up together. Sometimes we can even tell where one of the others is, like I can tell about Juan, but . . . I don't know." He shrugged. "We're still trying to figure it out, to know how many are left now."

"What do you mean, 'now'?"

"The men who tried to kidnap Juan today have gone after a bunch of the others. Sometimes they killed their families. Sometimes they just killed the kids they were trying to kidnap. I think they're after us all."

Marguerite sat back down on the couch, stunned. She had always known there was something special about her cousin, but never anything like this.

"Why did the men try to take Juan and the others away?"

"I don't know."

"Where did they want to take them?"

"I don't know."

"Then what are we supposed to do?"

"Save them," Paul said with conviction. He rubbed furiously at the side of his head. His eyes held an expression of pain.

Then Marguerite remembered Juan's most recent dreams. "You are the dream friend," she said. "You are the dream friend Juan said would come." That would explain everything, Marguerite thought. This must be part of Juan's dreams from God.

"Not me," Paul said. "But the dream friend *is* coming. I've dreamed it, too. So have a lot of the others. That's why we have to save them. For when the dream friend comes."

Things had moved past Marguerite's comprehension. "When is he coming?"

Paul held his hands to his head. Something seemed to twist within him. "His voices speak to me almost every day, now." Paul was having trouble talking. "He's coming closer all the time. His voices say he's coming soon. Very soon." Paul gasped and stumbled to the floor. Johnny walked leadenly to him, knelt beside him and cradled his head.

Marguerite stared in helplessness as the convulsions tore through Paul's body. She ran around the partition wall to her cousin. Perhaps he could help.

He couldn't.

Marguerite froze when she saw her cousin. He floated three

feet above the bed. From his eyes blazed beams of harsh white light. From his mouth a thousand voices came. He turned to Marguerite, transfixing her with his glowing eyes, and a voice from within the voices spoke.

"*We must all be together when the dream friend comes,*" it said.

Marguerite screamed.

SIX

"You sure you're not going to get in trouble for this?" Susan Foster asked as she piloted her Prelude along Interstate 95 into Connecticut. Foster had been so busy tracking down the women in Wyndham's records in the past weeks that she realized she hadn't been keeping up with Hyams's predicament with the NYPD. It was only after they had crossed the state line that she had remembered that Hyams had been told not to leave the city while Burch's murder investigation was continuing.

But Hyams seemed unperturbed as he sipped his road coffee through its perforated plastic cover. "I doubt it. I think Detective Ioannou gave up on me a few weeks ago. I haven't been followed for at least that long."

"He really thought you might have been involved in Detective Burch's murder?"

"I really don't know what he thought. My theory is that he was faced with a case that didn't have any easy answers, so he assumed the worst about anyone remotely involved, just on general principle. He even had some poor patrolman in Tampa arrested for possession of Burch's credit cards."

"How did a policeman in Tampa get his cards?" This was better than the late show, Foster thought.

"That's where it gets interesting. The guy in Tampa, an old friend of Burch's as it turns out, says that Burch gave him the cards and told him to use one of them on a particular night in this really seedy bar."

"The particular night being the night he came back to New York and killed the landlord in Paul Almagro's apartment building," Foster guessed.

"Absolutely. Just like he was setting up an alibi."

"But if Burch needed an alibi, then he expected to return to Tampa, and his death had to be a murder instead of the suicide it first appeared to be." Foster was proud of her analysis.

"Don't count on getting your detective shield yet. Despite the fact that he tried to set up an alibi, the evidence of suicide is still really compelling. Powder burns. Fingerprints. No sign of a struggle. So Ioannou has to consider that Burch may have intended to kill himself *but* make it look as if Paul had killed him. Sort of a noble sacrifice to finally bring *El Niño* in."

But Foster could see there was one more step to go. "Except, since Burch killed the landlord, even if *El Niño* came out of hiding and confessed to killing Burch, he could make a strong case for self-defense. Especially since it appears that Burch was deliberately hunting for him."

"And that, Detective Foster, is why Detective Ioannou isn't sleeping too well these nights. The man has a reputation for not letting anything get by him and here he has to deal with a case where everything's whizzing past at the speed of light."

"You don't seem to feel too sorry for him," Foster observed.

"Not at all," Hyams said happily. "He's a detective. That's his job. And as soon as he delivers a report that officially removes me from the case, I go to Mexico and recuperate."

Foster felt a vague sense of what might have been jealousy. Hyams seemed to be saying he was only helping out on the planning committee because he had nothing better to do. Did she feel hurt by that, or was it just the realization that he had something more to look forward to, and she didn't? She tried to keep her feelings from her voice.

"You're not going to be continuing on with this?" she asked. "Thorkel is covering my time. I'm sure he'd cover yours as well."

"Oh, of course I'm going to follow through with you," Hyams said quickly. "But, ah, doesn't it seem as if we're coming up to a few too many dead ends?"

Foster thought about that as she prepared to slip into a line of cars in the passing lane. She had been behind a slow-moving Greyhound for too long.

"We had fifteen kids on my list to begin with," she said, watching her side mirror carefully. "One of them has disappeared. That's Paul. Another died during a suspected kidnap attempt in Montreal. Five we can find no records of. Three we know died before their first birthdays. And another one we're going to visit today. We've got three more dead ends left after this one. Then we can start tracking down the Pennsylvania kid who got kidnapped, and who knows how many others." She floored the accelerator and swerved into the passing lane to the accompaniment of an angry horn blast.

"Well, as long as we have something to check into, then I'm staying with it," Hyams said. He made it sound like an apology.

"But why?" she asked. She knew she shouldn't, but she felt like being perverse.

Hyams made two false starts and then said, "I want to. It's like playing detective without the messy bother of finishing at the Academy. Besides, maybe when it's finished we'll all get our pictures in the paper."

None of those sounds convincing, Foster thought. And then she had the first glimmer of what she felt might be his real reason for deciding to keep working with her. But she didn't want that. Even if her body weren't rebelling against her, she wouldn't want that. She didn't say anything in reply.

"So why are *you* sticking with it?" Hyams asked after a mile of silence.

"I'm a writer," she said automatically.

"With a dead scientist, incomplete records, a wacko collection of Catholics who are working without the direction of their Church, and a story with so many loose ends you probably couldn't even sell it to the *National Enquirer*," Hyams said. "Surely there are better stories to be spending your time on."

"Maybe," Foster said, her voice as insincere as his had been. "But this is the one I'm working on now. I'll give it a couple more months at least."

"And then what?"

Foster tapped her hands against the steering wheel. She fought against the desperate feeling that threatened to engulf her. "No plans," she said as if she didn't care.

Another half mile went by.

"Ever think of going to Mexico?" Hyams asked in a disinterested tone.

"Never," Foster said. And the conversation ended there.

Not too far from Litchfield was a pleasant collection of five immaculate colonial houses, linked by meandering cobbled walkways and low picket fences. The houses' sidings gleamed with fresh white paint. Their trim and shutters were strikingly picked out with dark hunter's green. The lawn and gardens surrounding them were laid out with precision and an artist's eye for color. Except for the sign out front, they would have been a proud addition to any town in the vicinity. The sign said Vicker's Convalescent Home. It was a euphemism for garbage dump.

Foster had told Hyams what kind of place it was before they had set out.

"Convalescent home?" he had asked after she had parked the car in the neatly marked-off visitors' lot. He stretched his legs after the three-hour drive and awkwardly adjusted the camera he wore around his neck.

"Even the rich and famous can have defective genes," Foster had explained. Once inside, she didn't have to explain anything else. Hyams could see for himself.

"We get so few visitors in the middle of the week," Mr. Vicker said as he led Foster and Hyams along a brightly painted hallway. A "Sesame Street" counting song was playing in the distance. Children were laughing. At least, they sounded like children.

Mr. Vicker stopped in front of an open doorway. Foster looked in past his shoulder. The room resembled a well-equipped kindergarten classroom. Childish finger paintings covered most of the walls. Large construction-paper letters spelled out "Summer Fun" over some of them. A television set was built into the wall and Big Bird was dancing on it. Seven children and their teacher watched. Four of the children had hands and could clap in time to the music. Three others were in electric wheelchairs and rocked silently back and forth. Mr. Vicker waved to the teacher. The teacher smiled and waved back.

"They just love that show," Vicker said and began walking again. "We have more than two hundred episodes of it on videotape so the children can see it whenever they want." He was a happy man, Foster could tell. He spoke of his home with pride.

A teenager suddenly burst into the hall and bumped into Foster. He stopped dead. His features were grossly distorted as if they had been blown up like a balloon to twice normal size and then melted. Mr. Vicker made the introductions.

"Andrew," he said, slowly and carefully, "this is Ms. Foster. Can you say hello to Ms. Foster, Andrew?"

Andrew stared at Foster with his right eye. His left eye twitched up toward the ceiling.

"Say, 'Hello, Ms. Foster,' " Mr. Vicker repeated.

Andrew said something. Foster couldn't understand what it was.

"Very good, Andrew!" Mr. Vicker said with enthusiasm. He reached out and ruffled Andrew's hair. Andrew's face twisted into an immense happy smile and he said something else that Foster couldn't follow.

"No," Mr. Vicker said in reply, "Ms. Foster and her friend have come to visit Suddam today."

The smile left Andrew's face and he said something more.

Mr. Vicker smiled at the boy. "I will tell her that, Andrew. And now you must go and help Mrs. Monroe in the kitchen. All right?"

Andrew nodded like an excited puppy and ran off down the hall.

"He said he hopes that you'll come and visit him some time," Mr. Vicker translated.

"What's wrong with him?" Hyams asked.

"Oh," Mr. Vicker explained patiently, "we like to think that there's nothing wrong with any of the children in our care. They are living human beings, after all. They need food and shelter and love like anyone else. We prefer to think that if there is fault anywhere, it's with a world that cares so much about moving quickly that it won't stop to care for those who can't keep up." Foster felt sympathy for the look of embarrassment on Hyams's face.

"I'm sorry, Mr. Hyams," Mr. Vicker continued. "I don't mean to be rude. But truly, there is nothing wrong with any of the children here. Believe me."

"Does anyone come to visit Andrew?" Foster asked to change the subject.

"The mother comes from time to time," Mr. Vicker said as if it weren't really important. "The father is with some large bank. Very busy. Moving quickly. But Andrew has many friends here. He isn't lonely."

Foster decided against trying to explain that that wasn't what she was trying to suggest. Mr. Vicker was very defensive about his home. And for good reason, she thought.

Suddam Hussein was fourteen years old, according to Dr. Wyndham's records. The boy in the hospital bed in the playroom looked no older than nine or ten. His arms were little more than skin-covered bones. His face was sunken and hollow. But the resemblance was there, the genetic legacy of donor #72/SXM/4308.

Hyams fell into his role of Foster's photographer easily. He roamed around the playroom, squinting through his viewfinder as if searching for the best angles. Personally, Foster thought he may have seen *Blow-Up* one too many times. If such a thing was possible. But Vicker paid no attention to him.

Before Foster asked her first question, she paused to choose her words carefully so she would be spared another lecture. "Isn't it unusual for a child such as Suddam to be placed in a playroom?" she asked judiciously.

"In other homes, perhaps, but not here. Just because Suddam doesn't seem to be aware of his surroundings doesn't mean that that is actually the case. By having him share the playroom with other children, he can hear the sounds of playing, listen to their songs and games. Perhaps he can hear them, perhaps he cannot. But it does no harm to have him here and it is better than keeping him isolated if he does have some awareness."

"That is a very kind attitude, Mr. Vicker," Foster said as she made notes in her open pad.

"It is the only attitude. Food, shelter, and love. And the other children who play in this room feel that love, I can assure you. There is something very pleasant about being in this room." His eyes sparkled at Foster. "The children feel it. Can you?"

Foster stumbled over a response. Yes, she thought, I am feeling better than I felt during the drive up here. But she had attributed that to Mr. Vicker. It was so refreshing to meet someone who cared about his work and did it well, without hypocrisy. "I feel good about your home, Mr. Vicker. I'm sure my readers will, too," she offered.

"No," he said, eyes narrowing, "it's more than that, Ms. Foster. It's this room. The children look forward to coming here. Do you know they don't fight in here? They share their toys and never argue over the television? It's Suddam who does it. I don't know how, but he feels our love for him and returns it to us." Mr. Vicker laughed suddenly. "How do you think your magazine will react to that?" he asked.

At least he knows what he's saying may seem a bit odd, Foster thought. "I'm sure they'd be fascinated, but I'm not sure how I could write about it without some explanation," she said apologetically.

"Ah well," Mr. Vicker sighed as if he had heard it all before. "The children don't require any explanations. Not like us adults." He stepped out of the way as Hyams began to take pictures of Suddam lying motionless in his bed.

"But please do tell your readers what is possible," Mr. Vicker added. "There is a quality to every life, no matter what those more able may think. You will tell them that, won't you?"

"Of course," Foster said in keeping with her cover story. "That's why Father Panati suggested I come and visit your home. He's quite eager to see the work you do here publicized."

Mr. Vicker beamed happily at Foster's statement of intent. The rest of the afternoon visit went smoothly. And though she wouldn't admit it, she did feel less content the farther away they moved from the playroom where Suddam Hussein lay, motionless and staring and unaware.

"I hope the photos come out okay," Hyams said as they headed back into New York state.

"It's an automatic camera. As long as you remembered to push the button, it takes care of everything else."

"The button I knew about. It was the on-off switch I forgot until I was halfway through the first roll. Oh well, those were just my setup shots. The ones I really want to see are the close-ups of Suddam."

Traffic was lighter than it had been that morning. Foster felt lighter, too. As far as she was concerned, Suddam Hussein was the proof they needed that common genetic material was present in all four boys.

"The resemblance was there," she said. "We're building up the circumstantial evidence at least."

"It's not the resemblance I'm concerned about," Hyams said. "What did Wyndham's records say? Suddam was born with less than two percent of the amount of brain tissue that most people have?"

"That's right," Foster agreed. "No higher brain structures at all. Just a nodule of the original limbic system." Even though clones were supposed to be identical, from the differences Foster had seen in the photographs of Paul Almagro, John Danylkiw, the dead boy in Montreal, and the handicapped boy today, it was apparent to her that Wyndham's methods had somehow allowed minor genetic variations to creep into his reconstruction process. That would also explain why so many of the women implanted with the clones had miscarried, she thought. And also why three of the children had died as a result of severe congenital deformity before their first birthdays.

"So, with no higher brain structures," Hyams went on, "Suddam has no sensory processing capability, no motor capability, and even the way his autonomic system operates is a mystery. Right?"

"That's about word for word what I told you this morning," Foster said. Get to the point, kid, she thought.

"No muscular control at all, right?"

"Get to the point," she said, consciously leaving out the 'kid.'

"Then why did he have all those restraints on him?"

"What restraints?"

"One on each leg. They were under the sheet but you could see the outline. Plus one on each arm. *And* a restraint vest."

"Big deal," Foster said. "It keeps him from accidentally rolling out of bed."

"Don't you remember what his arms looked like? The boy didn't have any muscle in there at all. It's all atrophied after fourteen years in bed. Plus, he doesn't have the brain tissue to control it even if he did have muscles!" This was the first time Foster had felt real excitement in Hyams over the investigation.

"So, you're saying that the kid can't move, even accidentally, and they have him restrained as if he could.'' Foster still didn't see the point.

''Therefore,'' Hyams said triumphantly, ''the kid *can* move.''

''Without muscles?'' Now she understood what he was driving at. Hyams nodded. ''But that's not possible,'' she said.

''You mean, not human.''

SEVEN

''It just doesn't seem right, Bobby Jay,'' Randolph said. ''There should be some way for them to have a Christian burial.''

''I'm afraid not,'' Bobby Jay said with deep, caring sadness in his voice. ''They have reaped their rewards in Heaven, but we can't have them linked to me.'' He took a deep breath and stood up from his desk. He closed the copy of the L.A. *Times*, folded it, and then threw the paper and its story about the tragic barrio fire and the unidentified victims into his wastebasket.

''But this has been our *proof*,'' Bobby Jay said in a voice of studied righteousness. ''Beyond any shadow of a doubt, those five boys in the old studio are murdering demons!'' Bobby Jay strode to the window of his office as if he carried the sorrow of the world. But the sight of America's Glory lifted some of the weight from him. The reflecting pool was in. Next week the fifty-five-foot cross would be hoisted into position. Even the sod was going down in some of the completed areas.

''So what should we do with them?'' Randolph asked. Uncomfortable as he had felt with the idea at the beginning, even stronger doubts had been growing in him over the past month. He had seen the children in the old studio. He had been there when the tables had moved, when their eyes had changed and the voices of hell had burned from their gagged mouths. Except for the little fat one, of course. That was one of the doubts Randolph felt. He didn't think the fat boy belonged with the others. He felt there might be a soul in there worth saving. But

Bobby Jay didn't agree, and this was the reverend's show: the final episode of the greatest "Bobby Jay Good News Glory Show" ever.

"What do you mean, 'do with them'?" Bobby Jay answered as if the question had been absurd.

"Well, if they're so all-fired dangerous, and we don't have brother Eric and the rest to help look after them anymore, how are we going to keep those boys down there?" Randolph didn't like the look of anger that came to Bobby Jay's eyes. He knew he should never question one of the holiest men the world had ever been blessed with, but he couldn't help but feel that things were somehow getting out of hand.

"I hope I'm not detecting doubt in your voice, brother Randolph. I *pray* I'm not detecting doubt in your voice. Don't forget that the Lord Jee-sus is the Lord of Truth! And truth never caused a believing man to doubt. There's only one thing causes doubt, friend: only lies cause doubt. And we know who the Lord of Lies is, don't we?" Bobby Jay spread his arms across the windows and the buildings and dreams beyond. "Here is this greatest glory of the greatest nation of all the world, the only lies that are spoken, brother Randolph, are lies from Satan's own mouth. If I thought I was hearing doubt coming from your lips, I could only believe that you had been conversing with the devil. That's why I pray I didn't hear it. That's why I *know* I didn't hear it. Isn't that right?"

"No doubt at all, Bobby Jay," Randolph said rapidly. Dear Lord, he hated it when Bobby Jay could only see things as right or wrong. He acted as if any question anyone had was a personal attack. "No doubts at all, praise the Lord. Just wondering what I should be doing next, that's all."

"Very good, my friend. Praise the Lord, indeed." Bobby Jay went back to his desk and slid open the drawer with the Jack Daniel's. There was a lot more of that going on, too, Randolph noted.

"As to what you should be doing next, Randolph, you should be continuing to look after those boys in the studio."

"Bobby Jay," Randolph said nervously, "I don't mean to sound like I'm doubting anything, but is it safe to keep them here? I mean now that that one in Los Angeles has gone and killed Eric and the others?"

Bobby Jay smiled magnanimously. "It's never completely safe as far as the devil's concerned, brother Randolph. But we only have to keep them for another four weeks. Four more weeks and we can show them off to the President."

"Couldn't we show them to the President now?" Randolph asked cautiously.

Bobby Jay's face became stern and cold. "Randolph, any time the Lord Jesus comes to me and tells me that *now* is the moment for the President to see the instruments of Armageddon, that's the time I'll show him. As it happens, the Lord Jesus has *already* come to me and told me the proper time. He's told another, too."

It was news to Randolph. "Who is that, Bobby Jay?" Just please don't say it was Louella, he thought.

"Barbara-Jane Fuller," Bobby Jay said as if naming a saint. "Lord Jesus came and told me the place of Armageddon. Came and told Barbara-Jane the time. August twenty-ninth, ten fifty-two P.M. Quite a miracle, wouldn't you agree, Randolph?"

"Praise the Lord," Randolph said softly. It wasn't *getting* out of hand. It already *was* out of hand.

"Yessir, it's all been laid out by the hand of heaven, Randolph. Lord Jesus *said* America's Glory will be the site of the final battle. He *gave* me the information we needed to track down the Antichrists by directing us to that doctor's files. He *showed* me how those Antichrists have the devil's gift of a silver tongue. 'Course, it cost me that demon child in Montreal to learn how their evil voices alone could turn the souls and cloud the minds of true believers. But that was just the Lord's way of telling me to be sure and send the deaf to gather up the rest of those boys because those who cannot hear the devil's voice *cannot* be swayed from God's own work. And that little piece of strategy has turned out just fine now, hasn't it?

"And, Randolph, why the whole time Lord Jesus was talking to me and telling me all I need to know, he was *showing* a picture, just like a big old movie screen, to Barbara-Jane. Showed her when it was to happen, and showed her who was going to be there. Including the President." Bobby Jay knocked back another shot of Jack Daniel's and smiled his most saved smile.

"Did Barbara-Jane see the boys there, too?" Randolph asked.

"Can't rightly say," Bobby Jay replied, filling a glass for

Randolph and another for himself. "Haven't talked to the woman yet."

"Then how do you know about what she saw?"

The anger danced in Bobby Jay's eyes again. He set the bottle on his desk with a thud. The amber liquid sloshed within it.

"The President told me what Barbara-Jane told him," he said evenly, eyes burning into Randolph's.

"The . . . the President already knows about . . . about this?" Randolph asked. He knew he shouldn't ask any more questions, but he had to.

"Something wrong about the man who's been chosen by God to make sure that the forces of Heaven win the battle of Armageddon being told about his role by God's own messengers?" Bobby Jay asked, voice like ice.

"Chosen by God to make sure the forces of Heaven win . . . ?" Randolph repeated weakly.

"Randolph," Bobby Jay said sharply, head shaking with amazement, "what's wrong with you, son? The devil is a liar and a cheat. Don't you think he's going to try every trick in the book to make sure *he* wins? We've got to *outsmart* the devil, Randolph. We got to trick him the way he's trying to trick us."

"How's he trying to trick us?" Randolph asked. He felt as if he were drowning. Bobby Jay wasn't glowing with the inner light of the Lord anymore, he thought. It was the heat of insanity.

"Think of the weapons on his side, Randolph. He's got all those demon boys as the Antichrist. Not just one, mind, but as many as thirty! See the trickery? And then he has his earthly weapons, too. A-tomic bombs. Nuke-cue-lar missiles. All in the hands of the greatest pack of atheists the world has ever seen! The Reds, Randolph! Red like the fires of hell! You can't tell me that's a coincidence."

"I . . . don't understand, Bobby Jay." Randolph was afraid to leave and afraid to stay. He had no choice but to follow Bobby Jay's revelations to the end.

"Of course you don't," Bobby Jay said, and the way he said it and the way he looked at Randolph made Randolph feel as if Bobby Jay were a stranger. "You see, son, the devil knows that the time of Christ's return is near, so what better way to thwart him than to make sure that the Lord has nothing to return to?"

"How's he going to do that?"

"By lulling us with a false sense of security," Bobby Jay explained so sincerely. "All this crap from the Reds about the New Détente. And arms reductions. And allowing the Jews to go back to Israel. They're all lies, Randolph. They're all the devil's lies. Trying to get us to let down our guard. Make us weak. Turn our backs. And then . . . they attack!" Bobby Jay slammed his fist on his table and laughed as Randolph jumped. "A nuke-cue-lar holocaust, Randolph. The world destroyed. Nothing left for Jesus to return to. The devil will have won. But that's where we're going to outsmart him."

"How . . . how's that, Bobby Jay?"

"Why, strike first, of course," Bobby Jay said. "We're not just going to wait patiently for the devil to call for Armageddon when *he* wants it to be. We're going to surprise him! Preempt him! And that's what the President is prepared to do, God bless him. He's pretending to go along with those Red lies. But he knows the truth. He's prepared to fulfill the destiny that God has chosen for him."

Randolph felt the room spin. Four weeks, he thought. Four weeks.

"But won't an American attack destroy the world as surely as a Ru—"

"What's got into you?" Bobby Jay shouted. "Have you no *faith* in those useless bones? Can't you *feel* the Lord's presence in your work anymore?" Bobby Jay was out of his chair and instantly kneeling in front of Randolph. "The President will be doing the Lord's work! How can you think that the Lord will then repay us with destruction? Jesus is the Lord of Love and Forgiveness, Randolph. Have you forgotten that? Do you honestly believe that God will allow one missile to land on his chosen country? Does that sound like a kind and loving God to you? After we have destroyed his enemies for him?"

The words echoed blankly in Randolph's mind. All he could think was that there was a small bubble of spit in the corner of Bobby Jay's mouth.

"But . . . but why this way?" Randolph asked weakly. He felt himself begin to tremble.

"Why, Randolph," Bobby Jay said tenderly, with a smile of love and kindness, "surely you can see that it's the only way that makes any sense."

EIGHT

With Foster beside him, Jim Hyams walked along the sidewalk in front of his apartment building and wondered why he felt so uneasy. He hadn't been nervous about having friends from his classes come over for dinner. He hadn't been remotely on edge about inviting over any of the officers he had worked with during Operation Superbowl. And having Marjorie come over never bothered him at all. So why should I feel tense now? he asked himself. Maybe I don't really want to know, he answered.

After he had unlocked the front door, he held it open for Foster. He didn't think he was risking a feminist lecture by his action, since she was carrying the two bags from the deli and the wine store. In fact, he thought, in the almost two months he had been working with her, a discussion about women's issues had never arisen. He felt that had to be some sort of a record for New York. Nothing had even been said at the planning committee meetings either; four conservative male Catholics and not one condescending remark about Foster or any questioning of the way she had taken over most of the investigation process. Maybe the world is changing after all, Hyams thought.

The lobby of his building was small but well lit. There were marks on one of the walls where a planter box had been attached thirty years ago. But it had been too inviting a spot for someone to hide behind so it had been removed at the same time the windows on the ground floor had been barred. Other than that, the building was clean and well maintained. Hyams tried to remember if his cramped studio apartment was equally tidy. He doubted it.

"How long have you had this place?" Foster asked as they crowded into the tiny elevator. Hyams had to swing shut an outer hinged door and then pull a folding metal screen across the front of the car.

"About a year," he said. "Sublet from a friend of a friend. Absolutely no chance of it going condominium so I should be able to hold on to it for another six months." Even the small talk about apartments—the city's equivalent to discussing weather anywhere else—was making him nervous. He looked forward to getting into his apartment and starting to work. At least with Wyndham's medical reports and the latest printouts from Records spread out before them, he'd know what to talk about. Comfortably.

Hyams fiddled with the lock on his door. "Pardon the mess when we get in," he said, hoping that he had left no underwear on the couch. The smell of stale cabbage in the hallway was bad enough.

"No problem," Foster said. "You should see my place since I unpacked that trunk." She smiled reassuringly.

Hyams forced himself to look away from that wonderful smile and concentrate on the lock. Lift, wiggle, pull, and push. It clicked.

"There we go," he said with relief. But not a lot of relief. The thought of being alone with Foster, in the privacy of his apartment, with a bottle of wine and dinner in the deli bags, was making him feel like he was fifteen and his parents weren't home. Get a grip on yourself, he thought. It's going to be a fine, quiet, ordinary evening. He opened the door. Detective Ioannou was waiting for him.

"Jim Hyams, come on down," Ioannou said, smiling like a predatory game show host.

Hyams saw Foster tensing. She didn't know Ioannou. She stepped backward. Detective Sandra Heaslip was waiting for her in the hallway, the stairwell door slowly closing behind her. The detective held out her badge.

"Let's join them inside," Heaslip suggested as she took Foster's arm and led her into the apartment.

It took five seconds for Hyams to get over the shock of Ioannou's presence. Then he became furious. "Show me a warrant or get the hell out of here!" he shouted. "I'm getting sick of this!"

"Sick of what?" Ioannou asked innocently. "We haven't said boo to each other for the past month, kid. You're just upset that I've broken up your little party. Marjorie know about this?"

The mention of Marjorie brought red to Hyams's face. "Let's see a warrant or I'm charging you with harassment."

Ioannou shook his head sadly, long hair swaying. "If you wanted to, you couldn't be making it any worse." He reached into his inner jacket pocket and withdrew a folded-over document. "Here's your warrant, kid. Welcome to the majors."

When Hyams saw the warrant, he felt as if he had been kicked in the stomach. He grabbed it from Ioannou's stubby fingers and began to read. Then he felt as if he had been kicked in the groin.

". . . evidence pertaining to murder . . . kidnapping . . . assault?" he read. "What the hell is this?" The anger was gone from him. He only felt fear.

Ioannou studied Hyams's reactions then pointed to Foster. "Why don't you put those bags down and make yourself comfortable?" he suggested. "I've got another warrant for your place."

Foster sputtered. "What for?" she managed to say.

"That's what I'm hoping you'll tell me. Sandra, the purse."

Foster yanked her shoulder bag back from Detective Heaslip's grip. The detective pulled back, three silver crosses and a miniature razor blade jingling from her left ear. "Don't resist," the detective said. "It only makes it harder in the long run. And messier." Foster surrendered her purse.

"Will you at least give us a hint about what's going on here?" Hyams pleaded. He hated the look of shock he was seeing on Foster's face as she watched her purse being emptied. He felt responsible.

"All right, kid. I'll start storytime. But you better finish it, okay? I don't mind taking *you* in, but I'd hate to spoil the rest of the evening for your friend."

Hyams could tell Ioannou's threat of arrest was serious. "Whatever you say," he agreed.

"Once upon a time," Ioannou began, leaning back on the two-cushion couch with his hands behind his head, "a *good* cop was found with his brains all over the wall of an apartment just a few floors down from where a nasty teenage punk lived. Did the good cop try to kill the punk? Did the punk kill the cop? Was there a conspiracy involving other people who might have been involved with the good cop? The—"

"I told you I didn't have anything to do with it!" Hyams protested.

Ioannou raised a cautionary finger. "Simon didn't say speak, kid. Now, as I was saying, the noble detective called in to solve this mystery started trying to put the pieces together. But, there didn't seem to be too many pieces lying around, except for pieces of the good cop. So, the noble detective started following other people who might have been involved. One of the people he followed was a kid. The kid met a pretty lady. The kid took the pretty lady back to the police station and the kid had his girlfriend in the records department start to look for all sorts of interesting things from all over the country. Things that are on the magic warrant, for example. Murder, kidnapping, assault. And the most interesting thing of all"—Ioannou reached over to a large brown envelope that was beside him on the couch and slid out its contents: photographs—"was that everybody seemed to be one, big, not-so-happy family."

Ioannou held the photographs up: a mug shot of Paul Almagro, a missing child photo of John Danylkiw, a Montreal coroner's photo of Ahmed Shamir, a recent photo of Suddam Hussein, tied to his playroom bed, and then four more photographs of boys Hyams had never seen but who were the same as the first four.

"*Now* Simon says it's your turn." Ioannou settled back in the couch.

Hyams looked at Foster. At least she's lost that shocked look, he thought. He had no idea what he should say.

"I'd like to make a phone call, please," Foster said.

"You're not under arrest. Yet," Ioannou grinned. "I want the kid to finish the story for me."

"He doesn't know the story," Foster said. There was challenge in her voice. She was going to take on Ioannou. Hyams was impressed. Worried, but definitely impressed. "Give me that warrant," Foster said to Hyams.

She quickly scanned the front sheet. "This is a pile of shit and you know it," she said to Ioannou, pointing to the warrant for each item she dealt with. "First off, Jim told me about the Burch shooting and we both know you have nothing to link him to it. Otherwise you would have arrested him two months ago.

And if you *have* been following us, then you already know neither of us was anywhere near Larkin's Mill, Montreal, Los Angeles, or any of these other places. You're fishing, detective. And this license won't hold up for ten seconds in court." She tossed the warrant onto the floor. Hyams expected a lightning bolt to strike her for what she had done.

Ioannou tapped his little finger on the side of his jaw as he considered his next move. Then Heaslip held up Foster's notebook. She had taken it from the shoulder bag.

"She's got four of the names in here, Greg," Heaslip said. "Plus another eleven we don't have." She held up the can of Mace. "Plus a restricted substance."

"See? You're involved," Ioannou stated calmly. "Maybe not in the actual perpetration of what's on the warrant, but you do have knowledge pertaining to the offenses. If the warrant won't hold up as it's written, then I'll have it rewritten. I'll throw in your fancy spray can for free."

"I'm calling your bluff, detective," Foster announced. "Arrest us so we can call our lawyers or get out of here."

"Are you going along with that, kid?" Ioannou asked.

Hyams nodded. What else could he do?

There was a long pause. Ioannou scratched his beard. Heaslip slipped a small card from her purple-and-silver leather jacket and began to read.

"You are under arrest. You have the right to remain silent," she began. Hyams felt his insides turn to ice water.

Ioannou held up his hand. "Rewind, Sandra. I didn't say to arrest them yet. Let's give them a bit more time to think about what they're getting themselves into."

Hyams almost gasped out loud with relief. He began to consider how he could begin to tell Ioannou about the children.

"Oh, can the crap, detective," Foster said angrily. "You're so pitifully transparent it makes me wonder how you've kept your job. You have nothing to go on so you try to put on the pressure by threatening to arrest us. I say go ahead, knowing full well you have no possible grounds, and you scratch your beard to signal your partner to start reading us our rights so you can stop her and be a big hero. That kind of good-cop/bad-cop crap went out with J. Edgar Hoover."

Hyams felt as though he were in a tug-of-war. But he could

see that Foster was right. Ioannou had been trying to set them up. He must have had only a hunch to go on.

Foster picked up the warrant from where she had tossed it. "In fact," she continued, "even if you don't arrest us I'm still going to show this to a lawyer. And I'll give you ten to one that it's been improperly sworn to, which gives us grounds for harassment, just as Jim said."

Hyams couldn't believe it, but for the first time he could remember, Ioannou was speechless.

"Okay, lady," the bearded detective sighed. His first plan had failed. He shifted instantly to his second. "All on the table, then. Personally, I don't think Jim's bright enough to have had anything to do with Burch's death. I don't think you two had anything to do with what's been happening to the kids in these pictures, either. But I'm convinced that you two know what the *connection* is among these kids. It's obvious from the resemblance that they're related but what that relationship is . . . ?" He shrugged. "Anyway, my assumption is that you two are investigating the link between the kids. You are either doing it with or for Father Francis Panati at St. Joseph's University. And Alexander Thorkel of Thorkon Industries is involved." He paused to see if his openness was having any effect on Foster. "We *have* been following you."

"Go on," Foster said.

"So, I say to myself there's a link here. One of the elements of it is Paul Almagro. I suspect that Almagro was involved in Burch's murder. Therefore, I ask myself if, in the course of whatever you two are doing, you've uncovered anything that might help me prove my suspicions. Perhaps, I answer. So I go looking for you. That's it, lady."

"And what if we *have* uncovered anything?" Foster asked.

Ioannou took a deep breath. "Then, very politely and without warrants, I would ask you to share that information with me. All I'm interested in is getting whoever was responsible for Burch's murder. Good or bad, the guy was a cop."

"What's it worth to you?" Foster asked bluntly. Hyams choked. What was she trying to do?

Ioannou watched Foster carefully, trying to understand her motives. "You tell me," he said.

Foster pointed to the photographs. "There are four boys there we haven't seen before. We want all the information you have on them. Plus, we have reason to believe there could be up to twenty more boys who are involved in this. We'll want information about them as it becomes available."

"And I get Almagro?"

Foster shook her head. "You get the people who killed Burch," she said. "From what Jim has told me of your investigation, I don't think it was Almagro."

Ioannou's eyes widened. "You know who they are?" he asked, stroking his moustache like a grooming cat.

"The same ones who kidnapped the Danylkiw boy, killed the other boy in Montreal, and killed a priest and another man in an apartment building in New Jersey."

"You have names for any of these people?" Ioannou asked suspiciously.

"No, but if we can track down the rest of the children before they do, you can catch them in the act."

"What's the connection between the boys?" Ioannou asked.

"Do we have a deal?"

Ioannou nodded reluctantly. "We've got a deal. What's the link?"

Foster looked over at Hyams. "It will work out," she told him. Then she turned back to Ioannou. "The children are clones."

"Clones," Ioannou repeated as if he was learning a foreign language.

"Exact genetic duplicates of each other," Foster explained. "Think of twins. Identical twins are formed when a fertilized egg cell splits into two separate cells and then each begins to develop as an individual, right?"

"Okay," Ioannou said tentatively.

"In this case, fourteen years ago, the original egg cell was removed from the mother and instead of splitting into two separate cells on its own, a doctor made it split into about thirty separate cells. Then he implanted the cells back into thirty different women and what are, in effect, thirty twins were born."

"No shit," Ioannou said. "Why would anyone want to do that?"

"We're not sure. The scientist who did it found out he was

dying so he told his priest what he had done. The priest told Father Panati. I'm a science writer. Panati had worked with me before, so he asked me to look into it for him, just to see if it was true. I got hold of some of the doctor's records. One of the kids in the records was Paul Almagro. Jim came up to me when I was poking around Almagro's building after Burch had died there."

"So who are the people you say killed him?" Ioannou asked. The clones still weren't as interesting to him as the identities of Burch's murderers.

"About the same time we started trying to track down the children, another group of people started doing the same. Only they're out to kidnap the children."

"Why?" Detective Heaslip asked.

"Don't know," Foster said.

"Is this cloning business illegal?" Ioannou asked.

"At the time the doctor tried it, I don't think it was," Foster explained. "But there are new laws covering biological experiments and according to them, an experiment involving human cloning would be illegal if conducted without approval from the state government."

"Are the clones dangerous in any way?" Ioannou tried again.

"They're just fourteen-year-old boys," Foster said.

"What's Thorkel's involvement?"

"He's a friend of Panati's. He's paying the bills for our investigation."

Ioannou turned to Hyams. "You're not saying much, kid. Is she telling the whole story?"

"Absolutely," Hyams replied. But damn it, he thought, I hesitated. Did Ioannou pick up on it?

"So what happens if I tell my captain about clones?" Ioannou asked Foster. If he had noticed Hyams's hesitation, he wasn't doing anything about it.

"He'll laugh at you," she said lightly. "I'd recommend keeping their pictures to yourself and telling your captain that the children's parents or families are involved in Middle East politics. That is, if you have to tell him anything."

Ioannou sighed again and stood up. He nodded to Heaslip. "Ten o'clock tomorrow morning. The kid knows where my office is. We'll have all the files put together from our end. You bring what you have." He took the warrant back from Foster.

At the door, he paused and asked, "Do you people feel you're in any danger because of your investigation?"

"Not that we know of," Foster said. "But thanks for asking."

Ioannou looked at Hyams. "That's what partners do," he said pointedly. Then he and Heaslip left.

Hyams watched through his viewer as the two detectives squeezed into the elevator. After the door had shut and he was sure they couldn't overhear him, he said, "I almost believed that story myself."

"Why not?" Foster asked as she took off her jacket. "It was the truth."

"But not all of it."

"It was as much as he needed to hear."

"And what are we going to give him tomorrow?"

"Wyndham's records. There's no mention of the shroud in them."

"And then what?"

"And then we have Detective Ioannou on our side instead of trying to arrest us," Foster said. "After all, I've always heard it was a good thing to have a friend in the police." She smiled tightly at Hyams and started taking dinner from the deli bags.

Hyams helped. The nervousness had returned. From the way Foster had said 'friends in the police,' it was embarrassingly obvious to him that she had caught Ioannou's comments about Marjorie. But if I'm not involved with Susan, he argued with himself, if I don't even *want* to be involved with Susan, then why should I care if she knows I'm going out with Marjorie from the records department?

Thankfully, it became apparent that Foster had not interest in becoming involved with him because, for the rest of their evening of work, she never once mentioned Marjorie. Much to his dismay, Hyams found himself liking Foster even more for her tact in the matter.

NINE

Bobby Jay's Bible college had been the first building constructed on the site of what had become America's Glory—part Disneyland, part Heaven-on-Earth. But for Randolph Dewitt, working in a small storage room in the basement of the college, the religious message of America's Glory was threatening to become a nightmare. That is what he felt his last meeting with the reverend had turned into.

For years, Randolph had completely devoted himself to Bobby Jay. Not blindly, but for reasons that had to do with things other than the religion he shared with the reverend. What it came down to was that Randolph could see that Bobby Jay was a born leader of men and women. When the reverend spoke, people listened. And Bobby Jay spoke of the good things there should be in the world: honesty, trust, even patriotism. Any fool could see the world was in rotten shape and getting worse. Bobby Jay was a force against that dark transition. And if he was sometimes bombastic and overbearing, sometimes egotistical and given to fantastic statements about his relationship with the Lord, well then, Randolph felt accepting those qualities—and forgiving them—was better than the alternative: a leader who was calm and measured and reasonable, but not, perhaps, on the side of right.

Randolph was having a hard time trying to decide what side Bobby Jay was on these days. The uncertainty growing within him made it difficult to concentrate on his task of sorting through the medical records in the trunks brother Eric and the others had retrieved two months ago from the apartment building basement in New Jersey, before they had perished in that terrible fire in the Los Angeles barrio.

At first, the sorting had gone slowly. Bobby Jay had wanted to lessen the chance of someone outside his organization finding out about the boys so he had limited access to the operation to only a handful of workers. After a preliminary look through the records, Randolph had asked Bobby Jay to provide a doctor or a biologist to help him understand what was written on the records, but Bobby Jay had refused. "Let the Lord guide you," he had said.

Randolph stared at the piles of documents arranged on the tables—cloth-covered plywood sheets on wooden sawhorses—that filled the room and decided he could no longer feel that right was being served by this. For the first time in more than twenty years of devoted service and firm direction, Randolph Dewitt felt lost.

There was a knock on the door. Randolph checked to see that the lock was engaged, then asked who was there. It was Louella.

"Bobby Jay said you might be working too hard down here," Louella said as she entered the room. "So I thought you might need a bit of help." She smiled at Randolph. "Or some company."

"I appreciate that," Randolph said. Lost as he felt, twenty years of pleasant manners didn't vanish overnight. Besides, he was glad for the company, especially company that looked so nice. Randolph assumed that Louella had just come from a rehearsal because of her makeup and clothes. To his eyes, her extravagant eye shadow and trim two-piece maroon suit were stunning.

"You seem to have everything under control here," Louella said as she walked among the tables to the center of the room.

"The organizing's not all that bad," Randolph said. "It's when it comes to reading what the doctor wrote on the forms that it's slow going." He gestured at the ceiling in an attempt to say something nice about Louella's husband, despite his own doubts. "The new lighting Bobby Jay had put in for me sure makes it a lot easier, though."

Louella glanced up at the bright fixtures. They were attached by unpainted metal brackets to the acoustic ceiling tiles and all their wiring was exposed as it ran to a large ceiling-mounted junction box near the door. She hunched her shoulders up and shivered.

"It's sort of exciting, isn't it?" she asked. "Reminds me of some kind of emergency war headquarters." Again she smiled at him. Randolph decided he was feeling too uneasy after his meeting with Bobby Jay. If he thought about it, he couldn't say there was really anything different about Louella's smiles today.

"Well," he said flatly, "as Bobby Jay says, 'preparing to spread the word of the Lord is like preparing to go to war.' "

Louella's smile disappeared for a moment, leaving her face soft and vulnerable. "Bobby Jay's been talking a whole lot about war these past weeks, hasn't he, Randolph?"

"Yes, ma'am," Randolph said. And how do you feel about it, he wanted to ask.

Louella held his gaze a moment too long and then turned suddenly and said, "Now tell me what you've got going down here and how I can help. Bobby Jay's in a big meeting for the President's visit and I don't have anything to do for at least two whole hours." She turned back and there was that smile again.

Randolph ignored it and stared at the first table. "These are most of the records from the Harris fertility clinic," he began. "Apparently the Catholics' planning committee in New York took one of the trunks before we had a chance to get to them but they haven't been able to figure them out as well as we have."

"You mean as well as *you* have," Louella interrupted. "Bobby Jay told me how you're the only one doing this good work down here, all alone. That's one of the reasons he's worried about you, Randolph."

Randolph couldn't think of anything to say in reply. How could he tell Louella that he was just as worried about Bobby Jay? He continued.

"Anyway, each table represents a different type of patient at the clinic. Over here, we have all the women who were infertile because of physical reasons. Dr. Wyndham seems to have referred most of those to other clinics." Randolph walked along to another table. "This table is all the men who were infertile because of physical reasons."

"What kind of reasons would those be?" Louella asked. Her voice sounded controlled, as if she was trying to hide her interest in the subject.

"Um, I'm really not too sure, Louella. I asked Bobby Jay if he might find a doctor to help me go through these records, but he didn't want any more people than absolutely necessary to know about them." Randolph was feeling a bit embarrassed talking about this subject with Louella.

"I was wondering if the doctor's notes said anything about possible treatments," Louella said softly.

"Probably not," Randolph said. "He seems to have referred away most everybody who wasn't a candidate for artificial insemination. That's how he implanted the clones into the women who became their mothers. Anyway, over here are all the records of the women who were artificially inseminated." He touched each pile on the table as he described it. "Here are all the women who were given their husband's seed"—for some reason, he found himself extremely awkward about using the word *sperm* in front of Louella—"and gave birth to girls. Here are all the women who were given their husband's seed and gave birth to boys." He paused for a moment because Louella didn't appear to be paying attention. She was flipping through the records of the infertile men.

"Go ahead," Louella said when she realized Randolph had stopped talking. "Just browsing."

"Okay," Randolph went on, feeling warmth build in his cheeks, "this is the section from which the boys in the old studio all come from so this is the one I'm spending most of my time on. These are the women whose husbands were infertile so they were inseminated with a stranger's seed."

"Oh my," Louella said softly. She put down the files she had been glancing at and walked over to Randolph. "Those lights sure do make it hot down here, don't they?" she said as she slipped out of her suit jacket. Randolph looked away from the tight ivory blouse she was wearing and had to think for a few seconds to remember what he had been saying.

"Now, it appears that each stranger was given an identification number the same as the patients were, so I can tell how many times a stranger's seed was used. And it's this pile right here that has all the women who were given seed from the same stranger." He put his hand on the thickest pile on the table. Louella put her hand beside his.

"He certainly must have been busy," she said suggestively.

"Well, ah, it wasn't like that," Randolph said. It was Louella's perfume that was making the air seem so hard to breathe, he decided. He hadn't really smelled it until she came so close to him. That was what was making the room so stuffy and hot: the perfume and the lights.

"What was it like?" Louella asked with her warm smile glowing.

Her lipstick was stunning, too, Randolph noticed. "It wasn't really seed that was being given to the women. It was the special cells that Dr. Wyndham had cloned. What I've been trying to do is to cross-check all these files with the main patient records so we can find out the full names and addresses of the women from fourteen years ago so we can track them down today."

"Is that very difficult?" Louella asked. She had her hand on the files but wasn't looking at them. She was still standing close and staring up at Randolph.

Randolph tried to keep his eyes fixed on the files. It was no use, though. He could still see the taut fabric of Louella's blouse. He realized he was taking short, shallow breaths.

"Not too difficult," he said. His throat was dry and he had to stop to cough. "Just time-consuming. I have no way of knowing which files are hidden somewhere in all these piles and which files are in the trunk the planning committee has. I really don't understand all the ways the doctor divided up his files. By procedure. By referral. By sex." The last word came out as a hoarse croak.

"But you must understand some of what's in these files," Louella pointed out. "After all, you did manage to track down seven of the boys."

"Yes, ma'am," Randolph said. But it was really nine, he thought. Montreal and Los Angeles had been disasters. Two more reasons for the doubts he was feeling. Randolph moved away to a smaller stack of files. "That's these boys here. But there still could be up to twenty-one more. I just don't understand all the details he's put down in here." The confusion in Randolph swirled around like water disappearing down a drain. "Sometimes I don't feel I understand what anyone's talking about these days," he whispered.

"Why, Randolph," Louella said as she came over to him and reached out her hand to lift his head. "Are you crying?"

"No, ma'am," Randolph said, wishing it were true. "Just tired, I guess." Her hand was cool and soft against his skin. He felt his heart flutter.

"Sometimes," Louella asked, slowly taking her hand away, "do you feel you don't understand what Bobby Jay's talking about these days?"

Randolph looked into her eyes for an instant and then looked away. More uncertainty raged within him. "Yes, ma'am," he said reluctantly. "I truly don't. It's over, he thought. I've confessed myself as being unworthy. And then he felt Louella's arms encircle him, felt her body crush against his.

"Oh, thank God, I'm not alone in this," Louella cried. "I was so full of despair thinking I was the only one."

With surprise, Randolph's hands went to Louella's shoulders, eager to comfort her but wary because of who she was. He felt her tightly bound breasts move against him as she cried into his chest. He slid his arms around her back and held her as she held him.

"You know what I'm talking about?" he asked nervously.

"Oh, yes," Louella said between sobs. She looked up at him, mascara streaking. "Oh, yes, Randolph, he's been like a different man. A . . . a possessed man. All this talk about war and the President and I don't know what all . . ."

Randolph felt his tears come, too, from the relief that he was not alone with his doubts. He squeezed Louella tightly against him and realized that he had been wanting to do exactly that for a long, long time.

"You don't know what it's been like," Louella said. "He's given up interest in everything else, Randolph, to concentrate on what he's going to show the President. *Everything* else," she sighed. Randolph felt her breath warm against him.

"Everything," she said again, then pulled herself away and, keeping her arms around him, looked up at Randolph and did not let him look away. "That's why I was looking in those files, brother Randolph. I was looking for an answer. An answer for why there is no love between Bobby Jay and me. It's very hard for a woman like me to live that way, Randolph. Especially when I feel the love of others around me so deeply. Do you know what I mean?"

She pushed her hips against him and Randolph knew that what she felt would answer for him. The lights, the perfume, the sight of her as she backed away and slowly undid her blouse made him reach out to a table to steady himself. It's wrong, he thought, so wrong. But because she was Bobby Jay's, it made it important that he get something back for the wrong Bobby Jay had done him. And Bobby Jay had wronged Louella, too, so Randolph knew it was just as important to her.

Louella pushed files out of the way and sat on the edge of a cloth-covered table. She held out her arms to him, mouth trembling, eyes imploring. There was no more room for thought in Randolph's mind for what he was doing. He just went to her and placed his hands and his lips on her breasts so gloriously free.

Bobby Jay would be in his meeting for at least two hours, Louella had told him. And for all that time, and all that they did, Randolph was oblivious to the newly installed ceiling junction box and the faint hum of the video camera that came from within.

TEN

Detective Ioannou asked Foster and Hyams to wait in interrogation room three while he went to find Heaslip. The room was dimly lit and what features it had were unremarkable: no windows, drab tan walls, scarred wooden floors, and the scent of old sweat. Foster sat down on an ancient metal folding chair that squeaked against the floor. She placed her briefcase on the battered oak tabletop and turned to Hyams to comment on their surroundings.

Hyams held his finger to his lips and hushed her before she began. He tapped his ear and then pointed to the walls. Foster nodded. It probably wasn't legal, but it didn't surprise her that the police would bug a room where lawyers and their clients could supposedly talk in private. Part of Hyams's limited police training appeared to have paid off.

Ioannou kept them waiting for ten minutes. They sat and said nothing for all of it. Hyams seemed to be more composed this morning, Foster noted. Not like last night when she had fought back against Ioannou's high-handed tactics. At first she had thought that Hyams was upset because of the way she had gone against someone who must still be an authority figure to him. But the more she thought about it, the more she realized that Hyams's flustered reactions had flared each time Ioannou had made mention of Marjorie—the girlfriend in Records. It was almost as if Hyams didn't want me to know he was seeing someone, Foster thought. Which was a ridiculous notion. In New York, the only men who weren't seeing women were priests like Panati, gay, or dead. Every other man lasted about five minutes between relationships. But even so, though she had tried not to speculate too often on what Hyams's sex life was like over the months they had been working together, she found herself feeling a vague sense of disappointment when Marjorie's name had been spoken. Oh well, she decided, it just made her original decision not to get involved more valid.

Ioannou walked in without knocking. His hair hung in long, slick strands and his face was puffy, as if he hadn't slept the night before. His partner had on yet another outrageous outfit, primarily red, yellow, and blue, and the large-lens Vuarnets she wore prevented Foster from assessing her level of alertness.

Ioannou's chair groaned as he settled in it. Heaslip slid a cardboard box onto the table. When she sat down her own chair didn't make a sound, but an irregular smacking noise kept recurring. It took Foster a moment to realize that Heaslip was popping gum.

"Show-and-tell time," Ioannou said. He tapped the side of the box. "This is everything. Photos. Local police stats. FBI reports." He raised his eyebrows at Foster's look of surprise. "Like I told the kid, lady, welcome to the major leagues. Kidnapping is a federal offense. Anyway, what have you got for me?"

Foster snapped open her briefcase and handed over sixteen file folders. "This is the important material we have from the doctor's files."

"But not all of it," Ioannou said with tired annoyance. "That wasn't the deal."

"This is all the material that pertains to the fifteen boys on the list," Foster continued, ignoring him. "Their mothers' records, the artificial insemination procedure records, and any cross-referenced material from the insurance files. There were a couple of hundred other patients not involved whose records you are more than welcome to pore over whenever you have a spare month or two. The top file is a chronology I typed up, giving the dates of operation for the clinic, address, phone numbers, supplying companies, anything which might lead to other information."

Ioannou split the pile into two and handed half to Heaslip. "Okay" he said, "here are fifteen and you said there might be up to thirty. Where's the rest?"

"Originally, there were five trunks of records," Hyams said. "The doctor kept them in the basement storage of his apartment. When Susan and Father Panati located the trunks, Susan was able to get one of them back to her place. The others were stolen when Father Montgomery and a fellow helping him were killed."

Ioannou pulled a file from his cardboard box. "The Montgomery homicide is right here," he said. "New Jersey, right? No suspects. No witnesses. No hope. So, anything else not in these files? Like some sort of direction, at least, to the guys you think got Burch?"

Foster sighed. "This is the only thing we have to go on: After Father Panati and I found the trunks, only three other people were told about them. One of them, we believe, is associated with the people who want to go after the boys. When he heard about the trunks, he got in contact with whoever he's working for, and they sent some people over to steal them."

"Like, really keen," Heaslip said in disgust. "You *know* you've got an informer on your committee and you go ahead with all this work anyway. Ace move, Jim."

"We're not quite that stupid," Foster countered.

"The planning committee hasn't been told anything about the information in the records," Hyams added. "As far as anyone knows, with the exception of Father Panati, Susan has drawn a blank."

Ioannou rested his head in his hands. "I don't believe it, kid. Didn't you take any of the courses they were giving you? You've got a conduit into the group of people who are threatening the lives and well-being of maybe thirty innocent kids, and you didn't think to exploit it." He breathed some sort of comment that sounded Greek to Foster. "Give me the names of the rest of the people on the committee. Panati, Thorkel, you two, and who else?''

Foster gave him Delambre and Carey. She had phone numbers in her notebook and supplied those, too. ''Anything else?'' she asked.

''For obvious reasons,'' Ioannou explained, ''I can't let you take any of these records from the station. I can't even let you photocopy them. However, you're free to copy down as much information as you need from them. And you've got as long as you want, too. In the meantime, we're going to track down whatever we've got on the rest of these names and the rest of the committee. Questions?''

There were none. The detectives left and the work began.

Two hours passed. Foster found it awkward to work when most of the questions she and Hyams had for each other had to be written down to avoid possible eavesdroppers, but most of the time was spent simply reading. And it was disturbing reading. The FBI had definitely linked two of the kidnappings by their MOs: administration of drugs, no ransom, young teenage boys. How long would it take for an agent to notice the resemblance between the two boys? Foster doubted the situation would remain under control much longer.

Ioannou came back carrying an orange plastic tray heaped with Ronald McDonald's version of a smorgasbord. Heaslip had lost the glasses and gained a sheaf of computer printouts. ''Any luck?'' Ioannou asked.

''The FBI reports make me nervous,'' Foster said.

''They should,'' Ioannou agreed. ''The Feds are sure not going to be as understanding as I am. Big Mac?''

Foster shook her head. Hyams took it.

Heaslip dropped the printouts by Foster. ''We have something for you,'' she said. ''Jamie Estevez, one of the children on your list. One of the ones you couldn't track down. He's in the criminal wing of the Yorkwoods psychiatric treatment center in Maryland.''

''What for?'' Hyams asked around a mouthful of burger.

''Killed his parents,'' Heaslip said. Foster felt uneasy about the twinkle that seemed to be in the detective's eyes when she said that. "Not guilty by reason of insanity. Committal for observation. Official diagnosis is multiple personalities."

"Photograph?" Foster asked.

Heaslip pulled it out of the pile. "One of the family," she said and passed it over.

Foster held the police photo in her hands and saw the eyes of all the other boys look out at her. His hair was cut institutionally short. His face was broader, not just in the cheeks but in the cheekbones as well, and his nose just a hairbreadth wider. But it was in his eyes that the real confirmation lay. Despite the minor changes from boy to boy, the eyes were always eerily identical. Dark and shadowed, the eyes were the features that told the whole story.

"So, a question for you, science writer," Ioannou said. He hadn't touched the food on the tray but he was starting on his second cup of coffee. "I looked up cloning in a couple of books. The operative word seems to be 'identical.' I look at the pictures of these boys and I see a strong resemblance, but I don't see identical. Why's that?"

Foster understood enough of Wyndham's reconstruction log that she could answer Ioannou's question, but to do so would be to say that the original genetic material for the clones came from bloodstains anywhere between seven hundred to two thousand years old. "I don't know," she lied. "Flaws in the reproduction process, perhaps. Differences in the nutrition of the mothers during pregnancy. Different nutritional patterns as babies. Different childhood diseases. It's a brand-new field, detective. Not all the answers are in."

Ioannou shrugged, as if accepting her story. "So, you want to talk to little Jamie?" he asked unexpectedly.

Foster and Hyams exchanged glances. "I don't know what we'd have to say to him," Foster said. She suspected there was something more to the offer than Ioannou was making apparent.

"Would everyone on the planning committee share your lack of enthusiasm?" Ioannou asked.

Foster remained noncommittal. "Is that important?" she replied.

"You don't like giving anything away, do you, lady?" Ioannou complained. "Here's the plan. And we have to move fast on it before the FBI steps in and nails the people who got Burch. If they go up on federal charges of kidnapping, we won't see them back here for prosecution in Burch's homicide for at least three years. And by then, it won't matter to anyone. I don't want that to happen. Clear?"

Foster and Hyams nodded together.

"Okay then. The first step is to make the connection between the unnamed group who are after the children and the informer on the committee."

"That sounds easy," Hyams muttered.

"It *is* easy for anyone who's graduated, smartass. One of the oldest tricks in the book." Ioannou glanced at Foster. "Dates even further back than good-cop/bad-cop. We call it the party line. Ever hear of that, kid?"

"No, sir," Hyams said, appearing as surprised as everyone else that he had tagged on the 'sir' at the end.

"Everyone on the committee gets the late-breaking news that the science writer here has stumbled across the lost secrets of the doctor's files. She knows the location of one of the boys. She tells them."

"And each one gets told a different location and wherever the kidnappers shows up tells us who passed the word on," Foster concluded.

"Bingo. And if you had come to me a month ago with this, kid, we could have done the same thing a whole lot sooner." Ioannou was acting as if he was trying to make up for all the instructors Hyams never had.

"So what are the three locations?" Foster asked.

"Four," Heaslip corrected. "One for Father Panati, too."

"Not him," Hyams protested. "He knows everything we've done so far. No one's gone after Suddam in the Vicker home, have they?"

"Kid, I know this may surprise you," Ioannou pointed out, "but there's a pretty good chance that whoever's behind this might be a bit more experienced than you are. Maybe Panati doesn't want the kid without a brain. Maybe he only communicates with the unknown group when the moon is full."

"I trust Father Panati, too," Foster interrupted, "but there's no harm in going along with the plan. Why not make Suddam location four? If the kidnappers show up there, then it's Panati."

"Okay for now," Ioannou agreed. "For the others, the story will be that Jamie Estevez has been located. His case is available through newspaper files so the unknown group will be able to verify what we tell them. Up to a point. The point being that he's been transferred from the Yorkwoods Institute. Sandra's talked with the Yorkwoods director, and he's agreed to go along with our premise. He thinks we're stopping a writer from trying to get close to the boy for an interview with one of his many personalities."

"Did you give the writer a name?" Foster asked. She didn't like the sound of that.

"Relax," Ioannou said. "I didn't say *science* writer. Anyway, the director will tell his staff to tell anyone inquiring that Estevez has been relocated. He just won't say *where* the boy's been relocated. You'll tell Carey he's gone to Bellevue. Delambre gets MacGregor House. And tell Thorkel that Estevez has gone to Sector General. They're all medical facilities in the area and they're all easy to watch. We can even register a room to Estevez in each place."

"What's the procedure when the kidnappers show up at one of those places?" Hyams asked.

"Then we know who the informer is and we leave the driving to me," Ioannou said.

"And what happens if the kidnappers don't show up anywhere?" Foster asked.

"Then I figure it will be no more than two or three weeks before the FBI picks up on the resemblance between the children," Ioannou said in resignation. "Then they'll look for a link and find that all the mothers of the boys were treated at the Harris clinic. That will take them to Dr. Wyndham. That will take them to the murder in Wyndham's apartment building. From there they're going to find out that a detective and a student cop from Manhattan were poking around in a New Jersey homicide. They'll look into you and me, kid, and find the Burch case and Paul Almagro as our common links. A photo file on Almagro will show him to share a resemblance with the boys that started everything off to begin with. And then, when the Feds come calling at this precinct, I throw myself on my knees and tell them I was just about to pick up the phone and give them everything because it's more than a poor old city detective can figure out."

Ioannou stared meaningfully at Hyams. "And I suggest you do exactly the same thing, kid."

"An impressive chain of events," Foster said.

"That's how the business works, lady. Just like dominoes. If you know where they're going to land, you can jump out of the way. So, are we go on this?"

Hyams nodded. Foster agreed. "But how do I get word to the committee members individually so they won't compare locations?" she asked.

"That's your problem. You know them and how they work together. Just find some way they'll accept comfortably and call me or Sandra each time you tell one of them." Ioannou stood up. "You need more time with those files?"

Foster and Hyams decided they didn't for the moment and prepared to leave. They were walking to the station's main entrance when Heaslip came running after Hyams and said that Ioannou wanted to talk to him for a second; something about paperwork for his suspension pay. Hyams excused himself and went back with Heaslip. Foster waited in the busy entrance lobby, trying to stay out of the way of the ebb and flow of arrests and releases. Hyams was back in five minutes. He was shaken.

"*Was* that about your pay?" Foster asked. Obviously it hadn't been.

"No," Hyams said as they left the station and headed along the sidewalk to the police parking lot. "He wanted to give me a few words of advice."

"Such as?"

"Such as he doesn't believe that we're telling the truth. Not the whole truth at least."

"Which we aren't," Foster said, after looking around to make sure no one was within earshot.

"And which he knows, I'm afraid, especially because of the way I tried to tell him he was wrong." Foster unlocked the passenger door of her car for Hyams and walked around to the driver's side.

"I don't blame you for being nervous talking to him," she offered.

"You weren't nervous with him last night," Hyams said.

"No," she agreed. "But then, I had nothing to lose. I think somewhere inside of you, you still might want to be a police officer. He could be your boss one day. That has an effect on your dealings with him. Completely understandable. What else did he say?"

Hyams fastened his seat belt, a practice he had begun since driving with Foster, and said, "That he wasn't kidding about the FBI. At the very least we're looking at obstruction of justice charges. He says he's willing to stick with us for a week, through the party line scam against the committee, but that's all."

"What happens after the week is up?" Foster asked as she gunned out into traffic.

"He says our only chance is to tell him everything. If we don't, he's going to the FBI anyway and we're on our own."

Foster approached a yellow light and accelerated. "Did he give any indication as to what he thought we might still be keeping from him?"

"Hard to say. I don't think he's completely convinced by the cloning story but he does think it has something to do with the children's parents. He asked me if I thought any of the families, as in organized crime families, might be involved. I know that the only reason he's going this far with us is because he wants to get whoever killed Burch. It's a personal thing. Nobody likes the idea of a cop killer getting away."

"How did you leave it with him?"

"That I didn't know what he was talking about."

"How did he leave it with you?"

Hyams shrugged as he was rocked back and forth in his seat. Traffic was heavy and Foster was doing a lot of passing. "He said I had better come clean. Since I'm still technically part of the police department, I'm subject to internal discipline boards *and* the regular courts. He said that once the FBI was involved there was only one way I could get out of serious trouble."

"And that is?"

Hyams hesitated long enough that Foster could guess what it was. "Throw me to the wolves?" she asked.

"More or less," Hyams said. "The phrase he used was 'dump the lady.' "

"So, are you?"

"Going to dump you?" Hyams asked. He reached out his hand to hers on the steering wheel. "Never," he said.

ELEVEN

The limousine brought Barbara-Jane Fuller home at two o'clock. Her husband, Dean, was waiting for her. He squinted at the small blue flags fluttering from the car's front fenders as it drove away. Barbara-Jane walked up the front steps and passed him without a word. Dean followed her in.

"That was a White House limousine," he said. It sounded like an accusation.

"It certainly was," she replied. "The President got a bit concerned that some of his messages weren't getting through to me." Barbara-Jane unpinned her hat in front of the foyer mirror. The hat was pastel pink and about twenty-five years out of date. In both ways it matched her suit.

"You talked to the President two months ago," Fuller said. "What more did you have to say to him?"

"It's what he had to say to me," his wife answered. She went to the staircase, snapped down the seat of her elevator chair, sat on it, and began to glide upstairs. Fuller walked up beside her.

"What did *he* have to say to *you*, then? Has the President been having visions, too?" He knew he was sounding bitter. He could tell that Barbara-Jane knew it, too.

"No," she said smugly. "But there are those around him who have shared in my advance knowledge. Not everyone in this town thinks I'm a dried-up old gypsy, you know." She folded her arms and watched the stairs slide past beneath her, refusing to look at her husband.

"I never said anything like that," he replied weakly. It was going to be one of those arguments.

"And you never said that the President left three messages for me last week? Three, Dean. How do you suppose that makes me look? Not returning the President's calls . . ." The chair clunked at the top of the stairs and she stood up and lifted the chair seat back to the closed position. She headed for her study.

"Will you at least give me a hint about what the President had to say?" Fuller pleaded.

Barbara-Jane stopped in the doorway of her study. "He's doing everything just the way it's supposed to be done. You and I will be with him when the end comes."

"In the White House bomb shelter?" Fuller asked sarcastically.

Barbara-Jane tightened her lips and frowned. "America's Glory, the Reverend Bobby Jay's new broadcasting complex in Georgia. We'll all be together then because the President has invited me to join him on Air Force One for his Labor Day trip. He even invited you. He didn't want to because of those things you were saying to the *Post* reporter about his staff changes, but I told him that you were with me in my dream so you had to be with me for real."

Fuller almost choked at his wife's offhand comment. "What did the President say about the reporter and me?" he asked.

Barbara-Jane arched her left eyebrow in the way that signaled she had gained the upper hand in their argument and wasn't about to let it go. "The President has a lot of friends in this town, Dean. If you're determined to bad-mouth him to the press, you should make sure you choose a reporter from far away. A reporter who won't feel obliged to pass your allegations back to the press secretary. I think you might have to look pretty far afield to find someone like that these days. It's a moral revolution, you know." She put her hand on the knob of her study door. "Besides, in two more weeks, nothing's going to matter anyway."

"How can you talk like that?" Fuller could feel his voice rising in pitch. Was *everyone* in D.C. in on this madness except for him?

"Dean, my love, we have a chance to be part of history. Why not accept that? You've accepted my gift before. Why not now?"

The words were on his tongue: the truth about Galahad. But staring into his wife's lovely eyes, Fuller couldn't bring himself to tell her that her whole life had been a lie. She took his silence as capitulation, smiled and patted his cheek, then shut her study door behind her.

Fuller stood there a moment, couldn't think of a thing to say by way of apology or threat, and then went downstairs to his own study. He called Tom Jefferson at his new place of employment—consultant for a PAC group representing manufacturers of disposable glass containers.

"I need your help, Tom," he said. He wondered if Jefferson could sense the panic building in his voice.

"What can I do?" Jefferson asked. His own voice was plaintive and defeated. "All my people are gone. I have no contacts and absolutely no pull. It's like a Christian mafia in the White House these days."

"Tom, about ten minutes ago, Barbara-Jane came back from the White House. Things have gotten a lot worse."

"How?"

"Barbara-Jane says the President's doing everything just the way it should be done. He's following her dream exactly."

"I don't get it."

"The President doesn't just believe that the world is coming to an end in two weeks, Tom. The President believes it's his *destiny* to destroy the world in two weeks."

"God's will?" Jefferson said after a long pause.

"I don't know," Fuller said. He felt like crying with frustration. "All I do know is that it's all tied up with America's Glory and Bobby Jay."

"Seems a lot of things are tied up with Bobby Jay these days. Any thought as to what we can do?"

"One idea," Fuller said. Desperate, he knew, but the only thing he thought had the slightest chance of working. Two people couldn't face up to the resources commanded by the President. "We have to make it public."

"I thought you already tried talking about the staff changes with your friend at the *Post*. Nothing came of that, did it?"

"Wrong angle," Fuller admitted. "We have to keep it away from the President at first. Let the media pick that one up on their own."

"What are you talking about, Dean?"

"I'm talking about breaking the news of Barbara-Jane's vision. Tell the world the whole thing. Names and dates."

"What good will that do?"

"Barbara-Jane is news. The end of the world is news. Especially in August. You can bet that some enterprising reporter is going to ask the President what his reaction is to the prediction that he will start a world-destroying war on August twenty-ninth. If he confirms, then he can be relieved or impeached before the end of the month. I'll have to call a few of my colleagues in constitutional law to see how long the process will take, but the Twenty-fifth Amendment should cover it."

"What happens if he denies?"

"We can still raise a big stink. Foreign media won't be as circumspect when it comes to reporting allegations that the President's staff is being replaced wholesale with Bobby Jay alumni. The Joint Chiefs of Staff might get involved. SAC at least will pay close attention to any presidential orders coming through on the day."

"How do you suppose the Soviets are going to react to all this?"

"They think we're all trigger-happy fanatics anyway. It'll be one more proof for them. I don't think it will change anything. Unless, of course, the kind of control the President has over my friend at the *Post* extends across the board. If the story doesn't get reported, we'll have to take more direct action."

"I don't like the sound of that," Jefferson cautioned.

"And I don't like the sound of the commander in chief of the country's nuclear arsenal having delusions of biblical grandeur," Fuller stated bluntly. "That's not one of the reasons why I voted for him."

"Come over to my place at four this afternoon," Jefferson said. "I can be home by then."

"Let's keep it away from our homes," Fuller suggested. This was like the old days for him; all the safeguards falling automatically into place. "Parking lot of the Ambassador. Northwest corner. I'll be in the white Lincoln. Same time, all right?"

"All right," Jefferson agreed. "You're the one who knows what he's doing. I'll see you then. And God help us both, right?"

"Right," Fuller said and heard the click as Jefferson disconnected. But the line didn't go dead.

Fuller felt a chill go up his back. "Barbara-Jane?" he asked. Then the line went dead. He tried calling Jefferson back. The line stayed dead.

He tore out of the study and ran up the stairs, heart pounding.

Barbara-Jane's study door was locked. No matter how hard he pounded on it, no matter how loudly he called her name, she didn't answer.

Fuller was drenched in sweat. How could he have been so careless? How could he not have thought things through? The President knew about his talk with the reporter, Barbara-Jane had said. The President hadn't wanted to invite him to America's Glory. It all came down to the President knowing about him. He turned back to the stairs. Perhaps he could still drive away in time, get over to Jefferson's office in time, and then there was no more time.

He was halfway down the stairs when the front doors burst open. There were four of them—clean-cut, dressed in suits, and very young and intense. Fuller knew the type. Thirty years ago he had been one himself.

He didn't even think of resisting. From experience, he knew it was easier that way.

TWELVE

In her entire life, Marguerite had never seen more cars in one place than in the Disneyland parking lot that day. Row after row, they shimmered off into the summer heat. She wondered how there could be enough money in the world to buy them all. But then, she remembered, sometimes money wasn't necessary.

She shifted in the front seat of the Vanagon camper so the rush of the air-conditioned breeze could blow in her face. After all those years in Esperanza's stifling hot house, a machine that could create cold air in the middle of summer was nothing less than a miracle. And the fact that the camper van had been *given* to Paul—just by asking a man for it!—was even more of a miracle. Marguerite really didn't understand what Paul and Juan had been trying to do over the past few weeks. So much of what they communicated to each other seemed to go by ways other than words. But Marguerite had faith in her cousin. He asked her to look after Paul's friend, Johnny, so that is what she did, with no questions and no doubts. Well, one question.

"Do you think we might be able to go in?" she asked. Even as a child in Mexico, she had heard stories of the fabled Disneyland. Machines that walked and talked and let children fly through the air. *El Ratón Mickey*. Until Paul had driven into the parking lot and she had caught a glimpse of the single-track train rushing by overhead, she hadn't really believed that such a place could exist.

"Not today," Paul said. He was stern and unmoving behind the steering wheel of the van, waiting without watching, but for what, Marguerite didn't know. "Sorry," he added.

It was unusual for him to be polite like that, Marguerite thought as she dealt with her disappointment. Some of Juan's good manners seemed to be rubbing off on his brother from New York. If only Paul's sight would somehow make a similar transference to Juan.

They had been sitting in the lot for an hour, Paul in the driver's seat, Marguerite beside him. In the back, Juan slept and Johnny Matches sat and stared at the floor. Juan had tried healing the poor boy with the sunken chest many times after Paul had described what had happened to him. But, Juan had finally said, even God's power must have limits. The second time death had claimed Johnny, Paul should have let him go. She could see in Paul's eyes that he had disagreed with Juan, but he had said nothing. Or, perhaps, they had argued in a way that she couldn't hear.

Marguerite was watching the monorail go by again and wondering what things she might see from it when someone tapped at her window and made her gasp with surprise. She looked out through the tinted glass. She crossed herself.

"Roll down the window," Paul said.

The boy outside the van blinked as the cold air escaped in his face, a face that could be Juan's. Or Paul's. Or theirs could be his.

The boy didn't say anything. Neither did Paul. Marguerite leaned back in her seat so she wouldn't intrude on whatever silent communication was passing between them.

Finally the boy spoke. "This is too intense, man. Like, all day I've been thinking about this van, you know? So like I come out into the parking lot with my folks and the van is, like, right here. I mean, godzillous or what, you know? And then *you're* in it. So like, those dreams I've been having are for real?'' His voice was different from the others', but he was the same.

''They're not even dreams,'' Paul told him. ''We're interwoven. We're seeing through each other's eyes.''

The new boy thought about that for a while. Paul looked at the gas readout and shut the van off.

The new boy leaned closer to the van and put his head through the open window to look in the back.

''Like, sometimes I see more than you two. And there are some sort of weird numbers. Like, here.'' He tapped at his forehead.

Juan spoke from the back. ''Those are the ones we are trying to find,'' he said.

''Will you come with us?'' Paul asked.

The boy leaned back. ''This is too gargantuan for me, man. I mean, really.'' He shook his head.

''Dream friend's coming,'' Paul said.

The boy looked nervous. ''Oh, shit. That's real, too? Like, the weird voices and everything?''

Paul stretched his arm out to the boy. There was a moment's hesitation and then the boy took Paul's hand. Marguerite could feel a heat emerge from those hands held before her. The new boy's eyes flickered like a light burning out. Marguerite bit her lip but was familiar enough with the sight not to gasp again.

''But what do I tell my parentoids, man?'' the boy asked.

There were no answers.

''And, like, my dog?''

''The dream friend's coming,'' Paul repeated. ''How can you say anything? What more is there to say?''

''I don't know, man.'' The boy's face wrinkled with thought.

''You can see them as well as we can,'' Juan shouted from the back of the van. ''You know what we have to do. And we have to do it before the dream friend comes. It's all of us or nothing, Byron.''

The boy leaned back to the window and was about to ask how Juan knew his name when he seemed to realize what a stupid question that would be. Instead, he opened the door and squeezed behind Marguerite's seatback.

"We better slice out fast, man," he said. "The parentoids will be looking for me." He handed Marguerite a pastel-colored paper bag. "Sorry you couldn't go in today. You can have this, okay?"

Paul started the van and backed it out of the parking space. Marguerite opened the bag and pulled out the blue sweatshirt inside. *El Ratón Mickey* waved from it.

Marguerite couldn't remember ever being given a present by someone who wasn't part of her family. It was several seconds before she remembered to say, "Thank you."

"He *is* part of your family, now," Juan said from the back of the van.

Marguerite shivered. Juan had known what she had been thinking.

"We're all part of the family," Paul said as he drove the van slowly over the speed bumps toward the exit.

It was as if there were no boundaries between her cousin and the others, Marguerite thought. What one knew, the other could say. Even the new boy, Byron, had said he was sorry she couldn't go into Disneyland today.

As Paul pulled the van onto the road, Marguerite turned in her seat to watch the theme park slide away. She held the sweatshirt tightly, crushing the fabric, a souvenir of a place she had never been.

It's not fair, she thought, to come so close to such miracles yet not be allowed to go in. What could she have seen from the train? What wonders had she missed? It just wasn't fair.

She felt a kind hand on her shoulder. She heard Byron's California voice.

"I know," he said. "Like, really, I know."

THIRTEEN

Randolph Dewitt didn't mind that Bobby Jay had been keeping him waiting for fifteen minutes. The delay gave him some sorely needed time just to sit and think. He didn't care that it was in Bobby Jay's office he waited, a wall of monitors showing "Good News Glory Show" tapes on one side of him, and wraparound windows showing the almost-completed vista of America's Glory on the other. It was only the silence that mattered to Randolph. The silence made it easier to plan his next moves.

Randolph leaned back against the couch beneath the wall of Bobby Jay's honorary degrees and closed his eyes as he concentrated. He had already decided that the reverend had gone too far. The good that Bobby Jay might do no longer offset the bad. The boys in the old studio had to be released. Louella might be able to help him out with that, Randolph thought. She had certainly been helping him out in a number of other ways over the past few weeks.

Randolph smiled at his memories of Louella. He had half a mind to go over and get Bobby Jay's bottle of Jack Daniel's, too. But the way tension had been building between him and Bobby Jay, he decided it was best not to risk being caught rummaging through the desk drawers when Bobby Jay finally decided to join him. In fact, Randolph thought, I wouldn't put it past the old coot to be setting me up in here, maybe even taping me on some of that video equipment he so dearly loves. Randolph was glancing around, trying to guess where the reverend would put a hidden camera in his office, when Bobby Jay strode in as if he wasn't planning to stop.

"Randolph, my boy, glad you could make it. Mighty glad you could make it." Bobby Jay moved rapidly, infused with some excitement that Randolph couldn't understand.

"My time is your time, Bobby Jay," Randolph said. Now that he had made up his mind not to follow Bobby Jay any longer, Randolph found he could remain calm in the man's presence. There was no longer a personal investment at risk.

"My time is your time," Bobby Jay repeated with a bemused smile. "What's mine is yours, right, brother Randolph? Sounds a proper Christian sort of thing to you, does it?" He sat behind his desk and made a big show of clearing all the files on it off to one side.

"Share and share alike," Randolph said.

Bobby Jay joined his hands together and laid them down on

his empty desk top. "So, brother Randolph, any idea why I asked you here today?" He smiled his television smile. He didn't usually do that for Randolph.

"I imagine it has something to do with those young boys we have tied up in the old studio in the Bible college."

"Nossir," Bobby Jay said, shaking his head like a close friend about to tell a good joke. "Nossir, Randolph, that's not it at all."

Randolph couldn't care less so he didn't say anything. Bobby Jay got tired of waiting for a reply. "You know, Randolph," the reverend continued, just as if he were delivering a scripted sermon for the brothers and sisters at home. "We all work here under the grace and the glory of *trust*. We all believe in the brotherhood of the Lord, don't we, son?"

"Praise the Lord," Randolph said with a noticeable lack of feeling.

"I said, we *all* believe in the brotherhood of the Lord, don't we, son." Bobby Jay's television voice was gaining an edge.

"Yes, we do," Randolph said. Though some of us have a slightly different idea as to what the requirements of belonging to that brotherhood might be, he added to himself.

"Of course we do. Of course we do," Bobby Jay went on. "You trust your production team to do their jobs right. I trust you to keep everything on schedule so I can continue serving the brothers and sisters at home, don't I now? And Lord Jesus trusts me to do a good job for him. Why, Lord Jesus trusts in *all* of us as much as we trust in him. Praise the Lord, Randolph. Praise—"

"If you got something to say to me, spit it out," Randolph interrupted. "I've been listening to your sermons for more years than I care to remember as it is." Lord knows he had tried but there was no way he could have said that without it coming out as a blasphemous insult to Bobby Jay's ears.

The reverend's face went red. "*What* did you say?" he blustered.

"I said, if you've got something to tell me, then go ahead and tell me." Randolph settled back in the couch to think through his plan. I'm an accessory to those boys being kidnapped, he thought, ignoring Bobby Jay's rantings, so I better go to the police first and surrender. Maybe even the FBI. Though there were quite a few FBI agents in Bobby Jay's congregation, he recalled.

"Are you listening to me at all, you filthy lying son of a bitch!"

That, Randolph heard. "What in God's green Earth are you going on about so?" he asked.

Bobby Jay trembled with rage and threw some switches on the control panel on his desk. The curtains slid along their motorized tracks, cutting off the light from the windows.

"Bobby Jay," Randolph asked again, "what's going on here?"

Bobby Jay threw two more switches on his desk. The "Good News Glory Show" tape running on the monitors cut out, replaced by a gray hash of static. Then a new image appeared. It was the storeroom where Dr. Wyndham's records were spread out. Even from the back, even without clothes, Randolph recognized himself in a second. Louella's high-pitched moans were also unmistakable.

Many thoughts went through Randolph's mind at that moment. Blackmail was one of them. But he had been a widower for as long as he had known Bobby Jay and no close family remained. In that respect, he had nothing to lose. Bobby Jay, however, did have something to lose: ratings. How Bobby Jay could expect the brothers and sisters at home to send in offerings without Louella on screen singing up a gospel storm, Randolph didn't know. But of course, with Bobby Jay expecting the world to come to an end by Labor Day, ratings sure wouldn't mean much to him anymore. In the final analysis, Randolph concluded, that tape meant absolutely nothing. So he laughed.

Bobby Jay smiled at the laughter as if he had been expecting it. "Now calm down, son," he said, anger subsiding. "No need to get hysterical over this. You did it once. The sin's no greater for seeing it a second time." He opened the Jack Daniel's drawer.

"Oh, I'm not getting hysterical on you, Bobby Jay. Why, not five minutes ago I was sitting here thinking you might want to try something like that. I was even looking round to see where you might have hidden the camera in here. Now that I've seen how you did it in the storeroom, I'd say you have a camera hidden in that gray box over by the monitors. That right, Bobby

Jay? Give you a good shot of this couch here?'' Each word Randolph said brought a new twist to Bobby Jay's mouth.

''Do you know what that . . . that *pornography* means!'' Bobby Jay shrieked, pointing to the monitors. The Jack Daniel's bottle trembled in his hand.

''Since you're the one who hid the cameras,'' Randolph said coolly, ''I say it means you're some sort of a pervert, Bobby Jay. Just like the ones you're always going on about.'' Randolph couldn't believe he said that but my it felt good.

The Jack Daniel's bottle smashed on the desk in a shower of glass and whiskey. Bobby Jay jumped to his feet and screamed fire and brimstone. ''You brand *me* when it is *you* who are the adulterer! *You* who are the fornicator! *You* who are lost to the Lord while Louella and I give all of ourselves to bring you back to *Jee-sus!*''

Bobby Jay strode out from behind his desk. He pointed the accusing hand of God at Randolph. But instead of an outstretched finger it held the ragged neck of the Jack Daniel's bottle. ''Get down on your knees, Randolph Dewitt. Get down on your knees and *confess* to the Lord Jesus! Tell Lord Jesus that you *are* a sinner!''

Instead, Randolph stood up to face the man. ''I may be a sinner but I'm not crazy, Bobby Jay. What happened between Louella and me is our business and the Lord's. I'll not confess to anything in front of you.''

''Get down on your knees this instant and *confess!*''

''I'll wait till I'm in holy surroundings,'' Randolph said, his voice as threatening as Bobby Jay's.

''*These* are holy surroundings, you blasphemer!''

''Not anymore, Bobby Jay. The spirit of the Lord left here when you decided it was time to kidnap children and brand them and—''

''*They are the Antichrist!*'' Bobby Jay looked like a man who had been in a fight, flushed and sweat-covered, panting and shaking.

Randolph was icy calm. ''You're insane, Bobby Jay. Louella was right.''

''She has no part in this,'' Bobby Jay snarled.

''No part? Good Lord, man! Look at her! She was the one

who came to *me*." Randolph pointed at the monitors where he and Louella moved so perfectly together.

"She was doing the Lord's work. Get down on your knees and confess to the Lord Jesus!"

"She wasn't doing the Lord's work! She was trying to find a little bit of love, Bobby Jay. Because you had no time for her. You were too concerned about kidnapping young boys. Even killing one of them. Trying to deceive the President into starting a war."

Bobby Jay bellowed with rage and slapped Randolph across the face with his open, empty hand. Randolph staggered back against the couch but remained standing.

"It *was* too the Lord's work," the reverend said in a voice quaking with anger. "*I* sent her there. She *knew* the camera was there. We had to show you what a sinner you are to bring you back to the Lord." Bobby Jay moved closer to Randolph. "Show the Lord what a sinner you are, Randolph," he commanded.

Randolph couldn't believe what Bobby Jay had said. He looked over to the monitors. The tape had looped back to the beginning of the scene. Louella was unfastening her blouse. Randolph was bending to her breasts. "Then why do you have just that first time? Where are the rest of the tapes?" he asked.

"What rest of the tapes?"

"Of the other times," Randolph spat in the reverend's face.

"With *you*?" Bobby Jay's mouth stayed open in disgust.

"Twice a day for the past two weeks, Bobby Jay. That tape's just the first time. If you sent her, then where are the other tapes? The ones from my apartment? From your bedroom?" Randolph was shouting. Each revelation another blow to Bobby Jay. "Put it on the screen, Reverend Bobby Jay! Let's see *everything* your Louella and I did together. Let's hear *everything* your Louella and I said to each other. Let's hear what she really thinks of you."

Bobby Jay swung his arm into Randolph's stomach with all the force his anger could give him. Randolph grunted explosively and collapsed back onto the couch. His breath was gone. His ears were ringing. Just barely he could hear Bobby Jay's raving.

"*Show* the Lord Jesus what a sinner you are!" the reverend shouted from far away.

Randolph struggled to focus his eyes on Bobby Jay. He had

never had the breath knocked out of him so badly. Bobby Jay was standing over him now, leaning against him. Good Lord, Randolph thought as his vision cleared, Bobby Jay has an erection.

"I'll help you show the Lord Jesus what a sinner you are," Bobby Jay said in a powdery soft voice.

Randolph struggled to calm down and relax. My breath will come back if I just stop struggling so much, he thought. He remembered something from his childhood. He had fallen off a swing and landed on his back. I couldn't breathe then but I didn't die, did I? he asked himself. He placed his hands on his stomach. There was something else there.

Randolph opened his eyes and looked down. Bobby Jay's hands were on his legs. He couldn't feel what they were doing. He couldn't feel the neck of the Jack Daniel's bottle in his stomach, either, but there it was. Glistening with blood, right where Bobby Jay had stuck it.

Coldness swept through Randolph. He could hear his friends in the playground around him telling him to get up. He saw there was blood on Bobby Jay's hands. But it didn't bother him anymore. Not being able to breathe didn't bother him, either.

I'll just close my eyes and rest for a while, Randolph told himself. And then I'll be able to get back on that swing and everything will be all right again, forever.

He was wrong.

FOURTEEN

"Hello, Alex. It's Susan Foster calling." Foster nodded to Hyams from the couch in her living room. It was six-thirty Tuesday evening and this was the final call.

Hyams went back into Foster's kitchen to wait for the kettle to boil. Freshly ground coffee was ready in the filter of a Chemex brewer. The smell reminded Hyams of family vacations. By himself, he usually made instant.

The water in the kettle started to rumble. He could still hear Foster's voice as she passed on to Alexander Thorkel the last bit of information that Ioannou's party line operation required.

"Just fine, Alex. And you?" he heard her say. There was a pause and then she continued. "Well, I'll tell you. At Thursday's meeting, if you recall, I told everyone how I had finally managed to track down one of the boys. That's right, Jamie Estevez, the one who was being held in the psychiatric institute but who had been transferred. Right. Well, I have a contact with an ambulance service and he was able to tell me where the boy was taken. Now, I know that we made an agreement at the meeting that we wouldn't pass on any information except in the presence of everyone else on the committee, but since the next meeting isn't scheduled till Sunday, I thought that withholding information from you wouldn't be fair. I mean, you are being so generous with your support that I thought you might appreciate a bit of inside information, just so you know your money's being put to good use."

Hyams smiled to himself in the kitchen. He was impressed with Foster's ability to talk in a way that the person listening found most comfortable. With Thorkel, she acknowledged his financial support of the planning committee's work. With Father Carey, she had called upon his political knowledge of the Church: Was there any way that highly-placed Catholics might be able to use their influence to arrange a meeting with the boy? And with Delambre, she appealed to his rampant self-importance: She thought he'd better know where the boy had been taken because Delambre was obviously the only one on the planning committee who was capable of understanding the full importance of what was transpiring. All three people, of course, had been given a different location for the boy's whereabouts. Even Panati was being misled for the sake of discovering the informer among them. If there was an informer.

The kettle's rumbling changed to a gentle rush. Hyams wrapped a dishcloth around the black handle and poured the first half of the boiling water into the coffee brewer. The dishcloth was new, he noticed, like a lot of things in Foster's apartment. It was almost as if she were living in a friend's place and was going out of her way not to leave any evidence of use. Hyams emptied the rest of the water into the brewer and thought nothing more about Foster's living habits. They were the same as his back in the days when he would visit home and eat from paper plates and disposable glasses so he wouldn't mess his mother's immaculate kitchen. Maybe Foster just hated housekeeping.

He brought two white ceramic mugs of coffee into the living room. Each was decorated with a faded mission crest from the *Columbia*'s first flight. Foster was off the phone. He waited as she checked in with Heaslip to let the detective know the last false lead had been passed on.

"So now what?" Hyams asked after she had hung up the second time.

"We wait for Ioannou to give us a call saying who turns up where. If anyone does." Foster leaned forward for the coffee mug that Hyams had placed on a carved wooden trivet on the coffee table. Then she settled back into the corner of the couch with her legs pulled up beside her. Hyams took the chair opposite her. He wanted to sit on the couch too, but he knew he would feel awkward. Just as he felt uncomfortable sitting in silence with her.

"I want to apologize for getting the police all mixed up in this," he said. His voice sounded too loud in the apartment. The only room in it with full carpeting was the bedroom and he had only seen that through a half-open door on his way to use the bathroom. The living room area was oak-floored, with a single pastel-shaded dhurrie rug. It was the echo from the hard floor and walls that made his voice so jarring, he decided.

"You don't have to," Foster said. She cradled her coffee mug in her lap, as if warming herself with it. "From the reports Ioannou showed us, the police would have been involved sooner or later. At least this way, we'll be ready for them."

She smiled at Hyams and he thought it was the kind of open, unconsidered smile that she might use among her friends. He felt flattered.

"Well," Hyams said, "I was just feeling bad that the police were adding to your worries."

"What worries?" Foster asked defensively.

"About the boys," Hyams explained. Her reaction puzzled him. "I mean, it's got to be taking up a lot of your time. And, I don't know, you've . . . well, you've been looking *worried* the past week or so."

"I was born with knitted brows," she said and sipped at her coffee so he couldn't see any expression.

"Not that," Hyams said. He had noticed the way her forehead pulled in above her nose whenever she concentrated. He liked it. "I mean, you've just looked, oh, pale, I suppose. As if you haven't been sleeping too well." Please don't think that was a pass, he thought suddenly. Hyams poured hot coffee down his throat in atonement and prayed that he hadn't just said something tremendously stupid.

He felt Foster's eyes studying him. "I really didn't mean that the way it might sound," he began, and then had the hopeless embarrassment of realizing that whatever he said now could only draw more attention to what he hoped she would ignore.

Kindly, she said, "I appreciate your concern, Jim, but it's really nothing. The air conditioner in the bedroom isn't working and I haven't gotten around to having someone look at it. The worst thing for a light sleeper in New York is to have to sleep with the window open." She smiled again, but this time it was formal.

Hyams accepted her explanation, without believing it. The message had been received and he would avoid the subject of her worries. He hoped she would smile at him the other, friendlier way once more.

They talked about other things then: key money, restaurants, what it was like to decide to be a police officer and a writer. The conversation was amicable but seemed to go nowhere. Hyams thought several times about suggesting dinner but decided he would leave that up to her. He knew a dozen ways he could make a pass at her if he sensed she might be interested in going to bed with him, but, he thought sadly, he didn't know any way as direct to tell her he wanted to be her friend. The conversation eventually came around to the boys.

"So why *aren't* the clones identical?" Hyams asked, and forced himself not to smile as Foster's eyebrows came together.

"It has something to do with Wyndham's cloning method," she said. "But from reading his log, I'm not sure how much the differences between the boys are because of his deliberate intervention and how much are because of duplication errors arising because of his techniques."

"If he wanted to make genetic duplicates, why would he deliberately intervene to make differences among the boys?"

"For insurance. When Wyndham recovered DNA from the shroud, it wasn't as a whole structure, that is, as complete chromosomes. In effect, he recovered thousands, probably millions, of little pieces of what had once been the man in the shroud's genetic structure. Before Wyndham could begin to even think of cloning the man, he had to rebuild each chromosome by reassembling all those millions of pieces."

"That sounds like some sort of impossible jigsaw puzzle."

"A puzzle, yes. Impossible, no." Color had come into Foster's cheeks. She reminded Hyams of the way she had been the day in Panati's office when she had described the possibility of reconstructing dinosaurs. Knowledge was a passion to her. "First of all, with relatively simple genesplicing techniques like the ones drug companies use to manufacture insulin, Wyndham could make as many copies of the different pieces as he needed to experiment with. That is, once he had extracted the material from the shroud, he could produce an endless supply. Then, with an automatic DNA sequence reading machine, he could build up a list of all the different pieces he had along with the details of their nucleotide structure—that's the order in which the four different component parts of the DNA molecule appear. It's the order in which those component parts are arranged, sort of like lines of computer programming code, that controls all the diversity of life on this planet. With the possible exception of some bizarre viruses."

"So, to keep track of all this, he'd need a computer, right?" Hyams asked. He felt as if he were attending a private university lecture.

"Definitely," Foster agreed. "The program wouldn't have to be complex, but it would require a great deal of memory. Anyway, according to the notes in his record book, it appears that Wyndham spent about two years simply analyzing the material extracted from the shroud. Only then did he start putting the pieces together."

"Every possible combination of millions of different pieces?" Hyams asked in disbelief.

"Oh, no," Foster said excitedly, "only a few thousand

pieces at the most. And only in a few hundred combinations. You see, even though human DNA is incredibly complex, it follows a pattern. Understanding that pattern is the basis of Wyndham's reconstruction technique. He called it layering. It's like the method they use to remaster old music records. The sound engineers get fifty different copies of a record, pull little segments of the best quality sound from each of them, and then rerecord all the little segments together. The engineers don't have to fiddle with different combinations of the segments because by comparing each segment to a written score, they can say exactly where the segment fits in. What makes the layering technique of reconstructing DNA a manageable undertaking is that out of the entire hundred million nucleotides in a human's genetic structure, only about one and a half percent of that sequence provides the information required to construct a human body."

"So what's the rest of the DNA?"

"One of the biggest controversies in biology, these days," Foster said with her smile for friends. "One theory suggests that the extra DNA, which is mostly thousands of identical sequences repeated throughout the entire structure, is a type of parasite. You know, like a chicken is an egg's way of making another egg? In the same way, a person can be thought of as a DNA molecule's way of making another DNA molecule. Since the repeated DNA sequences don't seem to have anything at all to do with constructing a human body—for or against—they might just be extra baggage like moss on a tree. By using a variant of the Sibley-Ahlquist method, Wyndham could just ignore them." Hyams's face was blank. "The upshot being that he only had to reconstruct one and a half percent of the man in the shroud's genetic structure in order to start cloning," Foster summed up for him.

"So what you're saying is that what Wyndham did wasn't really all that difficult."

Foster's eyebrows came together. "I suppose so," she said, but didn't sound convinced. "Anyway, Wyndham still had to place those critical sequences at the proper spots among the extra, repetitive DNA structures. That's where I think the errors crept in. Or were put in. It seems that at some level of reconstruction, Wyndham couldn't be sure that all the important DNA sequences were in precisely the exact spot they had been in the original. His log isn't very clear on this part of his procedure, but I think he started tinkering at this point. His first step was to knowingly allow some minor genetic variations to exist on the chance that his first reconstruction was wrong and one of the variations might, by chance, be right.

"The next step was to *deliberately* create new minor genetic variations. Why? He doesn't say. But it probably had something to do with ensuring that a new generation of genetically similar individuals would be born so their genetic structures could be studied and the experiment tried again in the future with better techniques and technologies. That type of tinkering would account for the high number of miscarriages among the women he implanted with the cloned egg cells and the number of children who died shortly after birth. Those clones' genetic variations were too severe to be successful. The boys we see in the photographs have smaller, more successful—or, at least, less harmful—variations. More coffee?" she asked.

Hyams got up and took both mugs back into the kitchen, refilled them, and placed them in the microwave oven for reheating.

"How about the boy without a brain?" he asked when he returned. This time he sat down facing her from the opposite end of the couch. It didn't feel socially awkward but the way the wooden arm of the couch was digging into the small of his back, he knew he would have to change position soon. "Being born without a brain seems to be more than just a minor genetic variation."

"You'd be surprised," Foster said. "The growth of an entire organ may be controlled just by a single sequence of three or four nucleotides. Suddam probably has all the genetic information needed for a complete, fully functioning nervous system. The variation probably lies in a short triggering sequence that turns the rest of the DNA instructions on. Sort of like having a complete computer system shutdown because the sysop has forgotten a five-letter password. It is incredible when you think of the changes that can result from such a seemingly inconsequential difference. The genetic structure of chimpanzees, for example, differs from the human genetic structure by less than two percent."

Hyams widened his eyes appreciatively. "How close do you think the boys are to Jesus, then?"

"If the man in the shroud was Jesus, then I'd say for the most part that the boys are genetically identical to him. Maybe not as close as twins are, but closer than ordinary brothers and sisters. Of course, any one of them could be exactly identical, which was probably Wyndham's intent in his shotgun approach to creating variations."

Hyams shook his head and took the opportunity to move forward a few inches to relieve the pressure on his back. "No wonder Panati's upset," he said.

"I imagine the theological implications would be good for a few centuries of debate in the Vatican," Foster said. Her eyebrows drew back together. "Are you religious?" she asked.

Hyams thought it was odd the question hadn't come up before. Foster gave the impression that she wasn't very religious so perhaps she had been transferring her beliefs to everyone else. He thought of all the different ways he might answer her. "No," he said finally. "Maybe God, but not all the rest of it." His parents had done a good job on him, he noted. He felt guilty for what he had just said. "How about you?"

"Not even a 'maybe' for God," she said. There was a hint of bitterness in the way she had said it, too. Hyams had the feeling that she could say a lot more on the subject but, like him, she had decided there wasn't much more that was useful.

"Well, then," Hyams offered, "at least we don't have to worry about what God's reaction is going to be to science recreating umpteen versions of his only begotten son."

The phone rang. Foster laughed as if remembering an old joke. "That may be him now," she said and stretched out her legs and half stood up as she reached out for the phone.

Hyams concentrated on his coffee mug so he wouldn't be tempted to admire the way Foster's slacks were pulled tightly across her in that position.

Foster held out the phone to Hyams. "It's Ioannou," she said. "He wants to talk to you."

Hyams moved along the couch until he was beside Foster. She didn't move away. He took the receiver.

"So, we heard from one of our suspects, kid," the detective said. "If you and your lady friend want to get your clothes back on and come down to my office, I think we might have an interesting conversation with the guy."

Hyams pressed the receiver tightly to his ear and hoped that Foster, close as she was, hadn't heard Ioannou's comment.

"Which one?" he asked.

He could feel Ioannou's sneer through the phone line. "The guy you said it couldn't be, smartass. Francis Panati. My guys are bringing him down from Connecticut now so he'll be here in just over two hours. You can apologize to me then." The phone clicked off.

"He says it's Father Panati." Hyams's face was less than two feet from Foster's. Other than sitting by her in the car or being beside her while walking, he had never been this close to her before. Beautiful was the word for her, he decided reluctantly.

"That's impossible," Foster said. Her whole face drew together in concentration. She ignored Hyams's presence. "Otherwise everything else we put together out of those files would have been passed on, too." She stood up suddenly. "Does he have Francis at the precinct?" she asked.

"In two hours," Hyams said.

"This is ridiculous," Foster muttered. She picked up her mug, walked over to her stereo stand, and put the mug back down. Then she ran her eyes over the spines of books in a bookcase. "Absolutely ridiculous." She picked up the coffee mug again and walked back over to the couch.

"What's so ridiculous?" Hyams asked cautiously. "Maybe Panati didn't tell you the whole story because you aren't Catholic. Maybe—"

"Look," Foster interrupted. "I know people, all right? Every time Francis has tried to slip one by me, I've known about it. That's my job and I'm good at it. If Francis is behind the leaks, which makes him a murderer by the way, then I've . . . I've lost it. And I don't believe that." She picked up both coffee mugs and headed into the kitchen.

"Okay, okay," Hyams said. He got up and followed her. She was rinsing the mugs in the sink. "So, Ioannou made a mistake. Wouldn't be the first time."

"Ioannou's not the type to make a mistake, Jim."

"Well, if Panati's not the informer and Ioannou hasn't made a mistake, what other explanation is there?" Hyams was afraid

Foster was going to shatter the mugs against the metal sides of the sink.

"Ioannou's setting Francis up," she said.

"Oh, come on," Hyams protested. "That would mean he's working for whoever's after the boys in the first place."

"Exactly," Foster said with a tight smile. "Either way, Francis or Ioannou, I've been strung along. And time is short, Jim." Her voice had become harsh and brittle. "Time is just too *fucking* short!"

The metal sink clanged with the sound of the splintering mugs.

Hyams knew he was witnessing something beyond anything they had been discussing that evening. He waited silently for her to look up from the sink and come to him for comfort or reassurance but, in the end, she turned away and walked stiffly to the bedroom. Despite the tears he had seen in her eyes, he was unable to follow.

FIFTEEN

There were no comic books, Jason Coyle knew. There were no X-Men, no heroes, and no last-minute escapes. There was only pain and anger and hideous other things his young mind did not have the words to describe.

There was something else now, too. Hunger. Randolph, the red-haired man who fed them and let them use the portable toilet, hadn't come for two days. The air was filled with the stench of the toilet. If there had been anything in his stomach, Jason was sure he would have thrown it up long ago.

Four, maybe five weeks ago, after the third boy had been brought in and strapped to a table, they had all been carried to this larger room, which, Jason had guessed by the way the corridors had looked, was in the basement of a large building.

Randolph had called it the old studio. Rows of raised theater seats stretched away from the central area where the boys were kept strapped to their tables. Jason recognized a large TV camera on a rolling platform and some chairs and a table that were set up like they were used on interview shows. On the stage walls farthest away from the furniture, Jason saw a whole wall of televisions rising above a control panel that made him think of the starship *Enterprise*. Jason watched the television from time to time, but all they ever showed was the television guy, and only for an hour each day. He could tell it was an hour because of the large digital clock with glowing red numbers that hung beneath a giant picture window halfway up one of the walls. The picture window was slanted and Jason could make out more fancy control panels in the room behind it.

He had seen other parts of the studio only when his table had been carried into the studio. Now, with his head still tightly tied, Jason was unable to see anything else except for the empty tables and theater seats directly in front of him, and the televisions and clock off to the left. Whenever Randolph had let him use the toilet, by unfastening all the straps except for two which hobbled his legs and arms, Jason had to wear a black hood over his head.

Jason didn't mind the black hood all that much. It felt good when the man pulled it over his head and scratched the burns on his forehead. The tall guy from Saturday morning television had used his soldering iron to burn all the boys the same way: a number on each of their foreheads, 666, Jason had seen. Weeks ago, back when his own forehead throbbed with pain and he still thought that they might be rescued any moment, the number had reminded him of something he had seen in a series of movies on the Creature Feature. But, movies were like comic books: There were no such things anymore. There was nothing in the whole world except for crazy adults who wanted to hurt him without reason. Deep inside, Jason supposed he had been afraid of that possibility all his life. Now that that fear had come true, he wasn't even surprised.

Jason heard the door to the studio open. Someone was coming in. He strained his eyes to the right, twisting his restrained head the few inches it would go. It was the television guy. He was covered in blood.

The television guy disappeared from view for a moment and then Jason saw him dragging someone into the room. Usually, when someone was dragged in, it was another kid who looked like J.D. Jason had stopped trying to figure that one out weeks ago. He didn't care anymore. He had even stopped thinking about J.D. as his friend. And, usually, whenever another kid was dragged in, it was one of the kidnappers who did it. Jason hadn't seen the kidnappers for a long while now.

But this time, it wasn't a kid being strapped to an empty table by Jason's feet. It was a man, an old man with white hair and a stupid, drooling blankness to his face. It was from the drugs the kidnappers used, Jason knew. Randolph had kept giving them to J.D. and the others up to the day he didn't come anymore. For some reason, Randolph had stopped giving them to Jason weeks ago. The others had recently started to stir more than usual, so Jason figured the drugs were finally wearing off.

The boy watched as the Reverend Bobby Jay strapped the old man to the table. He wondered if the old man would have his clothes cut away and a number burned into his forehead by the soldering iron.

Apparently not. After the final strap had been tightened, Bobby Jay only removed the man's thick gold watch and wedding ring. For a moment he looked up from the old man and into Jason's eyes. There was blood all over Bobby Jay's hands, his sleeves, his shirt, and his face. But he wasn't hurt. He just winked at Jason like a Christmas elf, then moved out of sight.

The studio door didn't close, though. Someone else was being dragged in, someone with more blood on him than Bobby Jay. It was Randolph. Jason heard one of the other boys moan.

"Recognize your own, do you?" Bobby Jay said to the moaning boy as he dragged Randolph to another empty table. "Thought Lord Jesus wouldn't tell me what you're up to?" He began to laugh.

Jason had never heard the television guy's voice sound that way before, high-pitched and trembling. Something had changed in him. He hoped it meant that the reverend was hurting somehow. Jason could tell that Randolph was hurting. He kept groaning softly the whole time he was being tied to the table.

Bobby Jay walked back to the studio door. Two of the boys started shouting something against their gags.

"No more food," Bobby Jay said sharply to them. "You should have thought of that before you recruited Randolph."

All seven of the boys started yelling then, plaintive, muffled sirens of hunger and hatred.

"What do demons need with food?" Bobby Jay sneered at them. "What do any of you need except to be thrown back into the pit with your master?"

No food, no water, no toilet, he was saying to them. The boys howled.

"It's too late for that," Bobby Jay shouted angrily. "I know all about your master's schemes. I know how he's directing his evil influence against me and all those close to me. But Satan won't succeed, you know. *Jesus* is within me. The Lord *God* speaks to me. And not even when your master Satan possessed that man there"—Bobby Jay pointed to the old man on the table—"could he prevent the Lord God from speaking the truth to his own wife." Bobby Jay raised his hands and his head just as Jason had seen him do on television.

"Since the beginning of time," he said, his now deep voice flattened by the acoustical coverings on the blank studio walls, "Satan has prepared for this final battle between him and me. But he will lose within days." His voice dropped to a whisper. "Prepare yourselves, demons and sinners. It is almost at an end."

The boys' howling had stopped. But in the silence of the studio, Jason heard a familiar, liquid sound. One of the boys wasn't waiting to use the toilet. Bobby Jay jumped quickly away from the spot where he had been standing.

"You dare!" he shrieked. "You dare mock me like that!"

Jason heard something metal being scraped against the floor. He could hear the television guy howling something he couldn't understand. From the corner of his eye he saw something like a long metal pipe swing up into the air and then back down, quickly, savagely, into something that sounded soft and thick. After the third blow, it was something wet, too. Jason didn't hear the boy make a sound.

Finally, the television guy stopped. He was wheezing. The pipe clattered to the floor. Something dripped slowly and regularly onto the floor. Bobby Jay moved back into sight by the studio door.

"It's almost at an end," Bobby Jay hissed. Then he shut the door, locked it, and was gone.

Jason lay there for a long time before he fell asleep. He didn't know who Bobby Jay had beaten with the pipe. He supposed he hoped it wasn't J.D. But in the end, he decided, the only thing that mattered was that it hadn't been Jason Coyle.

He fell asleep peacefully then, secure in the knowledge that nothing would change in his absence. It was many hours before the sound of something dripping stopped and the studio returned to silence.

SIXTEEN

The precinct station was even busier at night than it had been in the day. That's the way to work, Foster thought. Lots of noise, lots of confusion, none of those deadly periods of silence and inactivity that sneak up and steal the present by allowing thoughts of the future. A black, senseless, endless future in her case.

She realized sadly that she was struggling to keep pace with Hyams as he made his way up the wide wooden stairs leading to the detectives' floor. The shortness of breath had arrived, along with the weight loss, just as the doctor had said. That's why she had cried in her kitchen that evening. Not because she thought Francis or Detective Ioannou had used her. But because they had wasted some of her last few hours. Wasted time had always been an annoyance to her before. Now, with so little of it left, it was obscene.

Hyams stopped at the top of the stairway, turned and waited for her. Plainclothes and uniformed officers moved steadily and noisily around him, escorting prisoners, witnesses, and victims alike.

"Are you okay?" Hyams asked as Foster joined him. There was a hint of embarrassment in his voice.

"Fine," she answered, grateful that he hadn't said anything more about her behavior that night, appreciating his concern and his respect for her privacy. "Just one of those bad days." She could tell that he didn't believe her. She felt that she owed it to him to say more. But all she could do was pat his arm, just as she had the day they had met in the dark hallway outside Paul

Almagro's apartment. Funny that I remember that meeting so clearly, she thought.

They walked together down the wide corridors, past wooden dividing walls fitted with an irregular series of clear and frosted glass panels. The khaki at the desk had said they were expected in interrogation room three, the same one in which they had first exchanged information with Ioannou. A lot of things seemed to be coming full circle tonight, Foster thought.

Detective Heaslip was waiting for them outside the interrogation room. A series of tiny red lights flickered across the printed-circuit brooch she wore attached to her multizippered black leather jacket. She held up her hand to stop them from entering the room. Foster noticed the detective's nails were painted alternately black and red.

"Detective Ioannou is in there with the priest they caught trying to see the boy at Vicker's Convalescent Home," she said. "Francis Panati. You know him, right?"

Both Hyams and Foster said yes.

"And he's the guy that brought you into the investigation of the boys?" the detective asked Foster, gesturing to Hyams.

"That's what I told Detective Ioannou," Foster acknowledged. She didn't know why Heaslip was covering old ground. She had an uncomfortable sense that a setup might be in progress.

Heaslip turned to Hyams. "And you got involved when her investigation of Almagro overlapped yours, right?" she asked him.

"Why the double check, detective? Is Father Panati saying something different?" Foster could see that Hyams was sharing the same uneasy feeling about the detective's questions.

"No," Heaslip said, shaking her head so the earrings in her left ear rattled against each other. "He's just saying a whole lot more." She stepped aside and pushed open the door. They went in.

Panati was in civilian clothes: slacks and sports jacket. He looked almost unrecognizable with an open shirt collar instead of a small patch of white at his throat. There was a warring mixture of exhaustion and relief in his eyes.

Ioannou sat across from Panati. His only attitude was anger.

"Exact genetic duplicates of Jesus created from the Shroud of Turin?" Ioannou snorted at Foster and Hyams.

"It's all right," Panati interrupted before either could reply. "I've told him everything."

"Do you believe it?" Foster asked. She sat down without waiting for an invitation. She was still winded from the climb up the stairs.

"Do I have a choice?" Ioannou shrugged.

Heaslip thought that was funny and started to laugh. She shut the interrogation room door and joined Foster at the table. Hyams pulled out a rickety metal chair and sat, too.

"Seriously?" Foster asked again.

"Look, Ms. Foster," the detective began, "I've known that you've been lying to me from the start. No, I take that back. You haven't been lying. You just haven't been telling me the whole truth."

"Have *you* been telling us the whole truth?" Foster was sure he hadn't been.

"Not to him," Ioannou admitted, nodding to Hyams. "But since I've been dealing with the both of you, yes. Straight arrow all the way."

"Like when you wanted to talk to Jim about his suspension pay and advised him to 'dump the lady'?" Foster said. "That kind of 'straight arrow' you mean?"

"The kid has a career to think of," Ioannou said flatly.

"No, the kid doesn't," Hyams said. "Not if it means working for people like you and Burch."

"Please, please," Panati interrupted again. "Recriminations will get us nowhere. Let's start with the here and now. With all parties knowing everything. With all parties working together to find the children and protect them from whoever's out to kidnap or kill them. Detective Ioannou is willing to accept the basis of our investigation for the moment, so why don't we settle for that and get on with it?"

Foster narrowed her eyes at Ioannou. "*You're* willing to accept it?"

Ioannou shook his head in resignation. "He's clean, lady. We've had two hours to check him out."

"I knew you weren't the informer, Francis," Foster said.

"Thank you, Susan," Panati said. He stared down at the tabletop, speaking like a small child caught peeking in a window.

"I just wanted to see one of them, that's all. The same curiosity that inspired Dr. Wyndham, no doubt."

"*Did* you see him? Suddam, I mean?"

Panati shook his head. "I'm afraid Detective Ioannou's men were too quick for me. They 'cuffed' me before I could lock my car door." Panati looked up and laughed. "It really was quite exciting. Just like television."

Ioannou rubbed his hand over his face. "Then you're sure going to enjoy what's going to happen next," he said.

"FBI?" Foster asked, feeling relieved that the detective and Francis really hadn't put one over on her. I've still got it, she thought. Should look good as an epitaph.

Ioannou nodded. "That's right. And unless we get a break from one of the other members of your planning committee, we have nowhere to go and nothing to do except wait for the Feds to appear on the doorstep. In fact, I'm surprised they haven't shown up already."

The same idea seemed to strike Foster and Ioannou at the same time. Foster spoke first.

"You don't suppose. . . ?" she said hesitatingly.

"What's the motivation?' Ioannou asked quickly, his face hardening with a look of worried concentration.

"Whose motivation?" Hyams asked, looking at Ioannou and Foster as if they were speaking in another language.

"The FBI," Foster said.

"FBI? Motivation for what?" Hyams's voice was rising.

"For going after the children," Ioannou answered. "Maybe that's why they haven't become involved even though someone should have noticed the resemblance among the kidnap victims by now. Maybe they're already involved."

"Or maybe another government agency is involved and the FBI has been told to stay out," Foster added.

"So what do we do?" Hyams asked.

Ioannou rubbed his face again. "Believe it or not, kid, for once we're in a situation that they don't teach you about at the Academy. I haven't got the slightest idea."

The silence that followed Ioannou's unprecedented admission was broken by three sharp raps on the door. Heaslip opened it. A uniformed officer peered in.

"That priest you wanted to talk to is in now, Greg," the officer said.

"I know, asshole," Ioannou said, rolling his eyes. He pointed across to Panati. "I've been talking with him for the past hour." He muttered again in Greek.

"Naw, naw," the officer said, after looking closely at Panati. "A *priest* priest. You know. Black jacket. White collar. The guy you wanted watched for at Bellevue."

"You sure?" Ioannou asked, eyes narrowing.

"All the way, Greg," the officer said. "Caught him trying to sneak into the room that was set aside for that Estevez kid. The priest had a case filled with hypodermics, too. Forensics got them and they don't look friendly. Know what I mean?"

"Who are you talking about?" Panati asked nervously. "What priest?"

"To find out who the informer was," Foster gently explained, "we gave each of the planning committee members a false location for the Estevez boy. Bellevue was the location I told to Father Carey."

"You do understand that you'll all burn in hell for this, don't you?" Father Carey asked in a conversational and completely reasonable tone of voice. He sat calmly and, for once, without slouching at the end of the table in interrogation room five. Hyams, Foster, and Panati had been allowed in the room only after Ioannou and Heaslip had had a long discussion with their captain and the captain had personally asked if Carey desired an attorney or a phone call. The priest had declined both.

"What are you talking about, Scott?" Panati asked. Hyams had never seen as much concern in someone as he saw in Panati.

"What a hypocrite you are, Francis," Carey said. "You claim to follow Lord Jesus and you know nothing about him. No one in the whole, sorry Church knows him anymore." He shook his head in sadness for his old friend.

"What do you know that I don't know?" Panati asked patiently. Ioannou and Heaslip sat still and remained as inconspicuous as possible. Evidently, they both thought that Panati could get more out of Carey than either of them. "Please, Scott," Panati continued. "If I'm all wrong, tell me how. Teach me."

Carey seemed to contemplate Panati's request for a few moments and then shook his head. "It's too late, Francis. Too late for you all."

"Why?"

"You've read your Bible enough to read the signs," Carey said. "Don't patronize me. Don't pretend you're blind to the portents."

Panati reached across the table to take hold of Carey's hands. "Scott, please. It's me. I'm not patronizing you. I'm just trying to understand why you're here. What you're saying. Why the police caught you sneaking into that boy's room with hypodermic needles. I truly don't understand."

Carey looked at Panati in surprise. "The *boy's* room? The *boy*?" He drew his hands away. "Jamie Estevez is no boy, Francis. He's like all the others. They have the powers of Satan. They're demons from hell. Antichrists."

Hyams watched as Panati's face tightened. He guessed it was the first time the priest realized what he was dealing with: his friend Carey was insane.

"How much do you know about the other children?" Panati asked.

"That we have them. That they're being prepared," Carey said smugly.

"Where do you have them? Being prepared for what?"

"You know what the presence of the Antichrist means as well as I do, Francis." Carey was beginning to sound annoyed.

"The Second Coming?" Panati asked.

Carey sighed deeply. "*Before* the Second Coming, Francis." He was annoyed.

"Don't play games with me!" Panati shouted, slamming his hand against the table. He stood up and continued to shout. "You're in trouble, Scott. I want to help you. But I'm not going to be able to do a thing if you keep acting like some pious little scholastic fresh from Rome! Now you either admit you're not saying anything because you're so disturbed you have nothing to say or you tell me once and for all what you were doing in Bellevue this evening, who sent you there, and *what you know about the children!"*

Panati sat down slowly. Hyams felt like applauding. Then they all waited for Carey's reaction. It was the right one.

"You really don't know, do you, Francis?" Carey said softly.

He looked around the room. "None of you do, do you?" He folded his hands as if in prayer. When he spoke again, it sounded like a lecture for disadvantaged learners.

"These are the end times which the prophets have foretold. The children, as you call them, spawned by godless science in a blasphemous mockery of the virgin birth of our Lord, are each of them a tendril of the Antichrist. And they are the proof we need to convince those who wield the weapons of Armageddon to thwart Satan's plans and strike first against his followers."

No one dared speak as Carey paused.

"Go join the brothers and sisters at home. Accept Lord Jesus and pray for forgiveness while there is still time."

Another long pause was finally broken by Ioannou. "Who did you tell about the trunks in Wyndham's apartment building?"

Father Carey bowed his head before his clenched hands, shut his eyes, and began to move his lips in silent prayer.

"Whoever you told just happened to murder two innocent men. Since when is murder the Lord's work, Father Carey?" Ioannou's voice had a threatening edge.

Carey's eyes popped open. "There are those who are born again in Lord Jesus and there are those who follow Satan. There the line is drawn. If those men were not helping in our work, then they were following Satan and they were not innocent. This is war, detective, and Lord Jesus is not unfamiliar with war." His eyes snapped shut and his prayers resumed.

Panati sat back, holding up his hands in defeat. Carey prayed on.

"So what happens now?" Foster asked.

Ioannou stood up, his metal chair squeaking against the floor. "SOP is to get a steno to take a statement, then arraign, and then ask for a psychiatric evaluation. What *we* do while all that's going on is something we'll have to think about. The captain is only—"

Carey suddenly shrieked and fell backward from his chair, gasping and writhing. Panati rushed around to him. Ioannou was next.

He's taken something, Hyams thought. He wasn't searched properly and his praying gave him a chance to slip something into his mouth. Without thinking, he placed a protective hand on Foster's shoulder as they watched Ioannou and Panati struggle to help the convulsing priest. And then everything changed.

Ioannou carefully backed away from the edge of the table as Carey and Panati slowly and awkwardly stood up, Carey's front to Panati's back. Carey held a gun against Panati's head, a standard issue .38. Hyams looked at Ioannou and could tell from the detective's sickened expression that it *was* his piece. The detective had been outmaneuvered by a priest.

"I wouldn't do that if I were you, whore," Carey suggested to Heaslip. "Hands on your head, please."

Heaslip lifted her hands away from the front of her jacket and placed them on her head.

"All of you," Carey said. Foster, Ioannou, and Hyams also raised their hands.

"You can't escape," Ioannou said. "There're two floors of cops out there."

"Oh, but I will escape," Carey replied unconcernedly. Then he whispered into Panati's ear. "Do you know why I despise you, Francis?" Panati didn't answer. His face remained calm. "Because you waste so much time and effort questioning things when the answers are right there in front of you." Carey glanced over to Ioannou. "One inch closer and I will kill him, detective."

"The only way we can find answers is to ask questions," Panati said. His voice was distorted by the pressure of Carey's arm across his windpipe.

"The Bible is God's gift to us, Francis. It relieves us from the necessity of asking questions. Detective, I'm warning you."

Hyams tried to catch Ioannou's eye. If the detective could somehow get a chance to push the table forward into the priests and make Carey reach out to catch his balance, then Hyams could rush him without endangering Panati.

Carey pulled Panati closer. "You have nine more days to read your Bible, Francis. Nine more days to discover the answer to all your questions on your own and then, I'm afraid, Armageddon. The whole world will be forced to see the truth. It will be too late for repentance then."

Hyams watched as Ioannou edged closer to the table. The detective had thought of the same plan. Hyams began to shuffle his feet forward so he would be in position to push Foster to the safety of the floor. Carey ignored them both.

"Please, promise you'll read the Bible, Francis. Please, promise that you will ask Lord Jesus to enter into your heart so you can be born again. Because, if you don't . . ." Carey looked up to see the subtle change in Hyams's and Ioannou's positions. He said nothing about it, looked back at the spot where the barrel of the gun pressed into the side of Panati's head. ". . . then I fear we shall not meet again."

Ioannou hit the table like a linebacker. Hyams swung one arm into Foster's side and used the other to steady his trajectory as he lunged over the table toward the priests. Too late. The gun erupted deafeningly.

The interrogation room was filled with officers before the echoes died. Hyams rolled off the table and returned to Foster. She lay on the floor, gasping for breath, holding both hands pressed tightly against her abdomen. Her face was drained of color. Her eyes were closed. Hyams guessed he had pushed her too hard and felt sick that he might have hurt her.

He crouched on the floor by her. Looking through a thicket of chair and table legs, he saw a crumpled headless body sprawled on the blood-slicked floor, a body dressed in black. Hyams looked more closely at the body and then saw who Ioannou was helping from the room. Panati was alive. The back of his head was blackened with blood and he held his hands over both ears as if to block out a terrible sound, but he was alive.

"Carey pulled the gun back on himself," Heaslip said as she knelt to examine Foster. "She's in shock. Might be internal bleeding. Go out and grab a paramedic when the ambulance comes."

Heaslip pushed Hyams to his feet and began checking Foster to make sure a bullet fragment hadn't caught her. Hyams stumbled through the throng of police officers in the interrogation room to the equally crowded hallway beyond. Paramedic officers rushed by with clanking orange equipment cases before Hyams could say anything. He looked through the doorway and saw them surrounding Foster. Hyams was trying to go back to her when he felt Ioannou's strong hand on his shoulder, pulling him back.

Ioannou dragged him down the hallway, away from the confusion and into an empty office. His steps were quick and his breath was short.

"Look, kid. He used my gun in there and that means in about ten minutes I'm going to get sucked into the bottomless pit of an IAD interrogation, so listen good." He pulled a small silver key from the inside pocket of his jacket. "This unlocks a fuse box upstairs in the locker room supply cupboard. There's a tape recorder there. Picks up everything in interrogation room five. You got that?"

Hyams nodded. This was serious business.

"Take the tape and don't leave any prints."

"Destroy it?" Hyams asked earnestly. He wanted to feel complimented that Ioannou was entrusting him with this, but he realized the detective was probably just desperate.

"Fuck no!" Ioannou spat at him, grabbing Hyams's lapels and throwing him against a wall just like old times. "Listen to it. Take down everything Carey said to us in there."

"The guy was incoherent." Hyams protested, trying to struggle out of Ioannou's grip.

The detective leaned into Hyams, immobilizing him against the wall.

"Whatever else he was, the guy was hooked into some organization that could track down children across the country and kidnap them. An organization that might even be able to lay some pressure on the Feds. And if the Feds can cave in, how long do you think the good old NYPD's going to hold out? I'm serious about not coming back from Internal Affairs, kid."

Hyams studied Ioannou's face. He was serious.

"Pull Carey's life apart. Phone bills, bank accounts, everything they taught you in the Academy. Hire a private detective if you have to but find out who he was working for." Ioannou dropped his hands to his sides.

"Carey was probably insane," Hyams said as he stepped away from the wall.

"Concentrating on the 'probablys' doesn't solve crimes, kid. You got to look after the 'what ifs.' "

"As in, 'what if he's right?' "

"As in, 'what if nine days from now some organization strong enough to put pressure on the FBI gets it in their minds to "strike first" with the "weapons of Armageddon"?' Want to try a quick three guesses on where a scenario like that might lead?" Ioannou's eyes burned into Hyams's.

Hyams thought it through for a moment. He shook his head. "That's taking it too far, man. That's crazy."

"Just like Carey," Ioannou agreed. "Maybe just like the people he's working for, too. Clones or no clones, kid, they killed a priest for some medical records. They killed a child. Maybe more than one. Whoever they are, they're serious shit."

A plainclothes detective appeared in the doorway to the office. "Greg Ioannou?" he asked. Ioannou nodded. "Captain wants to see you."

Ioannou stepped out into the hallway. The plainclothesman began to walk toward the captain's office. Ioannou paused and turned back to Hyams.

"Listen to the tape, kid. Prove me wrong." The detective nodded and winked and walked away, long dark hair swaying.

"I will," Hyams said, subdued by the enormity of Ioannou's suspicions. "I hope."

AMERICA'S GLORY

THE LAST WEEK OF AUGUST

ONE

Asleep, awake, from the boys with the numbers burned on their heads, from the boys still scattered but slowly gathering, from the dream friends past and the dream friends present, many voices called to Jamie. But the only one he listened to, the only one he cared about, was Dr. Hadrian's. When he heard that voice it meant he would get his needle and the needle was the only thing that would help Jamie forget how bad he had been.

He heard Dr. Hadrian's voice now. He opened his eyes expectantly and looked out from his bed. Dr. Hadrian had brought visitors to his white hospital bed.

"Is Jamie there?" Dr. Hadrian asked. His voice was so kind, Jamie thought. He could almost remember someone else who had talked to him that way: a man, or a woman, maybe both. But that was from before the dream time and the needles, when he had been bad. Dr. Hadrian gently called his name again.

"Hello, Doctor Hadrian," Jamie said. His tongue felt warm and soft and moved very slowly. It felt nice.

"Jamie, I've brought some visitors. Would you like to meet them?"

Jamie stared past the doctor at the two guests: a man who looked young and worried and a girl like on MTV. Dr. Hadrian said they were Jim and Sandra.

Then Dr. Hadrian looked closely at Jamie and said very clearly, "Jamie, are you afraid?"

Jamie shut his eyes and let the dream friend speak. *"There is no reason to be frightened by what you have experienced or will experience. It is important for you to remember that you are not alone."* He opened his eyes to see the doctor watching the visitors.

"Are you alone now, Jamie?" Jim asked.

"No," the boy giggled. "You're here."

"Before we came here today," the doctor said patiently, "were you alone then?"

"Uh-uh."

"Is Paul there with you?" Sandra asked. She crouched down by the side of Jamie's bed and smiled at him. Jamie liked her. He especially liked the big silver badge she wore that said "Sheriff." He nodded his head.

"Do you know Paul's last name, Jamie?" Sandra asked. "I promise he won't get into trouble."

Jamie realized he knew the name but he had never heard it spoken. He tried saying it but it came out slurred.

"Do you think it might be Allen?" Sandra suggested.

"Nope," Jamie said. Close but not quite.

"Martino?"

"Nope."

"Almagro?"

"Yeah," Jamie said. "Are you his friend?"

"I'd like to be," Sandra told him. "Can I be your friend?"

Jamie thought carefully and then decided it would be a good thing to be friends with someone on MTV. "Okay," he agreed.

"Do you think Sandra could talk with Paul for a little while?" Dr. Hadrian asked.

With all the adults asking him questions, Jamie was beginning to feel important. It almost made him feel as good as the needle did. But he couldn't let them speak to Paul. Paul was doing something very important and he couldn't be disturbed.

"Paul can't talk right now," he said. "Can I wear your star?"

The woman said she thought that was a good idea, took off her sheriff badge, and helped Jamie pin it to his pajama tops. Then she saluted him. Jamie decided he liked her a lot.

"Is Paul all right?" Sandra asked.

"Not really," Jamie said after stopping to think about it. He twisted the badge up so he could see his reflection in it. He was relieved to see that he didn't have any numbers burned into his forehead. Sometimes he woke up and felt like he did.

"Is Paul sick?"

"Nope." Jamie ran his fingers over his forehead just to make sure.

"Is he hurt?" the doctor asked.

"Nope. But J.D. sure is."

Dr. Hadrian leaned over and whispered to Sandra, "That's the libidinous personality."

"How is J.D. hurt?" Sandra asked.

That was a hard question. There were so many things wrong with J.D. "He's hungry," Jamie said. "He can't move. And the bad guy burned him."

"Which bad guy?" Sandra looked worried.

"The television guy," Jamie explained.

"Who's the television guy?" the doctor asked. He pulled out his notebook and wrote something in it.

"The bad guy," Jamie clarified.

Dr. Hadrian tried again. "Is he in there with J.D.?"

"No way," Jamie said. "He's the *bad* guy."

Jim stepped up to the bed and crouched beside Sandra. Jamie felt the worry that was in him. It made him feel sad.

"Can you tell us where to find J.D.?" Jim asked. "Can we go there and help him get away from the bad guy?"

Jamie just opened his mouth in surprise. "Yeah, you can *go* there," he said. "That's a great idea. You can help J.D. and Juan and Paul and—"

"They're all together?" Jim interrupted.

"Not all of them," Jamie said. "Just J.D. and the ones the bad guy got. Juan and Paul and the others are trying to find J.D., too."

"Where's J.D.?" Sandra took Jamie's hand. It made him feel funny.

"In the television place." Jamie narrowed his eyes. "The television guy calls it the studio. The old studio."

"Which studio? Where?" Jim's voice was so loud that at first Jamie thought the young man was mad at him or something.

Dr. Hadrian put a hand on Jim's shoulder. "Maybe I should ask the rest of the questions," he said.

"It's okay, Doctor Hadrian," Jamie said. "He's just sad."

Jamie tried to reach out and take Jim's hand the way Sandra had taken his, but Jim stood up too quickly. "And I don't know where the studio is. Sorry." He squeezed back on Sandra's hand. Yep, she was a good friend all right.

"Do you know why the bad guys are keeping J.D. and the others in the old studio?" she asked.

"So they can meet Number One," Jamie answered. Then wished he hadn't. He didn't like the way the three adults were looking at each other.

"Number One, Jamie? You're sure that's who they're going to meet?" Dr. Hadrian's voice sounded very serious, like the times he had asked about what had happened to Dr. Torchia.

"The television guy is always talking about it," Jamie said, watching the doctor's expression carefully. He hoped he wasn't being bad again. "Is it time for my needle now?"

Dr. Hadrian checked his watch and nodded. "Just a few more minutes, Jamie. Do you know who Number One is?"

"Nope."

"Do you know Washington, D.C., Jamie?" the doctor tried. "Do you think that's where the television guy might be keeping J.D. and the rest?"

"I don't know." He was convinced the adults were getting angry with him. "I really don't. Really, really." He started to cry.

Dr. Hadrian patted Jamie's head. "It's the medication," he said softly. "Don't worry, Jamie. We're not mad at you. We just want to save J.D. from the bad guys."

"That's what Paul wants to do, too," he said as his sobbing slowed.

"Do you know where Paul's looking for them?" Sandra asked.

Jamie thought hard. "Disneyland," he finally said. It was the only dream place he could remember seeing outside of a dream.

"That sounds like a good place to look," Sandra said comfortingly and stood up beside the bed.

"I'll get your needle now, Jamie," Dr. Hadrian said. "Our visitors have to go."

Jim and Sandra said good-bye. Sandra said he could keep the badge and that made Jamie feel good. But the sadness in Jim made Jamie feel bad. Just as Jim was about to go through the doorway, Jamie thought of something to tell him that could take the sadness away.

"It's not your fault, you know," the boy said.

"Sorry?" Jim said. But Jamie could tell the young man knew what he was talking about.

"You didn't hurt her when you pushed her down. It's o-va-reen cancer," Jamie said carefully. He had never heard those words pronounced, either. And for the few minutes he had to wait for Dr. Hadrian to return with the needle, he tried to understand why what he had said had made Jim feel afraid, and even sadder.

TWO

The flashing lights and howling siren took Paul by surprise. He checked the speed readout: seventy-three. He checked the side mirror: the Texas State Patrol car was gaining. Paul flicked on the turn signal and started to pull the Vanagon over to the side of Interstate 40 while the others in the back woke up. Though he had been getting better at sensing where the speed traps were, they had been stopped often enough that everyone knew what to do. Except for Johnny.

The camper sent a spray of gravel and dust into the headlight beams of the patrol car as it skidded to a stop. A sign thirty feet away said, Shamrock 65 mi. Paul checked over his shoulder. Marguerite was holding Johnny tightly, trying to keep him quiet. Paul looked at Juan and Byron and the two new ones who had joined him, Manuel and Peter, his maybe brothers. He could tell they were sharing the same feeling with him. It was getting stronger these past few days. Whenever a tense situation arose, they all felt the hungry itch for the needle. They weren't sure what the needle was, but their need for it was starting to interfere in the search for the others.

The trooper was like all the rest they had seen, approaching cautiously, large flashlight held distractingly off to the side to draw unfriendly fire. His hand stayed on his holstered gun until he saw who was driving the camper. Then the gun was drawn and pointed vaguely at the ground, vaguely straight ahead.

"Could you step out of your vehicle, please," the trooper said. He didn't ask.

Paul moved slowly and precisely, doing nothing to alarm the man. As he slid from his seat he checked out the police car behind the Vanagon. Almost hidden behind the glare of the high beams, a second trooper waited. He had a shotgun. Paul put his hands on his head, determined that everything would go smoothly. As long as no radio message had been sent, they knew from experience that they could handle two troopers.

The trooper stared at Paul for a few moments, not knowing how to react to the boy's decision to raise his hands.

"I didn't tell you to do that," the trooper said suspiciously.

"It's a dark road," Paul said. "You got a gun. Why make you nervous?" He looked to his side. The second trooper hadn't moved.

The first trooper shone his flashlight into the passenger windows. "How many others you got in there?"

"Six," Paul said.

The first trooper waved the flashlight twice at his backup. "Want to ask them to come out." Again, it wasn't a question.

Paul didn't like trying it with the other trooper so far away but he said, "No, they don't have to come out." Then he waited. Five seconds. Ten seconds. The first trooper stared vacantly.

"Harley! You okay?" the backup shouted.

The first trooper blinked. He waved his flashlight twice. "Want to ask them to come out," he said again, unaware of his repetition.

Paul wanted that needle badly. If only the other trooper would come closer. If only he could touch them. The needle itch was making things too complicated.

"Tell him to come here," Paul suggested.

"Come here," the trooper yelled.

"What's going on, Harley?" the backup yelled. Paul could hear the shotgun being pumped.

The first trooper blinked again. He waved his flashlight twice, hesitatingly. "Want to ask them to come out?" This time it was a question. He knew he had said it before. The power of Paul's suggestions fell off rapidly with distance. He would have to get closer.

Paul checked the backup. The shotgun was leveled. "Everybody out," the boy called to the others.

The trooper swore as he played the flashlight over them when they stood beside the camper. They all had their hands on their heads, except for Marguerite, who still hugged Johnny's head to her shoulder.

"You on the end," the trooper said to Johnny, flashlight held like a weapon on the boy's hidden face. "Look at me."

Marguerite released Johnny's head. The boy looked up. The trooper swore again and quickly aimed the beam to the ground. He started to gag.

It had been more than two months since Johnny Matches had died. He looked it.

"Harley! You move away from there!" the backup shouted. He was crouched behind the open door of the cruiser. His voice said he didn't like what he was seeing. "Move away, now!"

The first trooper stepped back, the afterimage of Johnny Matches still burning into his eyes.

"You punks lie down!" the backup shouted. "Now! Now! Now!" His voice told of fear and the decision to use his weapon.

The children hesitated a moment too long. The shotgun roared into the gravel at the back of the Vanagon, sending up a hailstone of shattered rock. Marguerite screamed. The camper slowly settled on two flattened rear tires.

When they were all spread out on their stomachs, half on the shoulder, half on the road, the trooper with the shotgun at last came out from behind the cruiser door.

"Harley," he said, "what the hell's wrong with you, son?"

"The one on the end there," Harley choked. "L-look at him."

The second trooper took Harley's flashlight and held it on Johnny Matches. The beam reflected from something yellow and green and shiny with moisture. The second trooper swore, too. He swept the beam over the rest of them. He stopped on Byron.

"Holy shit, Harley. That's the kid on the new FBI sheet! We got us a armed and dangerous!"

Harley shook his head. "But look at them, Steve. They all look like the kid on the new FBI sheet."

Steve ran the flashlight back over the boys, commanding them to look up at him. "We got the whole damned family," he said triumphantly. "You go back to the car and call for backup. We're going to need a truck to take these punks in."

"You don't want to call for backup!" Paul said loudly. Harley hesitated. Paul was sweating with his hunger for the needle. It had to be a link with another maybe brother. But who? Where?

"That a threat, you little punk?" Steve asked. He trod over to Paul, both the shotgun and the flashlight pointed in the boy's direction.

Paul moaned. It wasn't working. He couldn't concentrate. "You don't need to call for a backup," he tried again.

"Then how about an ambulance?" Steve asked and kicked Paul in the ribs. The pain shot up into the side of Paul's head. He writhed over onto his back. An attack was coming. He could feel it. His vision flickered.

"Omigod," Steve whispered as Paul's eyes flowed from empty black, to glowing white and back again. Paul's mouth stretched open. A rushing sound came from him. It stopped when the trooper kicked him three more times. The attack was over.

"Fuckin' drug addicts," Steve said in disgust. Harley hadn't moved.

And then the troopers heard the familiar sound of a car hood being popped.

"What the—"

Byron was standing in front of the patrol car. The hood was open. His hands were reaching inside. He looked over his shoulder at the troopers.

"Get away from that vehicle!" Steve shouted. He swung his shotgun around but was reluctant to fire at his own car.

Byron spun away like a gymnast. Blue arcs crackled from within the car's motor compartment. The troopers' mouths gaped as the three closed doors on their car flew open. Then the trunk lid sprang off. The spinning flashing lights flared blindingly and exploded as the horn and siren shrieked, peaked, and died. There was a second's pause, then the left headlight exploded. Two more seconds passed. Three more. The final right headlight dimmed and faded to black. The only light on the side of the highway now came from the interior passenger lights spilling out of the camper and the shaking beam of the flashlight.

Officer Steve's voice sounded as if it was struggling out from his belly. "You . . . god . . . dam . . . fuck . . . in' . . . *terrorists*," he rumbled. He blasted two shotgun rounds into the darkness where Byron had disappeared.

He listened for the sound of his target in agony, but heard nothing. Then the right headlight finally exploded.

Steve jumped and fired at the car. One round shattered the grille and then the shotgun clicked. The trooper swore and threw it to the ground. He ripped out his revolver and screamed at the children that the next one to move or even speak would be smashed worse than his car.

They lay there, quietly complying, as Harley tried to replace one of the tires on the camper with a space-saver spare and Steve delivered a lecture on why punks like them were killing the country. After ten minutes, they could hear the sound of an approaching vehicle.

"Harley!" Steve said. "You get out there and flag that sonovabitch over!" Then he kicked gravel at the children on the ground. "This is it, punks. Whaddaya say to the Labor Day weekend in my jail?" He kicked again. "Then, on Tuesday, I'll give the Feds a call to come and get what's left. Think you'd like that?" He was in a reverie.

The vehicle came closer. Standing in the middle of the highway, Harley could see the headlights grow brighter. He started waving his flashlight.

The vehicle stopped five hundred feet away. Harley could see orange running lights over the cab. It was a van or a small pickup.

"Make sure he sees your uniform, numb nuts," Steve called.

Harley shone the flashlight on himself. "Police officer!" he shouted and waved at the truck. "Police officer!" The truck rolled forward slowly. "It's a pickup, Steve! We'll be able to take them all in!"

"Happy Labor Day," Steve cackled and kicked more gravel on them. He was starting to concentrate on Marguerite.

The pickup stopped ten feet from Harley. "What-all seems to be the trouble, officer?" the driver asked through his open window. There was understandable suspicion in his voice.

"Caught us some dangerous criminals," Harley announced proudly, walking up to the cab. The driver adjusted the baseball cap he wore to keep Harley's flashlight out of his eyes.

"That so?" the driver said. He opened his door just as Harley came up to it. The driver slid out of the cab. He was short and fat and wore faded denim overalls. Harley escorted him over to Steve.

"'Fraid I'm going to have to commandeer your vehicle," Steve said, obviously relishing being able to use the word *commandeer*. "These terrorists are wanted by the FBI."

"That so?" the driver repeated, looking closely at the six children lying on the ground. Then he reached out both meaty hands to the officers' arms and said, "Y'all can give me your guns now."

Both officers handed over their revolvers without a moment's hesitation. The driver slipped one into a large overall pocket and held the other ready. "Now go into the camper and go to sleep for a day."

Harley and Steve walked over to the camper as if they were already dreaming. The children started to get up from the gravel, brushing themselves off. Byron emerged from behind the ruined cruiser, smiling at what he saw in the light from the camper.

The driver took off his cap. He was no more than a boy—with a full round face, and the eyes, the hair, the long, sharp nose of donor #72/SXM/4308. He smiled at his maybe brothers.

"We gotta all be together when the dream friend comes, y'all," he said.

THREE

"How long have you known?" Panati asked. He wore a thin turban of bandages and sat with Susan Foster in her living room. Two cups of coffee were cold and untouched on the table before the couch. Other things were more important that night.

Foster turned to look out the window. It was a hot August evening in New York. The pedestrians were making more noise than the traffic.

"The diagnosis was confirmed just after Christmas," she said.

"I'm sorry," Panati told her.

"So am I." She turned back to him. "Are you going to tell me about religion now?" she asked, and smiled.

"Do you want me to?"

"No." She looked away.

Panati leaned forward and took her hand. "When you do want me to, you call me. Anytime." His voice was strong and warm. The things he said, he meant. "I've never preached to you, and I never will. But I do have things to share with you. Things that can help you."

"Things that Jesus said?"

"Jesus says many things to many people. I know he has things to say to you, Susan. When you're ready."

Panati took his hand away and sat back. Foster was grateful that he wasn't going to give her a sermon or try to convert her or do whatever it was that Catholic priests did. But part of her wanted to throw herself into his arms and be told that everything was going to be all right and that death wasn't the end.

This is how it all started, Foster told herself, back when the first humans stood around the dead body of one of their tribe and realized that someday the same cessation would happen to them. Even in minds that had no language, the aching question would be there: for what purpose? And hundreds of thousands of years later, all of human history was only an absurd cycle of one tribe eager to subjugate and kill the other because each knew there was only one answer to that question and each knew that they were the only ones who had it right.

"Wyndham was a Catholic, wasn't he?" she asked.

"A lapsed Catholic, I'm afraid," Panati answered, curiosity in his eyes.

"I feel a link with him," Foster said. It was true but it wasn't anything she had ever thought she'd admit to anyone. "He had questions. I have them. He did something to try to answer them. I'm trying to figure out what it was he did. He had cancer and I have it. He killed himself when he realized it was useless to fight anymore." She stared at the coffee cups. Panati didn't interrupt. "I've thought about it." She looked at him for a reaction. Nothing. "I was thinking about it the day you called me. Remember that? Trying to make me think the Church was going to repeal its stand on birth control?"

Panati smiled in remembrance. "The old days. One hundred . . . Two hundred years ago was that?"

"I don't think I'll think about suicide again, Francis." There was conviction and purpose in what she told him. "I want to succeed where Wyndham didn't."

"I'm very glad," Panati said. She could tell he was holding back a flood of other things he wanted to say to her but she didn't encourage him. She was glad for the courtesy he was offering her and she wondered what price he might have to pay for that silence in the context of his own beliefs.

"What do you think Father Carey wanted?" she asked.

Panati shrugged, settled back in the couch. "The same thing we all want, I suppose. Understanding. Truth. I think everyone's motives always come down to the same thing. The differences lie in how we choose to pursue them." He sighed. "Though, really, I think he was insane."

Foster couldn't think of anything more to say. She knew the men had been friends. She remembered how Panati had stood up for all the members of his planning committee. What could be said about betrayal and madness? She got up to make fresh coffee, leaving Panati to the night sounds and his own inner dialogue.

Heaslip and Hyams arrived at ten that night. They had spoken to Jamie Estevez, and to his doctor. They had his records and transcripts. They knew more but they still didn't know enough.

"So instead of multiple personality, which was the first diagnosis, this Doctor Hadrian is willing to accept that Jamie and the rest of the boys are in some sort of *telepathic* communication with each other?" Foster felt her professional hackles rise. Time and time again, no matter how many uncritical articles and books were written, never had a single so-called psychic occurrence ever been reliably or repeatedly documented.

"Susan," Hyams restated, "Jamie *knew* Paul's last name. Over the past few months, all his references to Paul have been consistent with Paul's real-world activities. Doctor Hadrian was skeptical about Jamie being the focus for a network of real personalities until I told him they were all clones, and—"

"You told him what?" Panati asked with alarm.

Heaslip answered. "Father, you heard the tape of Carey's last few statements in the interrogation room. We have less than seven days now. We don't have the time or the luxury to hold anything back. We told him everything. Right down to the shroud."

"And Hadrian was willing to accept that clones can be telepathic?" Foster asked.

"Twins have increased sensitivity to each other," Hyams said, "so why not—"

"Most of that research on twins is anecdotal," Foster interrupted in annoyance. "Cyril Burt was responsible for the classic studies of twins that showed that even when they were raised apart, they exhibited great similarities. However, Burt also 'proved' that Gentiles were smarter than Jews and English people were smarter than Irish people. When he died in 1971, it was clearly discovered that he was a bigot who had made up the majority of his subjects and fabricated his data. His conclusions have been completely rejected."

"Will you *stop* it!" Hyams said bitterly. "I'm just saying what Hadrian told me. If you don't like it, then complain to him. Who cares why or how the boy can do it? He *can* do it, that's all."

"How about if we say it *seems* as if he can do it," Foster suggested. It was as close to an apology as she was willing to give.

"But there's more," Heaslip added. "Remember what Carey said about the children having the powers of Satan?" Foster did. "Well, according to Hadrian, Jamie's parents were both killed by simultaneous heart attacks. Jamie's first doctor, Rosalind Torchia, suffered a massive stroke after Jamie got mad at her for not letting him go back to his room—transcript's right here—and when Hadrian first interviewed Jamie and also got him upset, he claims the boy levitated from his bed."

"That's just laughable," Foster groaned.

"How about Suddam?" Hyams asked. "The boy without a fully formed brain at Vicker's Home? Remember I said he was restrained? He had no motor control, no muscles, yet he was restrained to his bed. Maybe he can levitate, too."

"Did Hadrian take any photographs? Gather any witnesses?" Foster asked. Where were these people's powers of rational thinking?

Hyams's face became grim, angry. "How about this, then? Just as I was leaving, Jamie told me . . ." He faltered.

"Told you what?" Foster asked, baiting him, wanting to make him say something ridiculous, wanting to humiliate him, as if every feeling she had for him could be turned around and used against him.

"Nothing," Hyams said, almost as if he sensed their argument reflected something other than the subject of discussion.

"Humor us," Heaslip said to Foster. "We accept that the boys are clones, so why not accept that they're different in other ways, too." She turned to Panati. "Jesus had special powers, didn't he?"

"Yes," Panati said cautiously. "But they came from God."

"But what if they were based in Jesus as a human?" Hyams asked. "I don't know what the Bible has to say about it all, but what if his powers were God-directed, let's say, but actually a physical part of Jesus the person? In his genetic structure? Inheritable?"

"Jim, I won't even begin to pretend that I understand the theological implications of what you're suggesting." Panati looked exhausted, skin almost as pale as his bandages. "I can see one side of the argument being stretched to say that Jesus carried genes from God, his father, so that the children are also sons of God. I can see another side being stretched to say that Jesus was no more than a freak mutation with nothing of God or heaven about him. I find both extremes unlikely and unpalatable."

"From a theological point of view?" Hyams queried, bordering on sarcasm.

"*And* from a moral and human point of view, also," Panati said.

Foster couldn't believe this conversation was going on in her living room: age-old history cycling through for the millionth time with theological debate leading to acrimony. How far can it go, she thought, before Jim and Francis decide to settle this like men?

"If Christians are still debating the true nature of Jesus after two thousand years," Foster said as peacemaker, "I don't think you two are going to solve anything tonight. Besides, the most important thing is to find out who's kidnapped the children and why Carey said we have less than two weeks to go to Armageddon."

Heaslip and Hyams looked at each other expectantly.

"Did Jamie have something to say about that, too?" Foster asked.

"Yes," Heaslip said slowly.

"The boys have been kidnapped so they can meet Number One," Hyams said.

"You mean the President?" Panati asked, startled.

"Jamie didn't know who Number One was. He didn't know if the children were in Washington. But he did use the name," Heaslip answered.

"In seven days the campaign officially starts," Foster said. She was suddenly aware of her heartbeat. It was speeding up. "There's the Labor Day parade in New York for the Democrats and . . . and . . ." She snapped her fingers impatiently. It wouldn't come to her. She looked anxiously around at the others. "Where's the President going to be when the campaign starts?"

Everyone's face was blank. Who had had the time to read newspapers? Hyams went over to a large woven basket where Foster accumulated her magazines and the Sunday *New York Times*. He started pawing through it. Panati's memory was faster.

"Of course," the priest said softly. "Scott told us to join the 'brothers and sisters at home.' That's what Bobby Jay calls his viewers."

"*Reverend* Bobby Jay?" Foster asked. "The television preacher?"

"Or television *guy*?" Heaslip suggested.

"What's that got to do with the President?" Hyams asked, flipping through a two-week-old *Newsweek* to see if it said anything about the election.

"That's where the President will be this weekend," Panati said. "At Bobby Jay's new Bible college and convention center and I don't know what-all it's supposed to be. I read about it in the *Christian Herald*. Oh, dear Lord."

"What?" Foster demanded. "Dear Lord what?"

"It makes sense," Panati groaned, and the exhaustion in his face was mirrored by his voice. "Bobby Jay has been broadcasting from his Bible college site for years, so that means there's a studio there. And the President will be there exactly within

Scott's time limit. And remember what he said: 'They are the proof we need to convince those who wield the weapons of Armageddon to thwart Satan's plans and strike first against his followers.' "

Foster felt the skin on her neck prickle. "Are you saying that a television fundamentalist intends to persuade the President of the United States to launch a nuclear first strike against the Soviets?"

"That's what Greg was afraid of," Heaslip said to no one in particular.

" 'I will send fire on Magog' the Lord said," Panati whispered. "Many who take the Bible literally claim that the land of Magog is the Soviet Union, and that the fire that rains down in the final battle will be nuclear fire."

"No," Foster said. It was insanity.

"And the President believes in a literal Bible. The President believes that this is the generation that will see the end times." Panati's words were marred by trembling. "The President wields the weapons of Armageddon."

"No."

"And in seven days, Bobby Jay is going to introduce the President to his collection of levitating, thought-reading, almost identical Antichrists, and tell him to take action."

"He can't," Foster pleaded.

"He's the President," Panati said.

FOUR

Dean Fuller remembered the instant he had known he was dead, and with that memory came the knowledge that he was still alive. It was a surprise he hadn't expected.

The knowledge of his death had come to him on the staircase of his front hall when the door had opened and the men had come in. Rose was in the house, probably in the kitchen. Barbara-

Jane was still in her study, where she had listened in to his conversation with Tom Jefferson. Obviously, someone else had listened in, too. If I resist, Fuller recalled thinking, both women might be in danger from wild shots or chemical sprays. And in any case, he could never have won against those odds. Dean Fuller wasn't a young man anymore. He regretted each lost and wasted day.

The men who had burst into his home had recognized the professionalism Fuller had shown by not forcing a messy and pointless confrontation. They had treated him efficiently, but with respect, as they led him quickly to the waiting car: a limousine, of course, dark windows and no flags. It was in the backseat of that car, wedged between two of the unsmiling, dull-suited young men, that Fuller had felt the prick of the needle in his leg and had known only seconds remained. No difference, he had thought in those last lucid moments, between the capitals of the present and the capitals of the past. Assassins crept along broadloomed corridors as quietly as they had lurked behind marble pillars, waiting for those who went against the ruling policies. The methods of governing were unchanged over the centuries. The only new slant Washington had added was that the deeds were generally revealed within a few decades, rather than centuries, and generally in best-selling books. Resigned to his place in the ongoing rush of history, Dean Fuller passed into oblivion.

Now, awake, head throbbing and throat sticking with grating dryness, he tried to understand why he returned from oblivion into what looked to be a television studio—a television studio thick with a foul and grotesque stench. He heard a moan beside him. He was not alone.

In his efforts to see who was moaning, he learned he was strapped onto a solid office table. Each arm and leg was held separately. Larger straps ran across his chest and thighs. Someone was taking no chances with him.

Fuller's head was not restrained so he was able to move it—carefully, to avoid the painful aftereffects of the drugs he had been administered—and see who his fellow prisoner was. It was a boy, naked, emaciated, and tied more securely than even Fuller was. The boy was also gagged.

Fuller felt a small rustle of fear pass through him. Wherever he was, he was not in the hands of professionals who could be counted on to carry out their duties like soldiers. The boy's condition was a warning sign: Fuller was in the hands of maniacs.

Learn the terrain, he told himself, reconnoiter, prepare for escape. He raised his head and began to examine the studio. As he did, the small rustle of fear grew into a dreadful wind. He was not in the hands of maniacs; he was in the domain of monsters.

Fuller saw there were five more boys gagged and bound to other tables, in addition to the one who moaned beside him. All were naked, hollow-stomached, and some, he could tell, were straining to roll their eyes to him. He also saw where the corrupt odor came from. To his right was the blue-white body of a man who had bled to death, well into its slow swelling as the bacteria within multiplied unchecked. To his left, farthest away, closest to the main studio doors, was another boy's body, gagged and bound as the others were, but crushed and torn like a primitive blood sacrifice. Fuller doubted that anything he had learned in his years of covert service would aid him against the people who were responsible for what he was seeing. At least he knew that if he survived long enough for his bonds to be removed, the disgust he felt would more than compensate him as he went against his captors' youth and strength.

He lay back, mind rushing through plans and counterplans, all directed toward deducing which organization was responsible for this outrage, what psychopaths would resort to such measures. Then the door to the studio clicked open and all was answered. Barbara-Jane Fuller, his wife, walked in, accompanied by the Reverend Bobby Jay.

Barbara-Jane waved her fingers beneath her nose as she walked over to him, trying to dispel the stench. But still she smiled at him, just as if she had stepped into his office and caught him sneaking a nap on his couch.

"I'm glad to see you're all right, Dean," she said. "They told me you reacted rather badly to the injection."

"You're glad to see I'm all right?" Fuller repeated. What was she doing here?

"Of course I am, dear. You're very important to the work to be done here." She looked around the studio as if surveying a dream home. "This is the *place*, don't you see?"

Fuller shook his head. Barbara-Jane was acting as if it were just another normal day at home.

"This studio," she said, cajoling him. "This is the great hall I saw in my vision. See the lights up there on the scaffolding? When they're turned on, Bobby Jay says, you can't see out into the audience. You can't see out to the walls. Just like my dream! And see, there? There?"

She pointed off to a wall where a large glass window slanted out from the wall eight feet from the floor. A dark wall of monitors and other equipment could be seen through it. "That's the control room, and see what's just underneath it?"

It was a four-foot-long digital readout showing the month, the day, and the time.

"And when it says August twenty-ninth, ten fifty-two P.M., my vision will come true and this sinful old world will come to an end." Her eyes sparkled, her cheeks were healthy and glowing, and she smiled at her husband. "That's why it's so important for you to be here, honey. You were in my dream."

"So was the President," Fuller said grimly.

"And he shall be here, too," Bobby Jay boomed out. "Lord Jesus showed me the way! Lord Jesus showed your wife the time and place! And together, we will show the President, and the world, the true path to righteousness, the true call to glory."

Fuller looked into Bobby Jay's small, dark eyes and saw the beast who was responsible for the ruined child's body strapped to the table nearest the door.

"Jesus has nothing to do with Barbara-Jane's visions," Fuller said, twisting against his straps.

Bobby Jay shrugged noncommitally. "Well, perhaps they come directly from God."

"They're a drug response." Fuller choked over the words he had sworn he would never say. "Hypnotics were administered. I would—"

Bobby Jay's slap made Fuller's eyes roll back with the sharp explosion of drug-sensitized pain. "I will not let you slander your wife," he snarled. "You claim she is an adherent of *pharmacopeia*? Satan's ancient way of seducing minds with the drugs of prophecy?" He slapped Fuller again and again. "If we had time, Mr. Fuller, I would give all my efforts to drive out the devils within you."

"Like you drove them out of that poor child by the door?" Fuller gasped. He could taste blood in his mouth. The whole studio pulsed with waves of pain.

Bobby Jay held a thick, padded strap over Fuller's head. Barbara-Jane looked on with love and concern. "That 'poor child' had no devils *within* him, Mr. Fuller." He pulled the strap tightly over Fuller's face, cutting deeply into his mouth. "That child *was* the devil." He leaned closer to Fuller's bulging eyes. "They are *all* the devil." Fuller looked desperately toward his wife. She did nothing but clasp her hands in caring worry.

Bobby Jay turned his head to see what Barbara-Jane's reaction was to Fuller's gagged pleas.

"You know, Bobby Jay," she said thoughtfully, "perhaps we better cover up the bodies of the dead. We don't want to distract the President, do we?"

Fuller screamed uselessly. This time, oblivion wouldn't come.

FIVE

This time, Hyams drove Foster to the police station. She still wasn't feeling too well, she had told him. Flu or a summer-time cold, she wasn't sure. And, by the way, she had added, sorry for the attack of the vapors back at the time of the shooting. She had tried to laugh while she said that, but she hadn't been convincing.

Hyams couldn't bring himself to tell Foster what Jamie had said about her. Maybe he was respecting her privacy, he told himself. Or maybe it was just easier to pretend it really wasn't happening. If he thought about it, her condition might explain the tension he had felt building between them. Better that than something more complicated.

But what Jamie had told him had convinced him. Despite Foster's protests, Hyams accepted what he had seen and heard. And Hadrian believed, too. That's why the doctor hadn't complained when Hyams had called him in the middle of the night.

That's why he had agreed to take a road atlas into Jamie's room and patiently explain the exact location of America's Glory to the boy. Hyams wouldn't admit it to Foster, but he believed the message would get through.

"What did you tell Thorkel?" Hyams asked, deciding to stay with the present.

Foster took a moment to answer, as if she had been thinking of something far away. "Just that Carey had given us a lead on the children's location," she said. "He was still shaken about Carey. Wasn't too interested in the details. Told me to just go ahead and book whatever tickets we needed through his company's travel agency and he'd take care of all the bills."

"Were they able to book us rooms right in America's Glory?" Hyams felt a chill whenever he had to use that name.

"Booked up months ago," Foster said. It seemed she wasn't too interested in the details, either. "The agent found a Holiday Inn about sixty miles away. There'll be a car reserved at the airport."

"Do we need tickets or anything to get in?"

"No. 'Admittance is free to all brothers and sisters.' " Foster grimaced. " 'Prayer offerings gratefully accepted.' You need passes for the special church services and the presidential luncheon is by invitation only, but the grounds are wide open. I guess the first thing to do is find out where he used to tape his television shows." She stared out the window, biting her lower lip, obviously impatient with Hyams's comparatively sedate, and legal, methods of driving.

He dutifully slowed for an amber light. "Can you believe we're doing this?" he asked.

"Day by day," she said, distractedly, "sure. But if someone had told me six months ago what I'd be doing this weekend, I'd have laughed."

Hyams thought about that for a moment. Then he did laugh. She joined him. As they pulled away on green, he sensed a bitterness in them both that he didn't like.

The parking lot beside the station was packed and Hyams no longer had a permit to show the guard. Two hundred feet along, he found a clear curb by a hydrant and pulled in. In the worst case, it was Foster's car and Thorkel could pay for the ticket and towing. He went around to the passenger side and opened Foster's door. He didn't go as far as helping her out, but he could see that in a few more days he might have to start offering.

"Did Ioannou say what he had for us?" she asked as they began walking toward the station.

"No," Hyams said, trying not to be too obvious about slowing his pace so that she could keep up. "It was just a message asking us to meet him. We'll probably have to give some sort of statement about the shooting. As far as I know, he and his partner never got around to completely explaining to their captain why Carey was brought in in the first place. Our best bet is to follow his lead and say nothing about the tape."

"I hope we do better with the captain than I did with you," Foster said.

"So do I," Hyams agreed, remembering the stories she had originally told him. He looked ahead to the main entrance of the station. The usual mix of those involved in the business of law enforcement moved up and down the wide stone steps. A short figure with downturned head suddenly walked from a storefront doorway and bumped into Foster. Hyams felt his chest constrict as he recognized who it was.

"Marjorie," he said, trying to sound at ease but knowing tension was forcing his voice into a tight, nasal parody of itself. "Have you, ah, met Susan Foster?" He knew the answer to that one, of course. He had done his best not to let either Foster or Marjorie know of each other. Except for the night when Ioannou had surprised him in his apartment and made his cracks about Hyams's girlfriend in the records department, Hyams felt he had managed fairly well.

Marjorie said nothing, grabbed their arms, spun them around, and forced them to walk quickly away from the station. She glanced furtively up at Hyams. She was frowning and it didn't suit her.

The records clerk was attractive, two years younger than Hyams, with a figure that all the old cops made hackneyed jokes about. The distinctive makeup she usually wore tended to be part of their jokes, too. But this morning, it appeared she wore none.

"Do you have a car?" the records clerk asked abruptly, not even turning to acknowledge Foster.

"We just passed it," Hyams said, gesturing over his shoulder. Marjorie changed direction again and began marching them back toward the car.

Oh, great, Hyams thought. This is what he had been afraid of—the scene—even though the only thing he had to feel guilty about, he told himself, was his own guilt. Yes, he had been seeing Marjorie all this summer and yes, they were lovers. But he had never slept with anyone else during his time with her and all the evenings and afternoons he had spent with Foster had been legitimate and work-related. Then why weren't you above-board with her, jerk? he asked himself. Hyams knew the answer to that one, too, and it appeared that now, of all times, was when he would have to pay for thinking there could be anything more between him and Foster.

Marjorie hurried them into Foster's Prelude, sliding behind Hyams into the backseat. "Drive," she said. It was a command.

"Look," Hyams tried, patting his hands resignedly on the steering wheel, "can't we just get this over with here? We have an appointment with Ioannou and—"

"Ioannou hasn't been in for three days," Marjorie said. "Get the hell away from this station! Now!"

Hyams pulled out with a squeal of tires. "I thought you said Ioannou called you?" Foster asked. She looked over her shoulder at Marjorie, appraising her.

"I said it was just a message to meet him there," Hyams said. "You want to tell us what's going on?" Marjorie looked out the back window. "Are you checking to see if someone's *following* us?" Hyams asked incredulously.

"Look," Marjorie said, keeping her voice low and urgent, "I don't know what you guys are up to." She held the pause a beat too long, so that Hyams would understand she was referring to more than just their work. "And I don't really care. At first I was worried because of the stuff you wanted me to look for in the databases, but when Ioannou said it was all right for me to continue, I figured it was legitimate police work. Was it?"

"More or less," Hyams hedged. "When we put it all together it will be."

"Yeah, well, anyway," Marjorie muttered, looking over her shoulder again. "The thing is, whatever you're doing, I figured it was worthwhile, so when I didn't hear from you after the priest ate it, I thought I'd keep running my checks for you. Kidnapping or crimes of violence against young teenage boys, right? Anyway, there's *nothing* in the databases anymore." She said it like a judge pronouncing a death sentence.

"You mean the databases have shut down?" Foster asked.

"The databases are fine. It's just that they're not reporting any kidnappings or crimes of violence against young teenage boys anymore."

"Maybe there haven't been any in the past three days," Hyams suggested. Unlikely perhaps, he thought, given the size of the country, but surely not impossible.

"I'm not talking about the past three days, Jimmy. I mean *there is no information in any national or regional law enforcement database concerning any of the cases you had me pull in the past six weeks!* Understand? Nothing! Someone's gone in and wiped the tapes."

"Does that happen often?" Foster asked. Her voice sounded fragile.

"It *doesn't* happen, period. Those databases are used in criminal cases all the time. They have to be inviolable, unerasable. Even if bad data gets put in, it has to stay in with a correction notice. If the databases were subject to arbitrary changes, think what someone could do with them. They could register you as an armed and dangerous psychopath wanted for fifteen brutal murders, and then after some local police force had shot you to death outside church or something, the false information could be removed." Marjorie was on the delicate edge of panic. Her universe had been violently altered. "If it were possible for data to be changed, records to be wiped out, the whole system would break down."

"But you're saying someone *did* erase files?" Hyams protested.

"Yes!"

"But who would have the capability?" Foster asked. "Or the authority?"

"That's why I'm scared," Marjorie said. "No one's supposed to."

Hyams drove for half a mile without saying anything. He knew who had the capability. And the authority. "Thank you, Marj," he said. "We appreciate your concern." It sounded cold, he knew, but that's how he felt, almost as if he were about to go into battle.

"But it's not just *you*," Marjorie said, voice trembling. "The system has safeguards, internal registers. Every time I requested a search or a printout, my operator number was recorded. They can trace me. And with Ioannou and now Sandra taken away by IAD and—" She shook her head in despair. "My supervisor called me this morning and told me not to come in to work today. I tried calling all over for you and they said you'd be coming in this morning so . . . I was afraid to stay at my apartment."

Hyams glanced at Foster. He could see in her face the same dark worry that he felt. The stakes were rising out of control. None of them would be safe now, not even in their homes. Six days to go.

"I know someone you can stay with, Marj. It's going to be okay," he said. For everyone's sake, he tried to sound as if he believed it.

SIX

She would be easy to find, Tom Jefferson knew, if he could just manage to make it inside. If you weren't on the list, getting into David's was about as easy as getting into Cheyenne Mountain.

Jefferson checked himself in the rearview mirror of the car he had borrowed. Favors without questions were easy enough to come by in D.C. because of the unspoken rule that each one must be paid back upon request, also without questions. Jefferson had had no problem in finding acquaintances who were more than willing to loan a car and cash to someone who had once worked within the White House and, all things being equal, might return when the administration changed.

The only thing Jefferson had to be grateful for in the past week was that his name had not surfaced in the rumors he had been expecting. His last phone call from Dean Fuller had clicked off an instant before he had hung up the receiver. Normally, he wouldn't have worried about an unfamiliar sound on the phone but, given their topic of discussion, he had decided to be prudent. The Fuller line had been busy for a full hour afterward. When Jefferson had finally rung through, a maid whom he had never known about—not Rose—had informed him that Mr. Fuller had been called away on business. Trying to tell himself he was the victim of too many Ludlum novels, Jefferson had arrived across the street from the Ambassador Hotel at three o'clock that day, taken a window seat at the Bon Marché, and watched for Fuller's white Lincoln to arrive in the northwest corner of the parking lot. By four o'clock, the Lincoln hadn't arrived, but three other particular cars had. Each was a different make and model, but each held two men with dark glasses and discreet earphones. Government cars. Government business. Jefferson had phoned home, told his wife to take the children and go to her parents' farm, and then vanished.

Now, tonight, it was time for his reappearance. He smoothed his hair in the mirror, and got out of the car. David's was ten doors down the street. He wondered if he'd make it.

The only thing apparently different about the street David's was on was that there were more and brighter streetlamps than the zoning codes required. A small, modern office building was on the corner of that street and a major avenue. One of the businesses with offices there did nothing but watch and identify everyone who entered the street. The streetlamps helped the business provide its services at night.

Jefferson walked slowly, making sure that whoever was on duty that night would have time to identify him. There was no way an unknown person could get close to David's. At the last minute, someone would invariably emerge from a nearby door and accidentally bump into anyone who was avoiding identification by walking too quickly or with head down. Jefferson didn't want to risk raising alarms in that way. If he was still on the "A" list, he would be allowed to make it to the front door. If he walked slowly, head up, like a regular customer, and a stranger suddenly appeared on a collision course, then it would be because Jefferson was no longer on any list. At least he'd have a chance to run back to the car. Not much of a chance, but he was counting on them—whoever they were—not to use guns.

The door to David's was unmarked, of course. It could have been just another of the plain front doors of the other townhouses that appeared to line the street, instead of an oak-covered steel blast shield. Even the surveillance camera mounted to the side of the doorway was common enough in this part of town to be unremarkable. When Jefferson pressed his trembling finger against the glowing button by the door, he felt relief. It lasted until he took his first step through the doorway. If a powerful enough government operation is behind this, he thought, then maybe they're just waiting to get me off the street before they take me down.

The door hissed shut on hydraulic hinges. The maître d' arrived after the entrance room was secure. It was Philip. The maître d's were all Philip there.

"Mr. Jefferson, sir, how good to see you," he said. "We weren't expecting you this evening."

Jefferson wondered if a brush-off were coming: sorry but there are no seats and perhaps if you'd care to make a reservation for another night? He prepared his lie.

"Wasn't expecting to be here myself, Philip," Jefferson said, surprised at how calm and natural he sounded. "Last-minute meeting. Table twenty-seven." Would it work?

Philip was good. His expression didn't change and the brush-off was instantly changed to a welcome. "Of course, Mr. Jefferson. Table twenty-seven." It was *her* table. "If you'll just give me a moment to announce you?" He began to back away. Jefferson followed, making a show of checking his watch.

"Actually, I'm about half an hour late already and I know she'll only want me for about five minutes. I won't be staying for dinner."

Philip paused awkwardly at the end of the entrance hall. A second blast shield could drop from its ceiling within a tenth of a second. "I'd hate to disturb her, Mr. Jefferson. I know she has another guest."

Jefferson remained motionless in the entrance hall, letting the metal detectors and chemical sniffers do their work; not that they meant much in these days of plastic Glocks and ceramic blades. But the message to Philip was clear: I have nothing to hide.

"I'll tell you, Philip, I'm worried she's going to be annoyed with me enough as it is, and by the time you get up there and back I'm going to be five more minutes late. I'm sure you know my career standing doesn't need that aggravation right now."

The maître d' glanced at the telltales surreptitiously placed on the wall outside the entrance hall. All were green.

"Very well," he said reluctantly. "If you'll follow me please?"

As soon as Philip turned his back, Jefferson inhaled slowly and deeply. He wasn't yet targeted. The people who had taken Fuller either didn't have the resources or the influence to watch for Jefferson throughout D.C. Now everything depended on how fast he could talk when Philip escorted him to table twenty-seven and realized that he really wasn't expected.

David's was busy that evening, as it usually was. But since the new guard in the White House had little use for bars and elitist perks, Jefferson wasn't concerned about being recognized at this point. The rules and decorum of the place, to say nothing of the weapons carried by the staff, would make a disturbance practically impossible. He hoped.

Table twenty-seven was upstairs. Philip led the way up the narrow oak stairway. It, too, could be sealed between blast shields, and the fire sprinklers studding the ceilings were equally capable of spraying an enervating dilation vapor as well as water.

The table-numbering system had begun when the restaurant was first opened in the mid-fifties, but the legends disagreed on how certain tables became associated with certain positions. The director of the CIA traditionally met guests at table forty-two, the director of the FBI at table thirty-eight. The numbers weren't arranged in any particular order, nor did they imply that any one table was better than another. Once a person was on the list at David's, all other distinctions were superfluous.

Table twenty-seven was in a far corner. Jefferson could only see one guest: the Speaker of the House. Interesting, he thought. Philip began to make his apologies but Jefferson interrupted before matters got confusing. If Philip thought a breach of propriety had taken place, Jefferson could be led away as easily as he had been led in.

"Mrs. Vice President," Jefferson began, "I'm sorry to be late for our appointment." The Vice President was at least as shrewd as Philip had been in the entrance hall. A look of surprise didn't even flicker across her face. "I do realize how important it is," Jefferson continued, "but I'm sure it will take no more than ten minutes of your time."

The Vice President stood up from the table and reached out to shake Jefferson's hand. "Philip," she said, "would you bring a chair for Mr. Jefferson. And, perhaps you'd like something to drink, Tom?"

Philip snapped his fingers and a white-coated waiter brought an extra chair to table twenty-seven, then departed to call up Mr. Jefferson's preferences on the bar computer.

The Vice President checked that no one but the Speaker remained in earshot and then leaned forward over her table. She smiled through clenched teeth and her eyes sparkled, but her expression was like a wild animal's warning display. All of Washington was in awe of her these days. Word was out: one more term with the President and she was going for the big one. Anyone who got in her way would have his heart ripped out by her bare hands. And her eyes would still sparkle in the same sweet way.

"I'm impressed, Tom," she said in her low, gravelly voice. "Not even my secret service groupies know where I am tonight."

Jefferson shrugged it off. He wasn't about to reveal his source in her office. "Does that worry you?" he asked, testing for her mood, her probable reaction to what he had to tell her.

"Should it? Number One's been telling some pretty strange stories about you these days. And some of the other dearly departeds, too."

"Do you believe those stories?"

"I guess I'll be able to answer that one after you tell me what it is that's so important you'd bushwhack me like this. One cough from me and you're in the basement, my friend. Now what is it?" She downed her shot glass of scotch and waited. The Speaker of the House sat well back, anxious to remain uninvolved.

"It concerns Number One," Jefferson said, trying to guess what she was thinking.

"Sort of thought it might. Anything in particular?"

Jefferson went for broke. "The Twenty-fifth Amendment," he said.

The Vice President leaned back from the table. Her face was

unreadable. "You thinking that the President might be unable to discharge the duties and the powers of his office?" she asked flatly.

"Yes, ma'am," Jefferson sighed. This was it.

The Vice President glanced over at the Speaker. She winked. "Seems like that's a hot topic of conversation these days, Tom. I gather you have some evidence in support of this potentially traitorous accusation?"

Jefferson nodded. Had she already been discussing the procedure with the Speaker? Did she know?

"Well then, Tommy, go ahead," the Vice President rasped earnestly. "Make my day."

SEVEN

Hyams was overwhelmed. Everywhere he looked he was surrounded by smiling faces and uncomplaining children. Almost everyone wore pins or buttons: cloisonné hands clasped in prayer or pointing one finger heavenward, the name Jesus formed into doves and rainbows, and proclamations that He was coming Soon. It was a colorful carnival and a noisy midway, a huge street party and an extended family reunion. Hyams also found it frightening. It was America's Glory.

"So where to now?" Father Panati asked. He had to bend over to Hyams's ear and speak loudly to overcome the combination of crowd noise and recorded hymns being played through the hidden speakers throughout the entrance courtyard, easily half the size of a football field and swarming with a born-again, Labor Day weekend crowd.

"She's got the map," Hyams said, pointing to Foster. The science writer stood glancing from the unfolded visitor's map she had been given at the entrance turnstiles to the buildings that stretched before them. Her hands were trembling, but she had refused to stay back at the Holiday Inn, even if this excursion was only to plan whatever action they should take before the twenty-ninth. This was the twenty-eighth.

Panati straightened up and waited patiently. Hyams looked at him and guessed the priest was wondering what it would be like to have this many people attending services at the Catholic church. Not that Panati looked much like a priest right now. He was in disguise, as he called it, with white pants, white weave shoes, and a painfully blue tropical print shirt. Unfortunately, he had chosen to tuck the shirt into his pants and the pattern was showing through the white fabric. Definitely not Vatican-approved apparel, Hyams thought.

The other way Panati stood out from the crowd was the way all three of them did. Their skin was New York pale in contrast to the healthy, tanned complexions of the predominately white crowd. Hyams looked up into the cloudless sky. A few hours beneath the Georgia summer sun and they'd be fashionably lobster red.

"Got it," Foster said. Hyams and Panati flanked her so they could see the map. The entire Bible college and family resort complex was laid out in the shape of a Latin cross. The entrance courtyard where they stood was at the foot of the cross. Just before them sprawled the interconnected buildings of the America's Glory Hotel, with a wide, open-air passage that ran beneath their crisscrossing elevated walkways to the Family Village. The shops, restaurants, and theaters of the village extended about half a mile to an outdoor stage and picnic area at the intersection of the cross. At the end of the right arm of the cross was the original Bobby Jay Bible College and at the end of the left arm was the America's Glory Corporate Center, which housed the organization's business offices and a state-of-the-art broadcast studio. At the head of the cross, farthest from the entrance courtyard, the multi-million-dollar glass-walled cathedral of America's Glory shimmered like an immense, improbable glacier beneath the morning sun.

"We're here," Foster said, pointing to the entrance courtyard on the map. "The new studios are in here." She indicated the Corporate Center. "And the President's luncheon and televised speech are scheduled for here." The cathedral.

"So where are the old studios?" Hyams asked.

"They have to be somewhere in the Bible college buildings," Foster answered. "The notes on the map say they were the first thing built on site. I suppose we can ask one of our 'friendly Glory Guides,' or take a tour."

"Sounds good to me," Hyams said, and the three of them walked to an information booth at the edge of the courtyard.

The smiling Glory Guide showed her immaculate teeth in a heaven-sent smile and said yes, the "Good News Glory Show" had recently been moved from its original studios in the basement of the Bible college to the brand new studio in the Corporate Center capable of seating eight hundred brothers and sisters, praise the Lord.

Panati praised the Lord right back at the Glory Guide and asked if there were any tours of the Bible college that day. There was one starting in forty-five minutes.

"Does that include a look at the old studios?" Panati asked enthusiastically.

"Now ahm real sorry 'bout that," the guide said. "But those old studios are bein' renovated to become a new broadcast facility for Reverend Bubba Jay's Glory College of th' Air."

Panati thanked the girl with another praise the Lord and he and Hyams and Foster walked toward the hotel passage to the Family Village.

"You're really getting into this, aren't you, Father?" Hyams said, intending it as a joke.

"Of course," Panati agreed seriously. "To be a successful undercover agent, one must blend in with one's surroundings."

Oh well, Hyams thought. This was the same man who thought being cuffed and arrested in the Vicker's Convalescent Home parking lot had been exciting.

Behind them, the Glory Guide waited until they disappeared within the passageway, then picked up her phone. Panati had been too interested in the old studios. The guides had been warned.

The Bible college buildings were the most conservative structures in America's Glory, erected when money was scarce and the rest of the complex was still to be described to Bobby Jay by Lord Jesus. That's what the guide map said. Hyams examined the buildings and decided the assessment was true. They were plain red-bricked buildings that seemed to have been designed by efficiency experts instead of architects: four stories high, full of right angles, and no decorations or changes in finish. Bobby Jay had obviously made up for their dull design when he had commissioned the glass eruption of his cathedral and the fifty-five-foot cross overlooking the reflecting pool at the hotel end of the Family Village.

About fifty other people were waiting by the tour sign on a path leading to the main college building. The pale New Yorkers found themselves eavesdropping on half a dozen conversations among earnest young men and women who were trying to decide if the Lord was really telling them to go to this college, or Jerry Falwell's. Hyams struggled valiantly not to whisper any facetious comments about the Lord's qualifications as a guidance counselor.

The tour guide arrived ten minutes after the scheduled time. Several people commented that it seemed to be an unusual occurrence for the normally well-run complex. Also, the guide wasn't one of the white-suited, perpetually smiling young men and women who were America's Glory official Glory Guides. He was a somber-looking middle-aged man wearing a large happy-face button that said, "HI! MY NAME IS HANK AND I'M GOING TO HEAVEN. ARE YOU?"

"Sorry to keep you folks waiting," Hank said, after he had captured everyone's attention by waving his hands above his head. "Our regular tour guide just found out his wife's gone into labor so he's off to the hospital to coach in another little player for the Lord's team." With three exceptions, the tour group laughed and applauded.

"Now, I'm going to have to ask you to bear with me on this because this isn't my regular tour," Hank continued. Then he explained that because some Friday classes were still in progress, the tour group would be broken up into smaller segments to be less disruptive. Within minutes, other guides had arrived and had taken the waiting people away in groups of five. Hyams, Foster, and Panati were in the last group to go, led by Hank and accompanied by two large men who hadn't talked about which college they should go to.

Hank chattered incessantly about Bobby Jay's personal call to glory until they arrived at the first stop in their tour: an empty lecture hall. Hyams had just begun to feel nervous when the arms of one of the men snaked around his chest and over his neck, pinning his own arms. From the corner of his eye, he could see that the second man did the same to Panati. It was a trap.

Just as he had been taught, Hyams brought his heel down on his captor's instep. But the captor had also been taught. The large man felt the buildup to the blow, moved his foot, and then jerked Hyams into the air so quickly Hyams could feel his shoulder blades snap together. Then he was rammed headfirst against the wall. If the man hadn't been holding him up, Hyams would have collapsed.

"Did you get it all out of your system?" Hank asked Hyams.

Panati was demanding to know what the meaning of this outrage was, but Hank ignored him, just as he seemed to be ignoring Foster. Hyams's desire to say something witty was stifled by the terrible sensation that some of his teeth had been pushed through his tongue. He groaned. It sounded as if someone else had done it.

Hank turned his attention to Foster. "Okay, lady, let's have it. How come you're so interested in the old studios?"

Foster looked over her shoulder at Panati, then at Hyams, and then back to Hank. Hyams saw the look of surprise on her face. Not because they had been attacked, but because she hadn't been.

"I-I've got a special message for Bobby Jay," she stammered nervously. Hyams had never heard her sound so insecure. She fumbled with her shoulder bag.

"Let's have it," Hank demanded and stepped closer to wrench the bag from her hands.

Foster whipped out her Mace can and the chemical spray caught Hank in the eyes. He yowled in pain and surprise. Then Foster's foot connected with his crotch like a thunderbolt and he went down with a pitiful squeak. Before he touched the floor, Foster had spun and screamed and clawed her nails across the face of the man holding Panati.

The man shrieked as four thick welts of blood erupted above and below his right eye. He pushed Panati at Foster and held both hands to his own face. Foster sidestepped Panati and, with the man's hands otherwise occupied and the priest out of range, doused his face with the irritating spray. Then she drove her foot into his crotch, too. When he slipped to his knees, she connected to the side of his head. The impact knocked her back onto the floor, but the man hit face down and didn't move.

The man holding Hyams screamed "You bitch!" at Foster, pushed Hyams at her, and ran out the lecture room door. Foster dodged the stumbling form of Hyams but didn't give chase. It was time to regroup.

Foster pulled a wad of Kleenex from her bag and began wiping the blood from Hyams's face. When she got to the right side of his mouth, he couldn't feel anything.

"I think you're about to lose a tooth in there," she said, examining the source of blood.

"Ruh hunh," Hyams agreed. Then he coughed as he saw what Panati was up to. The priest was going through the pockets of the two men on the floor.

Foster turned to follow Hyams's gaze. "Let's get out of here before the other one comes back with help," she said quickly, helping Hyams to his feet.

Panati stuffed the men's wallets into his pockets and ran to the lecture room door. He listened for a moment, pushed it open a bit, then all the way, and waved Foster and Hyams through.

Two young men carrying Bibles paused at the end of the hall when they saw Foster and Panati helping Hyams walk toward the exit.

"Can we help you?" one of them called pleasantly.

"No thanks," Foster replied, trying to hurry Hyams along. "Just a nosebleed." There was the sound of running feet, several pairs. "Move it," she ordered and began dragging Hyams by the arm.

Just as Hyams skidded around a corner, feeling like an extra in a Charlie Chaplin movie, he looked over his shoulder and saw four men racing after them. The man in the lead had four streaks of red across his face.

Panati pushed open a stairwell door and held it while Foster and Hyams ran in behind. He squeezed it shut.

A voice yelled from below, "Who's there? No entry, the sign says! No entry!"

"That way!" Foster gasped and they stormed up the stairs. Just as they reached the second floor, they heard the first-floor door open. They ran out into a second-floor corridor.

The corridor was empty. All the classroom and office doors leading from it were closed. Only the ceiling lights by the scattered fire doors were working. It had the look of a school closed for the summer.

"This way," Foster whispered, heading off along the corridor in the direction it was longest.

Hyams went unprotestingly in the direction Foster pulled him. He looked over his shoulder again. He saw a classroom door open. A young boy looked out. A dark-haired boy.

"Hay-mee!" Hyams grunted, twisting away from Foster. He started to run back along the corridor.

"Jim!" Foster hissed. "This way! This way!"

An avalanche of footsteps grew behind the stairwell door.

Hyams didn't hesitate until he reached the open door. Foster and Panati stared at the boy who waited there. Then at each other. They ran after Hyams.

The boy eased the classroom door shut just as the stairwell door burst open.

The classroom was dark, lit only by five ribbons of light which sliced through the venetian blinds covering the windows. Hyams could just see the boy hold his finger to his lips, telling the three adults to be silent. He pointed to an instructor's desk at the front of the room, motioning the adults to hide behind it. From the hallway came the sound of doors being thrown open, commands shouted.

The boy backed up against the wall by the door. Hyams watched from beneath the desk. The doorknob glinted as it spun. The door burst open. The man whose face Foster had torn entered like a bull, eyes drawn to the desk.

The boy swung his open hand into the man's belly. His movements were swift, but not powerful. The man barely slowed as he spun and raised his hand to strike the child. Hyams winced.

The blow didn't come.

Very precisely, the boy said, "The room is clear. They aren't in here."

"The room is clear!" the man shouted to the others. "They aren't in here!" He lowered his arm, stepped back into the doorway, looking around the room once more, as if to assure himself that the room was empty. He disappeared into the hallway, slammed the door, and locked it.

Panati sighed loudly enough to make the boy return his finger to his lips. He listened at the door then walked silently to the desk.

"You can come out now," he whispered. "But keep quiet."

Panati and Foster stood beside the desk, staring down at the boy—his hair, eyes, and nose intensely familiar. Hyams remained on the floor, leaning against the desk. His whole face thrummed with the beating of his heart.

Foster peered into the boy's eyes questioningly. "*Are* you Jamie?" she asked.

"Paul," the boy whispered. "Almagro."

Panati crossed himself. Paul's eyes flickered over the priest but sought out Hyams.

"You're Jim?" the boy asked.

Hyams nodded. It was too painful to speak.

"Jamie got us the message," Paul said. "Thank you."

There were more voices and running in the hall. The door to the classroom suddenly rattled as someone tried the lock. Panati moaned. Foster's hand reached into her shoulder bag.

Paul closed his eyes, held up his hand. "Not this time," he whispered. The rattling stopped.

"Are you making him do that?" Foster asked. "Keeping him out of the room?"

Paul shook his head. "I have to touch someone for that. Then talk to them. It used to be easier but . . ." His face looked pained.

"But what?" Foster prodded. Hyams could see her eyes sparkling in the band of light that fell across her face. Her skin was ashen and she was having trouble catching her breath, but the eyes told the true story. This was the woman he remembered from the weeks before—questioning, explaining, understanding, alive.

Paul rubbed at the side of his head. "Something to do with the needles," he said uncertainly. "Half the time it's confusing. The other half, it's still confusing but we don't seem to care." He shrugged. "Just getting harder to do things the past few days."

"Jamie's getting needles at the hospital," Foster said. "Tranquilizers, Jim said. Is that what it feels like? You need tranquilizers?"

"Get off it, I don't touch that shit," Paul sneered; the old Paul—*El Niño*. Then his eyes cleared. He stared at Foster as if trying to place her in his memory. "Do you know why we're like this?" he asked like a small child questioning his mother.

Foster turned to Panati, back to Paul. "I think so," she said.

"Complicated?" Paul asked.

Foster nodded her head.

"Thought so." Paul glanced back at the door. "We'll have to get you out of here so you can tell us." He looked at Panati and Hyams to make sure they were paying attention. "And we'll have to do it fast. Before tomorrow night."

Panati's eyes widened. "Do you know what's going to happen by tomorrow night?"

"Yes," Paul said.

"The President?" Panati continued. "Bobby Jay? First strike?"

Paul narrowed his eyes. "I don't know about that stuff." he said. "All I know is that we all have to be together when the dream friend comes. And the dream friend's coming tomorrow."

EIGHT

Death, death, and more death was all that Jason Coyle could think of. He was thirteen years old and he wanted to taste Bobby Jay's blood and flesh. He wanted to sink his teeth into Hank, the reverend's new helper who threw buckets of cold water at them to rinse off their filth, scraped their skin with the hard straws he shoved under their gags so they could eat without being untied, and ripped their flesh where he roughly injected the drugs that made consciousness indistinguishable from dreams. Jason trembled as he imagined his fingers pressing into Bobby Jay's eye sockets, nails peeling back his eyelids, knees and elbows and hands and fists all hitting and hitting until there was only death, death, and more death.

The digital clock below the control room window read: seven

thirty-one, Friday, August twenty-eighth. Jason had been tied to the table in the old studio for six weeks but was no longer aware of time. What was left of him was elemental, unchecked, and savage.

The door to the studio clicked and opened. Deep within his bound, constricted chest, Jason growled. Then he heard something he hadn't heard in all those six weeks: a young woman's voice. He strained to look at her. He recognized her from the TV shows that played on the wall of monitors every day. He growled again.

"Dear sweet Jesus," Louella Jay gasped. She held her hands to her face. Jason could hear choking sounds. He could smell vomit. He welcomed it as a mask for the other, worse smells of the studio.

Louella Jay began babbling. Jason could see her stumble forward into the room, hair flying around her head as she ran her wild eyes over the tables. Some of the boys began rocking back and forth, moaning softly beneath their gags. Jason recognized one of them as J.D., but he really wasn't sure who J.D. was anymore.

Louella walked stiffly to the table closest to the door. It was covered by a dirty white equipment tarpaulin. Something distorted and twisted seemed to be lying beneath it. Her trembling hands reached out to the tarp. Jason could hear her sobbing cries.

She pulled. The tarp fluttered away like a dying manta. The table beneath was a blackened mass of thick, sticky blood. But the bonds were closed over empty air.

Jason blinked and strained to see more clearly. That had been the table of the boy Bobby Jay had beaten with the pipe. No one else had been near it since Jay and the old woman had covered it with the tarp. Louella pushed a fist into her mouth as she stared at the gelatinous sludge that slick-coated the table. Jason saw her glance down to the floor, to the tarp.

Her shriek of terror filled the room, defeating the acoustical tiles, making Jason's ears ring.

All of the boys were brought back from their own nightmare visions with that sound. Even the old man with the white hair was straining against his bonds. The boys began to rock and moan. Louder and louder. Faster and faster. Jason could recognize the madness growing in Louella's eyes. He welcomed it.

Fed on it. Suffer, his mind screamed. Suffer, suffer, death, death, and more death.

The room was an ocean of rhythmic moans. Table legs scraped upon the floor. Louella's hair spiraled out like seaweed as she watched the tables move. Up and down. In time with the moans. In time with the madness. Only the old man's table was still. Only the old man's voice was silent. She stared at him. Then at the table beside him. The only other table to be covered by a dirty white tarpaulin.

Even as she walked through the bucking, thudding tables, she screamed at them to stop. "*Randolph*!" she shrieked. "*Raaaanndolph!*" But there was no answer.

Jason's blood roared past his ears. He yelled into his gag until his lungs felt as if they were ripping with the strain. He willed his table to move like the other boys', but it remained fixed in one spot, jiggling only when he rocked it physically. Jason had come to realize he was not like the others, but his fear and hatred were just the same.

At the second covered table, Louella didn't hesitate. She fell against it, onto it, and tore off the tarp at the same time. The tables bounced gratingly. Fingernails on chalkboards. Cats being skinned. Her mouth opened but her mindless sounds were lost and unheard in the cacophony of rage and fury.

Randolph lay on the table before her. Skin blue and moist and stretched taut over his swelling, days-old body. Mouth gaping open as if sharing his lover's scream, black lips pulled back in hideous grimace from blood-coated teeth. The room was an inferno of noise, a whirlpool of furniture. She focused on the one unchanging spot. The old man's table.

Her fingers flew at the buckles of his gag. "Help me!" she screamed to him. "Help me!" she whispered. "Help me!" she cried and she moaned. A table jumped three feet through the air and crashed into her legs. She collapsed beside the old man's table as if a shark had pulled her beneath the waves.

"*Stop it!*" Jason heard the old man shout. But he knew it was too late.

Then the woman was up again, tearing at the old man's arm straps, chest straps. She dodged another table. The man sat up. Together they freed his legs.

The old man stood unsteadily beside his table. Another table leapt up and at him. He struck out both hands and toppled it. "I said *stop it*!" he screamed. "I'll help you if you just stop it!"

Too late, Jason chanted in his mind, too late too late too late.

A gun blast tore into the ceiling. The old man folded his arms around the woman and pulled her to the floor behind the sideways table.

Another gun blast took out a ceiling-mounted television monitor in a gout of sparks and shattered glass. The jumping tables skidded to the floor, concentration broken.

"*I abjure thee, demons! Get thee behind me-e-e*!" echoed the voice of Bobby Jay. "Thou *shalt not* escape my vengeance!" He fired his Remington at the rotting body of Randolph. Its guts exploded in a liquid mass of yellow, red, and blue. Jason felt it splatter over his face, felt liquid creep down his face, soaking under his gag.

"Thus saith *the Lord*," spake Bobby Jay. The room was still.

Bobby Jay stepped into the studio. He closed the door behind him and reloaded the shotgun. He called for his wife.

"I know you're in here, swee'pea," he said lightly. "Lord Jesus told me." He stepped forward beside the blood-coated table of the boy he had beaten to death and looked at the ground. Jason couldn't see what had attracted his eyes.

"My oh my," the reverend said, smiling. "Things certainly do move right along now, don't they?" He looked up again, straight into Jason's eyes. "Do you know where my swee'pea is?" he asked.

Jason held his stare, didn't give him anything. Bobby Jay swung the shotgun up, aimed it at the boy. "Do you, you little turd?"

Go ahead and shoot, Jason's eyes said.

Bobby Jay swung the barrel around to another boy. "Or you?" he snarled. Then to another and another.

There was a sound by Randolph's table. Bobby Jay's head perked up like a hound dog's.

"Bible says a wife's place is by her husband's side, swee'pea. Won'tcha do the *Christian* thing and stand up? Stand up, I say, and be counted?"

The sound again: a sob.

Bobby Jay moved between the tables, closer to the ruined

corpse of his producer. "Come let Lord Jesus dry those tears, little girl," he pleaded.

Louella Jay stood up.

Bobby Jay spun. His face twisted in a hellish smile. His Remington was leveled. "That's a good girl," he said as if he were talking to a four-year-old. "That's a good, good girl."

The old man leapt on him from behind a table. Bobby Jay grunted and tried to pull back. The old man kept both hands on the barrel of the shotgun, twisting it up with incredible strength so that Bobby Jay couldn't pull away.

But Bobby Jay didn't try to pull away. He pulled the shotgun straight down. The old man lost his grip. The barrel slipped through his fingers. They closed over the gaping barrel of the gun. Bobby Jay turned his head and pulled the trigger.

Jason saw the spray of blood hit the double-height ceiling as the old man's fingers disintegrated in fire. White hair streaked with red, he fell back with his face distorted by a silent scream of outrage.

Bobby Jay's mouth hung open. He drooled. One side of his face was burned crimson from its proximity to the shotgun blast. He shook his head as if to clear his ears. Jason wanted him to die.

But Bobby Jay had no such intention. "What's it going to be, swee'pea?" he asked, breathing hard. "You just about ready now to see the light?" He loaded two more shells and pumped the gun.

"I'm coming to you," Louella said. Head down, hands trailing, she walked over to her husband.

He chucked her playfully under her chin. "That's my little swee'pea," he said. Then he reached around to his back pocket and pulled out a set of nickel-plated handcuffs. "I think your friend down there still has enough of a hand on his right arm for these to be useful, now wouldn't you say?"

Louella looked down at the floor. Jason could hear the old man moaning. Louella nodded.

"*Stand up* when you're in the presence of *my wife*!" Bobby Jay spat at the old man.

Jason stared in unblinking attention as he watched Louella Jay help the old man to his feet. The left arm ended in a bloody flipper of shredded flesh. The right hand resembled a glistening red mitt with one perfect pink thumb still attached. Louella clicked one bracelet of the handcuffs over the old man's right wrist.

Bobby Jay led them to the studio wall by the door near the video control console. Five metal pipes ran along it, floor to ceiling. He had Louella attach the other bracelet to the middle pipe. The old man was as white as the tarpaulins. Jason didn't think he'd last much longer.

"Too bad about those hands, isn't that so, Louella?" Bobby Jay asked. Louella didn't respond. "Did they used to feel good when he rubbed them all over you?" She took her head, staring at the floor.

Bobby Jay used the barrel of the Remington to lift her face up and meet his gaze. "Now don't you go lying to me, swee'pea. I know you been boffing him. I know you been boffing them all!" He tore the barrel away from under her chin in a sweeping gesture that encompassed all the boys on the tables. Perhaps all the people in the world. "Haven't you?"

Louella Jay looked long into her husband's eyes and then nodded. It was true. Whatever he was saying was gospel.

"I knew it," the reverend said, pleased with his clarity of vision. "I could tell. It wasn't the Lord's work anymore with you, was it? Not like me. Not like my selfless giving of myself to bring the sinners to Lord Jesus. You did it because you are a harlot, didn't you, swee'pea? I say, didn't you, swee'pea?"

"Yes."

"You did it because you are a whore, didn't you, swee'pea?"

"Yes."

"And you're a slut, too, isn't that right now?"

"Yes, Bobby Jay." Louella's voice was a sobbing whisper.

Bobby Jay's voice was a chilling roar. "Don't you dare say, 'Yes, Bobby Jay,' to me, slut!" He brought the barrel back to her chin. "You say, 'Yes, Lord Jesus.' Let me hear you say that. Say, 'Yes Lord *Jee-sus*!' "

Louella's eyes were the eyes of a trapped animal. Jason understood those eyes.

"Y-yes," she said, "L-lord Jesus."

"Amen, swee'pea. Ayy-men." The reverend patted her on the head and then wrapped an arm around her shoulders and pulled her tightly to him. He led her to the door.

"Now don't be all that gloom and doom," Bobby Jay joshed as he opened the door and helped her through. "Lord Jesus knows it's been a bad day and all, but you sure did come through a lot better than our godless Vice President, let me tell you. Ooo-eee, wait'll you see the news. And stop that there crying, too, swee'pea," he added as the door swung shut. "Don't you know that Jesus loves you?" The lock clicked. The studio was sealed.

In the new position the tables had taken, Jason could look down over his feet and see what was left of Randolph and, just past him, the old man cuffed to the wall pipes. The old man was looking straight at him. He had eyes like Louella's.

The old man looked back at his ruined hand, pulled on the cuffs, straining to slip free. The bracelet was too small to slide over the stump of his palm and his remaining thumb. He looked back at Jason, looked with eyes that Jason could understand. He turned back to his hand. Brought his mouth to it. Began to chew.

Jason watched it all. He tried to pretend it was Bobby Jay.

NINE

Eyes closed, Hyams stood before the mirror in the Holiday Inn bathroom and gingerly touched the side of his face. He felt the light pressure of his fingers.

He opened his mouth. His tongue moved smoothly and easily across his firmly set teeth. He opened his eyes. His face was unmarked and unblemished. The faint heat signature of Juan's small hands was all that remained of the damage that had been done when Hyams had been slammed into the wall in the lecture room. He felt goose bumps ripple up his arms to his neck. The children were real. It was all real. He left the bathroom.

The room was a standard-issue Holiday Inn double. The heavy drapes were drawn to block out the parking lot lights and the two double beds were serving as couches. Everyone was staring at the television as Dan Rather explained the blurred images showing the attempt on the Vice President's life as she was arriving to speak to a Chicago Board of Trade banquet earlier that evening. Two assailants were involved. One was dead. One was wounded. Both had been tentatively identified as former FBI agents. Still no word on the Vice President's condition, though a rumor was circulating that her ambulance had not yet shown up at the hospital, three hours after the shooting. CBS News was unable to confirm or deny.

Panati smiled bravely at Hyams as the young man sat on a dresser at the side of the room. The priest turned back to watch the television. Hyams watched the children, faces lit eerily by the set's blue glow.

Ashraf, the fat boy with the Texan drawl, was the easiest to identify. Next was Juan, the healer from the barrio who could not cure his own blindness. Byron seemed to be the youngest, with darker skin and lighter hair than the others, easily picked out whenever he began to speak because of his California slang.

As for the other children of donor #72/SXM/4308, the only way Hyams could tell them apart was by what they wore. Paul—*El Niño*—wore a white shirt and ripped, faded blue jeans. Mañuel, who could speak but rarely did, wore filthy gray jogging pants and a sleeveless Superman T-shirt. Omar wore thick-lensed, taped-together black-framed glasses and Peter had a fancy calculator watch that beeped on the half hour and hour. Without those identifying possessions, though, they were identical. Some of Dr. Wyndham's minor genetic variations must have been minor in the extreme.

The two children who were unlike the rest sat against a headboard as far away as they could from the television. They seemed to be inseparable. Marguerite was quiet and nervous and acted as if she were as proud of her cousin, Juan, as she was of her Mickey Mouse sweatshirt. Johnny, the boy she sat with, hadn't said anything since the adults and the children had met. He kept his hands jammed into the pockets of a red nylon jacket three sizes too large for him. It had a hood, which he had tied tightly around his face, exposing only his eyes. But his eyes were covered with mirrored sunglasses and his nose was plastered with white sunscreen. He was also drenched in some cheap and overpowering aftershave lotion, though a disturbing scent of something else lay buried beneath it. Paul hadn't answered any of the adults' questions about Johnny except to say he was a good friend who could never be left behind.

Dan Rather was asking questions of a hastily assembled board of political analysts. There seemed to be some surprise at the President's decisions not to remain in Washington or go to Chicago. He was scheduled to appear at America's Glory tomorrow, and as far as he was concerned, it was business as usual.

"Think there's a connection between the shooting and Bobby Jay?" Hyams asked.

"Probably Bobby Jay *and* the President," Foster said. "How can you make an ambulance with the Vice President disappear?"

"Maybe they think it was an inside job and don't want to let anyone know where she really is," Panati suggested.

"Or maybe the ambulance crew was in on it, too, and the ambulance is at the bottom of Lake Michigan," Foster sighed. She reached out and turned down the sound. "They're just repeating themselves now."

With a squeaking of springs, Ashraf rolled off one of the double beds and began rooting through the pizza boxes on the floor. Hyams had never seen a two-hundred-dollar Coke and pizza order before, but the kids were starving and Foster had a Thorkon Industries American Express card. Even though dinner had been a feeding frenzy, Ashraf obviously had a few cubic inches in him somewhere that had been left unfilled. Whatever else the children were, they were still teenage boys.

"Like, you think the dudes that hit the old lady are the same ones who canned the rest of us down in the studio?" Byron asked.

"Can't be sure," Foster said. Hyams had noticed that her voice had developed an odd brittleness since Juan had laid hands upon his face and healed the damage done to it. "But it wouldn't surprise me."

"And this television guy thinks we're going to blow up the world or something so that's why he's spazzed out?" Peter asked. He was the most educated one, the only one who had known about clones when Foster began to explain to them why they were so alike.

Foster nodded.

"What a shithead," Paul said angrily. It had been building

in him for hours. ''Let's get him now.'' The boys began to stand up.

''No,'' Foster said sharply. ''We've already decided on our plan and Jim's already made the phone call to Jamie. We have to wait for the morning when there're more people. More confusion. If you go in now, you'll be the only ones moving around. They have to be expecting us to go back. They'll spot you miles away.''

''We go back the same way we got you out,'' Paul said. Hyams knew the boy's plan was wrong, but the way he was speaking, Hyams was tempted to give it a try. ''Through the college auditorium, into the change rooms, and out through the side parking lot and the service roads. We bypass the whole main entrance that way. We can do it.'' They were all on their feet as one.

''And what happens if they have guns?'' Foster threw at them. She was standing, too. ''They won't have to worry about hitting anyone else at night. You guys are pretty clever when it comes to healing up a couple of scrapes and scratches, but how're you going to handle a machine gun barrage like the Vice President got? How are you going to all be together for your 'dream friend' if you're all *dead*?'' She was staring them down, Hyams thought. She was actually speaking against *El Niño* and winning. ''We go in the morning, just as we decided.'' She sat down decisively. After a few seconds, Paul sat, too. The rest followed.

The television showed the out-of-focus images of the carnage in the lobby of the Belmont Hotel. A small white circle indicated the blur that was the Vice President as she was engulfed by secret service agents. Other images showed a bloodstained stretcher being rushed into an ambulance that had driven over the hotel's red carpet and twisted the revolving door leading to the main lobby. The footage ran by again and again, in silence.

The adults and the children had been talking for hours—ever since Paul had led them from the Bible college and back to his companions—asking questions and answering them. Foster described clones. She told them about the Shroud of Turin. Some of the children remembered being told they were adopted in a special way. All of them carried the message of the dream friend. None of them knew who, or what, the dream friend was.

Through a series of questions that had made the adults feel as if they were talking in a barely understood foreign language, they had managed to come to a limited understanding of how the boys interacted with each other nonverbally. Foster grudgingly settled on the term *telepathy*, even though it wasn't shared equally among them all.

Juan and Paul and Byron were able to hold entire conversations without saying a word, but only Byron could communicate with Omar. Likewise, their powers seemed to be linked. Juan had a talent for healing. That talent had been passed along to Paul after communication had begun. Paul had passed into the network his talent of command. The ability to levitate seemed to have come from one of the boys held captive by Bobby Jay, and Mañuel seemed to have no special talent at all.

If all these abilities were simply single aspects of what had once existed in one person, Foster had said, it was no wonder that the man in the shroud had caused such a stir. Panati had taken exception to her conclusion but held back from a full-scale religious debate.

Finally, the conversation had ended in ongoing circles. No matter how many questions they asked, the adults couldn't share the experiences that the boys took for granted. There was only so much that angry and frightened teenage minds could absorb in one sitting. The pizza had been a truce. The silence in the hotel room was a respite.

Paul broke it with one last question. "Why does the television guy—Bobby Jay—think we're going to blow up the world, anyway?"

Foster held out her hand to Panati. "Take it away, Francis."

The priest reached for a green-striped can of Coke III and sipped at it, gathering his thoughts. "Prophecy is one of the roots of the Christian religion," he began, choosing his words carefully for his audience. "All through the Old Testament, prophecies tell of the coming of the Messiah. Christians believe the New Testament tells the story of how those first prophecies were fulfilled—with the coming of Jesus as the son of God and savior of all people."

"And we're like Jesus, right?" Peter asked. Hyams thought he was the one who was most intrigued by his genetic heritage. The rest really hadn't understood.

"*Physically*, yes," Panati reluctantly agreed. "Anyway, the New Testament also contains prophecies about the return of Jesus. That is, what will be happening just before he comes back. How he will come back. And what will happen after he comes back."

"Do any of the prophecies mention people like us?" Peter asked. All the children listened carefully to the priest's answer.

"No. Some scholars tend to view the prophecies as vague and unspecific; other scholars say they are clearly exact. But in any event, people like you are not mentioned."

Hyams interrupted. "But Bobby Jay thinks the children are fulfilling the role of the Antichrist, Father. Remember what Scott Carey said."

Panati nodded. "The prophecies say that just before the time of Christ's return, a great new leader will emerge. This leader will win the hearts of most of the people of the world until he sets himself up as a god before them. The leader is called the Antichrist because he will lead people away from the real Christ. He is supposed to have great powers. Be capable of performing miracles. Because of your origin, because of your abilities, I think that's why Bobby Jay has developed the idea that you, together, are that Antichrist."

Peter's face was drawn in concentration. "So how would we know" he asked, "if we were this Anti-guy anyway?"

"That's easy," Panati smiled. "If you go by the current way the prophecies are interpreted by fundamentalist Christians today, then the Antichrist will easily be identifiable by any number of signs. First, he will be a prince of the Roman Empire."

"There is no more Roman Empire," Peter said.

"Some fundamentalists interpret the Roman Empire as being today's European Economic Community," Panati explained. "Also, he will suffer a fatal head wound and then miraculously be restored. It's after that that he will become a god to most people and, while offering peace, will lead the world into the battle of Armageddon. That's a plain in Israel where the final battle is to be fought. Then, just before it seems certain that the world will end, that's when Jesus will appear in the skies and bring a thousand-year peace to the world." Panati looked around at the silent children. "The fundamentalists also believe that true Christians, born again in Jesus, will not experience this battle.

Indeed, they won't even be around for the Tribulation—that's the seven years of war and famine and pestilence that will lead up to Armageddon. Their belief is that just before the Tribulation begins, there will be the Rapture. That's when every true Christian, without dying, will vanish from the face of the Earth in one instant, rising up to meet with Jesus in the sky." Panati was speaking calmly and seriously. Hyams couldn't tell how much of what he was describing the priest believed himself.

"Does anyone know when this is supposed to all happen?" Peter asked.

Panati's eyebrows went up and down. "That's where the interesting part begins. The prophecies describe the signs to watch for just prior to the second coming. Wars and rumors of war. Earthquakes. Famine. All the things that seem to have gone on all through history anyway. Except the difference will be that there will be more of them at one time, worse than ever before. But the question is: who's to say when things will reach their worst? Almost every generation has seen itself as the last generation, with its own Antichrist, like Napoleon, or Hitler, or even Henry Kissinger, for God's sake. What gives the fundamentalists a boost in this century is that a major sign of the impending second coming is the rebirth of Israel. And that happened in 1948."

"But *when* is Jesus supposed to come back?" Peter asked. The boy sounded nervous.

"According to recent popular books and interpretations, within a biblical generation of the date Israel was reborn."

"How long is a biblical generation?" Hyams asked. This was beginning to sound spooky.

"Forty years," Panati said. "That puts Armageddon about four years ago in nineteen eighty-eight. No doubt certain writers are going back over their notes to see where they went wrong and start reinterpreting things all over again." He sat back in his chair. "As I said, every generation has had the vanity to think it was the last one."

"That's what you say the fundamentalists believe. How about the Catholics? How about you?" Hyams badgered.

Panati's voice was rich with authority and indignation. "I believe it is wasteful and presumptious—and probably even sinful—to piously try to second-guess God. As far as I'm concerned—and since Catholicism is a healthy hotbed of diverging opinions, I can only *hope* to speak for others in my religion—I believe implicitly in what Jesus himself said about his second coming when he talked with his disciples in Matthew twenty-four. 'No man shall know the hour of my return.' Catholics believe in getting on with life and not just sitting around smugly waiting for the world to end."

Foster grinned at Panati. "Francis, you're angry."

"Gives me something to confess at mass," the priest muttered. Hyams could see Panati's cheeks were flushed and that he was probably embarrassed for having become so carried away.

"Let's get this straight," Peter said. "*Before* Armageddon, we need a leader of the European Economic Community to come back to life after being wounded in the head? We need all the Christians to suddenly vanish? We need seven years of tribulations and *then* a battle at an *actual* place in Israel?"

"As well as the rebuilding of the Temple in Jerusalem and a fair number of other things," Panati agreed. "But, more or less, you have the right idea."

"But none of that stuff's happened yet," Peter said. "Why does Bobby Jay think that tomorrow's the big day?"

"Maybe the idea's to jump the gun," Foster suggested. "That could be what Carey meant by striking first. Take the devil by surprise before the Antichrist has grown up. Doesn't really matter why he believes what he does. All that matters is that he can do something about it and we have to be able to stop him."

"Well, I think he's a fucking asshole," Paul grumbled.

Panati slapped the arm of his chair. "By Jesus, so do I!" In his favor, he managed to look contrite for the rest of the evening.

TEN

The sun glared from the metallic finish of the airplane door as the ramp was rolled up to it. The familiar seal was swallowed by the harsh brilliance as the door swung open. "Ladies and gentlemen," the announcer's voice intoned, "the President of the United States."

Click. "Run Leonardo! Run!" Splinter cried. But the Shredder's minions had blocked the sewer. There could be no escape this time.

Click. "Form flaming sword!"

Click. "You knew the job was dangerous when you took it, Fred."

"Jamie! Leave the remote control alone." Dr. Hadrian stood beside Jamie's bed and held out his hand. Jamie looked away from the ceiling-mounted television and passed over the slim black remote-control transmitter.

"No cartoons today, young man," Dr. Hadrian said. "Remember our promise to Jim."

"Yes, doctor," Jamie recited in a small voice. "Watch the news channel all day. Keep track of every place they show the President." Jim was a nice guy and everything, Jamie thought, but news was a pretty dumb thing to watch on a Saturday morning. Still, Dr. Hadrian insisted and they were going to let him keep the TV after the weekend so it probably wasn't such a bad deal after all.

"Do you know why I have to watch it?" Jamie asked.

"It's an experiment," Dr. Hadrian said. "Like when you looked at the road maps that showed how to get to that America's Glory place a few days ago."

Jamie nodded. That had been strange, too. But as long as the doctor had the needle, Jamie didn't feel like arguing.

"Can I have my needle now?" he asked. He could feel his skin beginning to itch. That was always a sign that the last needle was wearing off.

But Hadrian shook his head. "That's part of the experiment, too, Jamie. Just for today, Jim asked us, no needles. You can have anything else you want, though," he added quickly.

"Ice cream?" Jamie asked.

"All you want," Hadrian offered.

"Beer?"

"*Almost* anything else you want," the doctor said, smiling. He pointed the remote control at the television set and the screen rushed through the channels until CNN was back. A motorcade of black limousines was pulling away from Air Force One. The scene flipped back to the newsroom.

"There you have it," Ross Whittaker said, "the President's first speech since his press conference about last night's tragic shooting and not a single mention of it or the Vice President. It's almost as if he's saying: 'Hey, this just didn't happen.' Gail?"

The scene cut back to a windblown woman standing on the tarmac by the presidential jet. "I think we've just seen a man who refuses to let tragedy stand in his way, Ross. We saw it two years ago, after the tragic car crash that took the life of the First Lady, and I think we're seeing that fantastic resolve at work again today. As the President said this morning in Washington: 'It's business as usual until there's no more business left to do.' Back to you, Ross."

"Do I have to watch all this stuff, too?" Jamie complained.

"As a favor for Jim, yes," Dr. Hadrian said. "And for J.D. and all the rest, too. You want them to get away from the television guy, don't you?"

"Yes," Jamie sighed. "But I didn't think it was going to be this much work."

"I'll get you some ice cream," the doctor said and left the room, taking the remote control with him.

Jamie settled back against his pillows and watched some dumb shot from up high showing the President's cars driving along the highway. Oh well, he decided, at least they said I could have the TV. He wondered if the dream friend would let him take it with them.

ELEVEN

Marguerite could hear the camper's motor straining to produce the cooling air as they waited in the main parking lot of America's Glory, but very little of it reached to the back where she and

Johnny sat. She liked the camper more than the van they had had to leave behind in Texas. There was more room in the camper, even a refrigerator and a bathroom. It was something made to be driven on the road—almost as long as some of the transport trucks they passed—yet it was better than the house Esperanza had forced her and Juan to live in. Marguerite didn't know which she understood least: Esperanza or America.

There was a table that folded out of the wall by the refrigerator in the middle of the camper. The nice woman, Susan, and the nice man, Jim, had been having a conversation with Juan there, and Marguerite was half listening as she cradled poor Johnny. She supposed the other man who said he was a priest was nice, too, but she had never known a priest who dressed in such a silly way.

"So Paul just asks people to hand over their car or their camper or whatever and the people do?" Jim asked Juan.

"As long as he can touch the person he's talking to, my brother Paul can be convincing," Juan said. He stared ahead with white, unseeing eyes, but Marguerite could tell he was enjoying talking to adults who treated him with respect.

"And no one decides to call the police a couple of hours later and say that their car has been stolen?"

"I don't think so," Juan said. "But Paul keeps changing vans and campers every other day, just in case."

Jim shook his head. "And he gets you food and gas the same way." He sighed. "Let's hope he never gets into politics." Then Marguerite thought the nice man's face took on a strange look and he excused himself to go up to the front of the camper where everyone else waited for a message from someone called Jamie so they could compare it with what they saw on the tiny television plugged into the camper's dashboard.

At the table, Susan moved closer to Juan, bent her head down, and began to whisper. Marguerite couldn't hear what she was saying, but she could see Juan take on his worried expression. He whispered back to the woman. Their conversation went on for two minutes. Then Marguerite was shocked to see her cousin's hand reach out to Susan's stomach, rub against it, and move down, below the belt of her slacks.

Marguerite felt her cheeks burn. What had that woman said to her cousin? Why was she making him do something so filthy and sinful? And then she saw Juan's eyes flicker with the light and she understood. The woman must be ill. She had seen what Juan had done for Jim's injuries the night before, and now she wanted Juan to heal her, too.

Marguerite watched the process carefully, wondering if she should leave the motionless, sitting body of Johnny and go to help. She could see the sweat shine on Susan's face. She could hear the soft whisper of prayers from her cousin's throat. The Savior's work was being done. Marguerite silently joined the prayers. And then Juan moaned in a chilling way she had heard fewer than a dozen times before. He removed his hand.

Susan barely kept herself from slumping across the table. Juan shook his head, whispered to her again. The woman's face was a mask of lost hope and despair.

"I'm sorry," Marguerite heard her cousin say, disappointment and strain forcing the volume of his voice to rise. "Sometimes the time is too late. It has progressed too far. I cannot change it."

Susan leaned closer to Juan. Her words were indistinct but her pleading tone was clear.

Juan shook his head again, pointed a finger. "You would be like *him*," he said. Susan's words were silenced. The blind child was pointing directly at Johnny Matches.

TWELVE

"More ice cream?" Dr. Hadrian asked.

Jamie shook his head. "Needle," he said. His voice was hoarse. He felt as if ants were crawling under his skin. "Please. Needle."

The doctor stood beside Jamie's bed. He took the boy's hand. "Jamie, hold on. Just for a few more hours. I know you can do it. For Jim and Paul and all the others."

"Noooo!" Jamie moaned. He tried to throw himself from the bed. The shoulder restraints held.

Hadrian pressed down on the boy's quaking shoulders. "You can't give up, Jamie. They need you to tell them where the President is. They need you to tell them how close they are to him. Do you understand? Where's the President, Jamie? Tell me. Tell them!"

"He's on TV," Jamie gasped. "Give me the needle."

"You can't say he's on TV, Jamie. Look at it. Tell me *where* you see him. Say it."

"America's Glory."

"*Where* in America's Glory?"

"The cathedral. He was talking in the cathedral. Now he's going to eat something in the cathedral. Please, Doctor . . ." Jamie began to cry. Hadrian twisted the boy's head so he looked at the set on the ceiling. "Keep watching, Jamie!"

"*You keep watching*!" the boy shrieked. He writhed against his bonds.

"I can't watch and let them know what I'm seeing! I'm not their brother, Jamie. You are. *You* can watch to see where the President is. *You* can tell how close he is to your brothers in the studio. You're the only one who can talk to them when they go into America's Glory. They won't be able to watch TV then. You have to do it."

Jamie flung his head back and forth. "*Nonononononono!*"

Hadrian slapped him across the face; and a second time, harder.

Jamie went rigid. His eyes shifted in some way so that only the whites remained. Brilliant whites. Glowing whites. His mouth opened. A storm gathered. Hadrian struck the boy again. And again. The light from his eyes flickered and died. The moment had passed.

"I'm sorry, Jamie. Dear God, I'm sorry. But you really are the only one who can do this. Really and truly. You're the only one who's linked in visually."

The pain of the doctor's blows had masked, for the moment, the craving for the needle. Jamie drew in a deep, quivering breath. "It's okay," he said shakily.

"Where's the President, Jamie? How close is he? Tell me so the others will know."

Jamie stared at the television set, trying to concentrate on the voices and images it presented. He described the President's location. He told Dr. Hadrian how close the President was to the old studio. And he knew that as he spoke those words, the message was going in other ways to other minds. But given the time that remained, Jamie didn't think it would do much good.

THIRTEEN

Hyams leaned over to look through the windshield at the late afternoon crowds still heading into America's Glory. He turned back to Paul.

"You all got that the same way?" he asked. "You're sure?"

"After the luncheon, he has a reception until six. Then the only thing they're saying is he's announced a press conference for eleven ten tonight," Paul replied.

"That much is on the radio," Hyams said. "I mean about his meeting with the other kids in the studio."

"Ten o'clock," Paul said. Then they all repeated it, a chorus of certainty.

"Finally," Hyams sighed with relief. That information had been a long time coming. With Jamie's help, the children had spent most of the day concentrating on the President's entourage, trying to pick up, through their telepathy, a sense of the President's plans for the day, the plans that were not announced to the public. He wondered what the boys might be capable of if they were released from the confusion of their shared craving for Jamie's needle.

Hyams checked his watch. "Finally. That gives us four and a half hours to get into position without having to try to avoid the press and the secret service on top of the Glory Guides." He turned to Panati in the seat beside Paul. "This is it, Father. Ready?"

The priest nodded.

"Okay," Hyams said loudly enough for his voice to carry down the camper to Marguerite and Foster. "This connection with Jamie and the President seems to be finally working. We know the President's schedule so we know where he will be and where he *won't* be. And that's where we're going to go. So, now, we do it just as we planned. The first group goes in to release the five kids that Bobby Jay still has trapped in the old studio. Remember, the boy who was kidnapped along with J.D. might be down there, too. Those kids will be taken out to the side parking lot where Ashraf will be waiting with the camper, ready to run interference, if necessary, with the second group. When you're all out safely, Father Panati will phone in the bomb threat to the networks and the White House so we can force an evacuation. Without the meeting with the kids and Bobby Jay, the President, we hope, won't have an excuse to start a holy war, especially if his bodyguards are rushing him away to someplace safe.

"In the meantime, the police crews should start looking for the bombs Panati will say are hidden in the basement of the Bible college. According to what you guys have been telling us about what's been going on down there, the police should turn up some interesting evidence. Then Susan, Father Panati, and I will find a news crew and start telling the whole story. Jamie's doctor will do the same thing in Maryland. Once it's out in the open, all we can do is hope that other parts of the government will be able to keep the President from acting."

"Why not call in the bomb threat, now?" Peter asked.

"Like I said, I don't want any of you guys, or your brothers, getting involved with the police. And I sure don't want Bobby Jay's Glory Guides deciding to kill the kids when they see the police coming in and ruining their plans. No calls until the kids are out of the basement, okay?"

"When will we see you again?" Omar asked.

Hyams shrugged. "Depends on how the police and the media react to our story. Depends on what happens when your 'dream friend' arrives. Any ideas, guys?"

The children in the camper shook their heads. "We must all be together when the dream friend comes," Mañuel said. He was drooling onto his Superman T-shirt. It was one of the few things he ever said.

"That's it, then," Hyams concluded. "We'll be taking care of the most important thing—stopping the President—and you guys will all be on this camper waiting for whatever it is you're waiting for." He turned to Paul. "You say the dream friend will be here by midnight?"

"More or less," Paul agreed vaguely.

"Okay, then, we all get back together tomorrow morning and see where we go from there. The first thing we'll probably have to do is get an agent to handle all the movie offers, right?"

The children cheered. Most of them liked the way Hyams thought.

"First group is a go!" Hyams announced and Paul, Marguerite, Johnny, and Juan left the camper. "Wait five minutes and then take the camper over to the side lot," Hyams said. He walked down the length of the camper to sit beside Foster.

"You okay?" he asked. He couldn't remember her having said more than a few words all day and her color was paler, even after yesterday's excursion in the sun.

"Yep," she sighed. "All set to charge in like a Blue Blaze Irregular and save the world. How about you?"

"I don't think I have the slightest idea what I'm doing," he admitted. "Phoning in a bomb threat against the *President*?" He shivered theatrically.

Foster made an attempt at a smile. "It's not as if you don't have a good reason. You're doing it because of a telepathic message received by a homicidal child who's strapped in a psycho ward in Maryland."

Panati joined them. "Are you two going to be all right?"

"Fine, Father. How about you?" Hyams answered.

"I'm nervous," Panati stated frankly. "But not about what *we're* going to do . . ."

"The dream friend?" Foster asked.

"That's it," Panati said. "I don't know, but . . . well, I keep feeling as if I'm missing something obvious. An important connection."

"Such as?"

He rubbed his hand through his hair. "What it comes down to is I don't believe in a literal Bible. It's not part of the Catholic tradition." He shrugged. "Adam and Eve. The six days of creation. They're stories that carry the essence of God's work, but not the details. I can live with that. God's all the more clever for making evolution and the big bang, I say. But it's that lack of detail that bothers me."

"Detail about what?"

"About Jesus." Panati looked shocked as he realized what others might think he meant by that. "Not that I doubt Jesus, not that I doubt my faith at all. It's just that, well, the New Testament is the story of Jesus. The *true* story of Jesus. But what if it's not the *whole* story of Jesus? What's there is truth, but what if not *all* the truth is there? What if there's more to what Jesus is? Things that the Gospels didn't report. More things like the shroud." He shook his head. The ideas were threatening to overwhelm him.

"I don't know why that makes you worried about what we're going to do tonight," Hyams said. The badgering tone he usually directed at Panati was gone. He was being kind. He cared for the man.

"Not what *we're* doing tonight," Panati corrected. "What *they're* doing tonight."

"But they're just waiting for their dream friend," Foster said, spreading her hands.

"Exactly, and I want to know what that dream friend is. Or *who* that dream friend is." The priest sighed deeply. "If it's linked to them then it is somehow linked to Jesus? Or to God? Or even . . ." He sighed again. "I want to be there when the dream friend comes back."

"The kids aren't saying 'come back,' Father. This is the dream friend's first time here," Hyams said.

Panati narrowed his eyes at the young man. "Is it?" he asked.

FOURTEEN

The handcuffs dangled empty from the pipes by the studio door and Jason Coyle knew why.

There was darkness in the studio. The glowing red letters and numbers of the digital clock read out August twenty-ninth, six oh eight P.M. There was something waiting in the darkness that ducked to avoid the glowing light of the clock. Jason Coyle knew what it was. His heart and his hate sang out to it. He knew what it planned. He wanted to join.

There was a scraping noise again. The tables were shifting. Slowly floating, carefully sliding their way along the studio floor, arranging themselves in the pattern. Jason's table could not move so the others formed around him. Jason was glad he was being included. Jason wanted everyone to die. Tonight, in this place, in this darkness, he felt the power that could make that happen.

The studio door clicked. The studio door opened. The stage lights came on, bathing the children and their tables but leaving the audience seats in shadows. Jason growled into his gag. The person who had entered was Hank. He carried some blankets and a large bucket of the cold soup he fed them through the straws.

Jason shifted his eyes to the shadows. Something dark moved there. The boy growled again, almost like a purr.

Hank wasn't going to be able to feed them this night, he knew. Hank was going to die. And by the time the night was over, he would not be alone.

For the first time in six weeks, Jason felt happy.

FIFTEEN

Marguerite said a silent prayer in the dimly lit basement corridor, then reached out and took Johnny's hand. It was slippery. She could feel things like wet ropes slip and slide within her grip. For Juan, she thought. For Juan and his brothers I must do these things. "This way," she whispered to Johnny and gently urged him down the corridor with the pulling of her hand.

Three times so far they had been stopped by cruel-looking men. Three times Paul had reached out his hands and clouded their minds and told them to look elsewhere. But each time had been more difficult. Paul and Juan looked terrible. The flesh around their eyes was red, their skin pale. Constantly, they scratched at themselves. Marguerite felt if she didn't keep talking to them, reminding them where they were and what they were supposed to do, they would wander senselessly until the cruel men were able to sneak up from behind.

Paul stopped just where the corridor they were in opened onto another. At the intersection, a sign had the word STUDIO and an arrow pointing to the right.

"What is it?" Marguerite asked. Juan held up his hand to silence her. His other hand held Paul's. Somehow, Marguerite knew, That was part of the way they talked with each other.

She heard footsteps from the corridor. She shrank against the wall. A man came around the corner. He was out of Paul's reach. He held a gun.

The man was different from the first three. He wore a suit instead of just a short-sleeved shirt and jeans. A small American flag was pinned to his lapel and a thin white wire ran up the side of his neck from his collar to his ear. The man looked from Paul to Juan and back again. He shook his head. Paul held out his hand and stepped toward him.

The man backed out of reach, warning them, "If you move again, I'll shoot. Do you understand?" Paul stopped. "You," the man said to Marguerite and Johnny, "come forward."

Marguerite hesitated until she saw Juan's hand motioning to her. She stepped away from the wall with Johnny.

"No," her cousin said.

"Just Johnny," Paul added.

Marguerite stepped back against the wall as if someone else was in control of her legs. Johnny Matches kept walking.

"I said come forward," the man repeated to Marguerite.

Johnny walked faster, legs pumping stiffly, thudding against the floor.

"I'll shoot," the man said. "Halt!"

Johnny ran.

The man's gun fired with a silenced *thwick*. Johnny's red nylon jacket leapt from his back with the passage of the bullet but Johnny kept running. Another, louder *thwick*. Johnny hit the man and knocked him to the floor. A third shot. A fourth. Johnny flailed his hands against the man's face. The man hit back at Johnny, knocked his sunglasses flying, looked into his rotting eyes, and screamed.

Then Paul and Juan were on the man and the instant their

hands touched him, he was silent. They dragged him back into the other corridor. Marguerite was forced to look away when Paul stood before the thing that was Johnny and embraced him.

"This way," Paul said, and they followed the arrow to the right. As she passed by the intersection where the man had fallen, Marguerite saw small white things lying on the floor. She recognized them as bones, just the size of fingers.

Johnny was ahead of her and she was glad she didn't have to hold what was left of his hand again. She tried not to look at the black holes in his jacket.

Forty feet away, an open door threw light into the darkened corridor. Beside the doorway, a large red light fixture had an angled sign: "Do not enter when light is on." The light was off. They had arrived at the old studio.

It was like nothing she had prepared herself for. She had heard the stories the boys told of what had been done to their brothers in the studio, but she had never imagined it the way it really was.

The boys were little more than flesh-covered skeletons, naked, bound and gagged like animals. Five of them resembled Juan and Paul and the others, but sick and beaten. Their foreheads were inflamed with hideous festering scars in the shapes of numbers, all the same numbers. Back in the hotel room, the funny priest had called it the mark of the beast.

The stench of the room was overpowering. Marguerite held her nose and tried not to gag. Paul stood before the tables and squeezed on Juan's hand. "Can you see it?" Paul asked in an incredulous whisper. "Can you *see* it?"

"Yes," Juan gasped. Marguerite heard overpowering revulsion in just that single word.

"We have to let them go," Paul said hurriedly. He stepped forward to the arrangements of tables that held the captives, five of which radiated like wheel spokes from a central sixth. There were some other tables scattered across the brightly lit stage area, but they were empty. Except for one that held something that Marguerite almost didn't recognize as a body. Paul took another step forward. He slipped.

Marguerite looked at the floor and saw what his feet had slid through. Blood. She traced it to its source. She screamed.

A body was sprawled on its back beneath one of the empty

tables. An armful of blankets was caught under it, an empty bucket lay beside it. Its head was a misshapen red pulp. A large happy-face name badge smiled from the body's jacket. She could read the name on it: HANK. Hank was going to heaven, the badge said.

Paul led Juan around the slick of blood, toward the boys on the tables. Each one was silent and motionless, but all of them watched with wide eyes. Animal eyes. Marguerite was scared.

Paul led Juan to the first boy: a brother. Juan placed his open palm on the mutilated forehead, held it there for less than a minute. When he took his hand away, the forehead was smooth and unbroken. Marguerite heard her cousin say: "No."

He placed his hand on the second boy's forehead. Again the mark of the beast was cleansed. Again Juan's trembling voice said: "No."

Paul had to guide Juan's hand to the third boy's forehead. Juan's hand shook as he healed his brother. "You cannot!" Juan called out.

For the fourth boy, it was the same. And the fifth. Juan was crying. The sixth boy was the one in the middle of the other five tables. Juan touched his hand to the sixth boy's forehead and then pulled back as if he had been burned.

"What's wrong, cousin?" Marguerite asked. She could feel terror move through her just by standing in this room. There was evil here, she felt.

"We must hurry," Juan said. "We must free them and take them away from here before they can carry out what they plan." Juan grabbed Paul's hand and held it on the sixth boy's forehead. Marguerite saw Paul's eyes flicker as the sixth boy's forehead was healed.

"Quickly, Marguerite," Paul said to her. "Unstrap them. If they stay here they will—"

"They will what?" a loud voice boomed from all around and above them.

Marguerite spun back to the door. Jim and Susan were there. So were Omar and Peter. But none of them returned her smile of relief and greeting. They walked into the studio in defeat. The man from television walked behind them. He had a shotgun.

Four more adults walked in behind Bobby Jay: his wife, Louella, an old woman with white hair whom Marguerite didn't recognize, and two more men in suits with small American flags and wires running from their shirts to their ears. Each of those men carried a thick-barreled gun. Behind her, Marguerite could hear the boys on the tables begin to moan.

"Go ahead there," Bobby Jay called out. "Answer the man. If they stay here, they're going to do what?"

Paul and Juan stood on either side of the boy in the middle of the tables. Neither spoke.

"I said, answer the man!" Bobby Jay shouted. "*Lord Jee-sus* commands thee!"

Paul muttered something.

"What was that, demon?" The reverend lifted the shotgun to his shoulder. "Answer now or the next words you speak will be to your lord and master in hell!"

Paul shouted, "They're going to kill you. They're going to kill everyone!"

Bobby Jay looked puzzled. "Of course they will," the reverend said softly. "That's their purpose as servants of Satan. You're not telling us anything new, you know." He pumped the shotgun.

Marguerite couldn't believe the television man. One moment he was ranting like Esperanza on her worst day, and the next moment he was as calm and as pleasant-sounding as she remembered her father to be. What was wrong with him?

"It's not their purpose!" Paul shouted angrily. "You've made them crazy down here. You should feel what they're thinking. The pain, the hate, the—"

"Wages of sin, I'm afraid," Bobby Jay remarked lightly. Then Marguerite saw the reverend had finally noticed that Paul and Juan were standing too close to the middle boy. "Get away from him and put your hands *up*!" Bobby Jay shrieked. "*Now*!"

Paul and Juan jumped away from the table, hands in the air. The boy in the middle table lay motionless with his eyes closed.

The men with suits were holding Jim and Susan and Omar and Peter against the wall with their guns. Bobby Jay shoved Marguerite over to join them. He stepped closer to the tables and rose up on the balls of his feet.

"Nice trick there," Bobby Jay laughed. Marguerite shivered at the sound of it. "Wiped their little slates clean, did you?" He was staring at the unmarked foreheads of the tied boys.

"Trying to keep the secret of your mission here on Earth, are you? Drag us down into sin and depravity until you're all grown up and can lead us to Armageddon?"

"You're fucking nuts, old man!" Paul said. "We just want to be left alone. We're just trying to get our brothers out of here before you suck the President into all this."

Bobby Jay's face twisted into a mask of rage. "Don't you *know* that the power of Lord Jesus can *see* through your lies? Don't you know that your knowledge of the President is *proof* that you are in league with Satan?" Spittle flew from the reverend's mouth.

"Don't you know you're too late?" a rich, familiar voice echoed from all the walls of the studio. Marguerite could hear Jim swear.

Bobby Jay laughed insanely. He pointed to the dark window of the control room. They all looked. They all saw a figure standing behind that window, microphone in hand.

"Say hello to the commander in chief," Bobby Jay cackled.

SIXTEEN

"What's that?" Jamie asked. He looked around his hospital room. There was no one else in it. He peered at the television set suspiciously. CNN was still on: some dumb show about gorillas fighting somewhere. Jamie had hoped it was going to be like *Planet of the Apes* but all he had seen so far was a bunch of people running around the jungle with guns. In any event, the sound was turned down so it hadn't been the TV he had heard.

Something was bothering him, though. It suddenly struck him. His skin didn't itch anymore. He didn't feel as bad as he did that afternoon. Even the way his stomach felt after the two tubs of Häagen-Dazs was better. "Oh yeah!" he said out loud. Now he knew.

Jamie got out of bed. The shoulder restraints pulled for

a second, but then fluttered uselessly from him. He walked over to the closet. He didn't even feel dizzy the way he had when they had let him use the bathroom earlier. He opened the small closet door. His jeans, a red shirt, some socks, underwear, and his favorite North Stars were there. "Should I get a jacket or anything?" he asked. He cocked his head as if listening for a reply. "Neat!" he said excitedly and started to get dressed.

The door to his room opened. Dr. Hadrian came in.

"What are you doing out of bed?" the doctor asked.

"Getting dressed," Jamie replied, tucking his shirt into his jeans.

Hadrian looked over at the shoulder restraints. "Who let you out?"

"No one," Jamie began. Then he corrected himself. "Dream friend," he admitted sheepishly.

Hadrian rapidly glanced all over the room, floor and ceiling. *"He was here?"*

"Nope," Jamie said, buttoning his cuffs.

"But he's coming?" Hadrian was sounding excited.

"Yep," Jamie said happily. "Almost here."

"And then what?" Hadrian had his notebook out and was scribbling in it.

Jamie sat down on the visitor's chair and pulled one foot up in front of him so he could reach his laces. He looked very thoughtful. "And then . . . and then . . ."

"Yes?" Hadrian encouraged, pen poised above his book.

Jamie looked up at him. In his notes, Hadrian recorded that he had never seen the boy look so at ease at any other time during the course of his treatment at Yorkwoods.

"And then," Jamie said calmly and assuredly, "I'm going home."

SEVENTEEN

Foster was numb. She had only one thought in her mind as she looked up to the familiar silhouette standing in the control room window: I voted for him. She didn't know whether to laugh or to cry.

At any moment she expected Bobby Jay to shoot either Paul or Juan and she knew there was nothing she could do to stop him. She and the others were being carefully watched by two men who could only be part of the President's secret service bodyguards. Foster knew that the two women behind Bobby Jay wouldn't be any help, either. One was Bobby Jay's wife and the other Foster recognized as Barbara-Jane Fuller. If anyone could be counted on to support a crazed fundamentalist's call for a holy nuclear war, Foster shuddered, a self-proclaimed psychic and astrologer would be just the type. There was no hope left, she decided. None at all.

Then Paul yelled "*Now Johnny!*" and he and Juan dove beneath the tables. Bobby Jay's shotgun blasted the space where Paul had stood and the leg of the boy tied up behind him was sprinkled with a pattern of red dots. Foster could see the child writhe in pain.

The two secret service agents spun with the sound of the shotgun. Foster gaped when she saw what was left of Johnny's face as he rushed the agent closer to him. The agent slashed his gun across Johnny's head, forcing the boy's neck to bend ninety degrees to his shoulder with a loud crack. Foster expected the boy to drop. Instead, he struck at the agent with savage, swinging arms.

The second agent held his weapon ready, waiting for his opening as the first agent fell back under Johnny's relentless attack.

The opening came and three shots slammed into Johnny. The boy twisted and came at the second agent, the loosened hood falling away from his head: a lopsided, grinning skull, barely held together by black and slimy strips of decomposing skin. The second agent wrapped his arms over his head, screaming. And then Johnny was on him, forcing him to the floor, digging splintered finger bones into the man's chest, into the man's heart.

Bobby Jay's shotgun blasted a second time. Johnny collapsed in his final death, a shredded mass of disintegrated flesh. The agent beneath him had been directly in the path of the reverend's shot. His struggles were also at an end.

"Did you *see* that, Mr. President?" Bobby Jay sputtered, his eyes burning as if he already saw the flames of hell dance around him. "Do you need more proof as to *where* these children come from? *Who* they serve?"

Foster heard the click of a PA system mike.

"No," the President said. "No more proof. There can be only one answer for what you have shown me tonight. America thanks you, Bobby Jay. God bless you. It is time for it to end."

Foster's mouth was dry. How could he think that way? She wanted to shriek at him. Barbara-Jane Fuller did it for her.

"*Mr. President, wait!*" she shouted to the figure behind the glass. She waved frantically.

"Yes, Barbara-Jane," the professionally measured voice replied through the overhead speakers.

"It's not time yet, sir," she explained. "In my vision, I mean. The time I saw the old world end was ten fifty-two. It's only ten forty-one now." She pointed to the digital production clock beneath the control room window.

The President's reassuring voice sounded like the grandfather everyone wished to remember. "Well now, Barbara-Jane, I don't think that's anything to worry about. I have to get on the phone here to call my aide with the activation codes. That should take a few minutes more. Ten fifty-two it shall be, if that's the way the good Lord showed it to you."

Barbara-Jane mouthed the words "thank you" to the President, gave him a little wave, and then turned to Bobby Jay while trying to avoid looking at what still twitched on the floor where Johnny and the agent had fought. "Now, if only my husband were here," she said to the reverend. But Bobby Jay was too busy trying to peer under the tables to see where Paul and Juan had gone to pay any attention to the woman.

"I *am* here," a hoarse voice rasped from the darkness of the studio audience seats.

"Dean?" Barbara-Jane said questioningly, shielding her eyes from the overhead stage spotlights as she tried to see where the voice had come from. Bobby Jay sprang up and stared at a place on the wall by the door. Foster followed his gaze and saw only an empty pair of handcuffs hanging from a pipe. She didn't know what they signified.

"Mr. President," the voice called out. "Can you hear me, sir?"

"Yes," the President replied over the speakers. "Who's speaking?"

"It's Dean Fuller, sir."

"Ah, yes, Mr. Fuller, I was told to expect you with us this evening."

Bobby Jay signaled frantically to the remaining agent to run into the seats and get Fuller. The agent gestured back, indicating he didn't want to take his gun off the people he held against the studio wall.

"I'll watch them," Bobby Jay snarled angrily and pointed his shotgun at Hyams. "Get Fuller! Get him!"

Reluctantly, the agent moved into the curved and shadowed expanse of seats.

"Mr. President," the voice of Fuller continued. "Are you here because you believe my wife has had a vision of the future? Do you believe you are fulfilling that vision?" His voice was ragged, like a man in pain.

"Well, sir, I believe that, yes, that is the case. Certainly what I've seen here tonight has not convinced me otherwise."

"Mr. President, are you familiar with Project Galahad?"

There was no response from the control room.

"I know Tom Jefferson was going to mention it to you. He said you had been briefed. Are you familiar with it?"

"Go ahead, Mr. Fuller."

Foster squinted into the audience section of the studio, trying to keep track of the agent's progress. If there was a disturbance now, perhaps Bobby Jay could be rushed. Perhaps the shotgun could be used against the President. There was another gun somewhere under the bodies of Johnny and the second agent, too. She saw that Hyams was also staring out over the seats.

Bobby Jay glanced nervously back and forth between the people against the wall and the boys tied to the tables.

"It began in Eisenhower's day, sir. Covert intelligence gathering. Lots of things we knew but couldn't act on without compromising our sources." Fuller was gasping like a man who was having trouble breathing. Foster was sure she saw shapes moving slowly among the seats.

"We knew so many things about the Soviet's intents. The plans for Cuba, for Sputnik even. We needed a way to get the word to other agencies, other countries, without revealing our sources, without risking interception by moles within our organizations. It was the fifties, sir. We thought they were everywhere." Fuller's voice was desperate. "I was working with Dulles then. Galahad was the way around our problem. Reveal our intelligence through a blind—an unconnected third party."

"No," Barbara-Jane said quietly.

"Galahad was implemented with the creation of a psychic, a predictor of the future. God forgive me, sir, but I volunteered my wife."

"That's not true!" Barbara-Jane shouted, stamping her foot against the floor.

"I would give her hypnotics. Drugs to induce a conscious dream state. I would read her our intelligence—"

"Lies! Lies!" The psychic shook her fists with each word. "I have been *chosen by God*!"

"You were chosen by my case officer!" Fuller shouted back. "Why would God concentrate on sending you visions about MIRVs and Soviet subs, and Soviet launches, and assassinations and technology and—"

"You are Satan!" Barbara-Jane's shriek hurt Foster's ears. Marguerite crossed herself over and over.

"*You* are a pawn!" Fuller bellowed. "Mr. President, she has *never* had a vision in her life. They were all chemically induced. They were all *Galahad*. You can't believe her now!"

"The world *will* end, Mr. President. I have seen it. I have seen the end!"

"Flashback drug reactions, Mr. President. You can't go through with this!"

"*Silence*," the President thundered into his microphone. No one made a sound except for Marguerite's whispered prayers and the moans of the tied-down boys. The speakers transmitted the sound of the President's breathing as he kept the circuit open. It was the regular and unstressed pattern of a man who was either in control or so far gone that control no longer had rational meaning. Foster closed her eyes, willing the President to believe what the man in the shadows had revealed.

"I have no recollection of the Galahad project," the President announced. The circuit clicked off.

"Mr. President, *no*!" Fuller shouted. Foster heard movement among the seats. She opened her eyes. Dimly, she could see two shapes collide.

A terrible howl of pain filled the studio. She could see the children cringe.

"The lights, Louella!" Bobby Jay snapped at his wife. "Turn on the rest of the goddam lights!"

Louella ran over to an electrical panel and palmed two rows of rocker switches. One after the other, five battens of spotlights illuminated the audience area. Bobby Jay's mouth dropped. The secret service agent lay dead over a row of seatbacks, his crushed head a ruin of blood. Dean Fuller hunched over the body. His arms ended in blood-soaked rags. A two-foot length of pipe was strapped to his right forearm and from it, blood dripped steadily.

Bobby Jay slammed the butt of the shotgun into his shoulder and fired. A seat near Fuller instantly burst into shreds. He jumped behind the agent's body.

Bobby Jay pumped and fired again. The body jerked wildly with the impact of the charge, but Fuller was gone.

Bobby Jay mumbled in incoherent rage. He pumped and fired, pumped and fired. Nothing happened. The gun was empty.

The reverend stared at the gun in shock. Then lowered it, broke it, and fumbled in his pockets for more shells. The chance had come. Hyams hit him waist level as hard as he could.

The two men skidded across the floor, Bobby Jay snapping and snarling like a mad dog, Hyams savagely elbowing and punching.

"In God's name, what's going on down there?" the President's voice boomed. His form could be seen pressed against the control room window, shading his eyes and straining to see what Bobby Jay had been shooting at among the seats.

Foster ran to help Hyams. He didn't need any. Bobby Jay's

face was swollen and bloody. His body was limp on the floor. Foster held out her hand and Hyams staggered to his feet. His breath came in trembling gasps.

"We're going to make it," he said to her.

"I think not," Barbara-Jane said. She held the second secret service agent's gun. It dripped with gore. Foster and Hyams raised their hands. "The time is now ten fifty, Mr. President," the astrologer said to the control room. "Two more minutes till all the world passes away."

"Thank you, Barbara-Jane," the President answered. "My aide has arrived and more secret service are on their way from the hotel. When the codes have been transmitted, I'll send the men down to help you."

Foster looked up to the control room window. She saw the President put down his microphone and turn away to an open case held by a second man. Her legs felt like ice water.

"Not like this," she said to Hyams.

Hyams looked at her, gesturing with his head and eyes. She saw what he was planning. She nodded. Not like this. They turned their heads back to Barbara-Jane. They began to lower their hands.

"I'm warning you," Barbara-Jane said threateningly, inexpertly brandishing the gun.

With a shocked expression, Hyams looked suddenly off to his left. Barbara-Jane had no training and the ruse worked. She turned automatically. They rushed her.

Barbara-Jane fired the gun once into the air when Hyams and Foster hit her. She smashed to the floor with a thick crunching sound coming from her hip. She brought the gun up against Hyams's head with a thud. He pulled a hand away from her to grab at the wound. She aimed the gun into his shoulder. Foster snapped her arm down over the barrel of the gun just as it went off. Hyams rolled away from the psychic, slapping at his smoking, powder-burned shirt. Barbara-Jane's eyes widened in surprise. The front of her dress darkened with blood.

She turned her head to look at the control booth and the clock beneath it. She blinked rapidly as she strained to read the time. It was ten fifty-two. Her eyes rolled up and stared into nothing. Her first and only real vision had come true. For Barbara-Jane, the world had ended.

Foster looked over to Bobby Jay and saw Paul and Juan crouching over him. Juan's eyes were glowing; his hands outstretched.

"No!" Foster shouted, pointing to the control room. "Up there! The President first! Stop him!"

Juan reached out and Paul took his hand. Then Paul turned to the control room window. He raised his other hand and pointed it at the figures behind the dark glass. A crackling, electrical sound grew. Foster could smell something that reminded her of machinery. Juan and Paul were rising from the floor, floating. Foster tried to see what Paul was holding in his hand: something blue, something with no shape but with—

The control room window dissolved in a roaring avalanche of sparkling glass. Paul and Juan crumpled to the floor like marionettes with severed strings, splattered with blood. Foster looked up to the control room. The President stood back in the shadows. Three agents leaned forward through the window frame, smoking Uzi machine guns in their hands.

"Thank you gentlemen," the President said over the speakers. "You arrived at a most appropriate time. For the rest of you down there, that will be quite enough. No one else is to move." Foster saw the President turn back to the aide with the open case.

Paul and Juan lay motionless on the floor. Bobby Jay was trying to sit up, rubbing at his face. Louella cowered against the wall, eyes clenched shut, tightly wrapped arms covering her ears.

There was blood everywhere. Bodies everywhere. This is how the world ends, Foster thought, not with a bang, with insanity.

And then the boy in the center table wailed like a siren. His arms and legs snapped out from the straps which Paul and Juan had loosened when they stood so close. His hands gripped the heads of the two boys on the tables by his arms. His feet touched the heads of the other two boys. The pattern was complete.

The crackling sound returned, louder, coarser, more threatening. The boy in the center began to shake, still keening. Foster held her ears. She saw the bonds and straps of the other boys burst open in small blasts of blue light. The radiance grew, enveloping them in a rippling field of crackling energy. They began to rise together in the air, connected as a giant, glowing X.

From above, the three agents sent down a torrent of machine-gun fire. Foster couldn't hear the guns over the roar and the crackle of what writhed around the children. The bullets had no effect. She felt her hair begin to rise from her scalp. Small static sparks jumped from her fingertips. The ball of energy was co-alescing.

Tendrils waved like pseudopods from the pulsating ball. One tendril snaked out and touched Foster's foot. She writhed with physical pain from the hate and fear she felt it bring. But she understood what it was. The boys were not creating it. They were focusing it. Gathering it from those people in whom it existed. Refining it, purifying it. Then giving it back. The tendril passed on, intertwining with others until they formed a braided, Weaving branch that grew in the direction of the control room.

The boys are going to *touch* him, Foster thought. They're going to let the President feel what is inside of him. They're going to make him understand. She knew it would kill him, but she had felt just enough from that small tendril that had touched her to feel glad.

The branch of energy was inches from the shattered window. It shot out like a neon squid to pluck the secret service agents and the aide from the control room. Foster could feel their agony as the hate penetrated them, crushed them, sucked them dry. Yes! She thought. Yes! Show them all! The digital clock exploded in a spray of plastic and circuitry. Spotlights flared and popped across the ceiling as the sound reached past the threshold of her hearing and her entire body began to quake with its fury. Foster screamed for the President's blood. She wanted to join the pattern, felt herself join the pattern. Blue flames leapt up the walls of the studio, converging on the control room and the cowering man within. This was it. And then it was over.

As simply as that.

The blue field of light collapsed faster than Foster's eyes could follow. The crackling was shut off like a circuit being disconnected. The floating boys suddenly dropped five feet through the air and back to their tables. The only sound was a horrified asthmatic wheezing which came from the huddled shape in the control room window. It was the President. Foster wondered how close those tendrils had come, what he had felt.

She heard footsteps behind her. She turned. Hyams was already staring, open-mouthed. Panati, Ashraf, and the other children from the camper were in the doorway. They were not alone.

Ashraf's chubby cheeks balled up in a joyous smile. "Dream friend's here, y'all," he said, and his voice was like a song.

EIGHTEEN

How disappointing, Foster thought. He's just a man. Well, three men, actually.

Two of them were quite ordinary. They could pass unnoticed in any crowd. Both were thin, fit, and wore light-colored jackets and slacks. Though their faces did not resemble each other, both had the same light brown hair and pale gray eyes. Perhaps there was a faint Oriental cast to their eyes, but nothing that Foster could point to and say was truly different.

But the third one *was* different: at least six-four and immensely, almost grotesquely fat. He wore a dark suit, unremarkable except for its size. His hair was black and hung in curls around his head, covering his forehead. The rest of his face was completely hidden by a thick black beard and moustache and large, out-of-place sunglasses—and the hair, beard, and moustache were so obviously fake that Foster knew they could only be a mask, hasty and imperfect, disguising any hint of whatever real features lay beneath. It reminded her of the way Paul and Margeurite had dressed poor Johnny, trying to keep the others from being frightened by what the boy really had looked like. But these children were anything but frightened now. They gathered around the fat man as if Santa Claus had just walked into the room.

Panati stood by the door with a strange expression on his face. Foster tried but couldn't get his attention. There was too much distraction from the babble of the children. At first she thought they were all talking amongst themselves, but as she listened, she realized she was hearing only one-half of a conversation from each of them, and each of the children seemed to be taking part in a different one simultaneously.

The two ordinary-looking men moved past the children, swiftly and lightly, reminding Foster of dancers. They panned their eyes across the studio like cameras but stopped their scan when they saw the bodies of Juan and Paul lying by the sitting and quietly babbling Bobby Jay. Instantly, the men were at the boys' sides. Foster thought she must have blinked because she didn't remember the men moving to get there.

As if answering an unheard command, three children—Mañuel, Omar, and Byron—peeled off from the rest and ran over to the men. Foster watched in fascination as they showed the children where to place their hands upon the bodies.

Loud laughter erupted around the fat man. Foster turned to see what had happened. Nothing as far as she could tell. The man was standing in the middle of the group, running his hands familiarly through their hair, as if he were greeting a favored child. Foster experienced an odd sensation and abruptly felt that she had been observing him for hours.

The children were reaching out to the fat man, clamoring for another touch, some more attention. This, whatever it was, was what they had been waiting for. They were no longer alone. Foster felt Hyams pull on her arm. She looked back to the other two men. Paul and Juan were standing unaided, holding their bullet-riddled, bloodstained shirts away from their chests and looking down at their unmarked skin with serious expressions.

Foster shook her head. Again she experienced an unsettling sense of dislocation. She felt as if she should be frightened or nervous, but a calm enveloped her. It reminded her of the feeling she had had as she stood by Suddam's bed in the convalescent home; a boy without a brain who somehow stood watch over a peaceful playroom where children always shared their toys and never fought over the television. This is coming from the fat man, Foster thought, and did not question the illogic of her sudden knowledge.

Again the dislocation. The voices and the sounds around her sounded thick and muffled. She suddenly felt she had to fight against something but didn't know what.

She saw Dean Fuller limp down an aisle, away from the seats.

He reached the stage area and paused with tears in his eyes by the body of Barbara-Jane. Then he looked up at the crouching form of the President in the frame of the control room window. Fuller's eyes were clear and unwavering. Head bowed, he walked stiffly over to the door marked Control Room, dripping pipe swinging with his arm. He pushed the door open with his elbows and Foster saw the start of a staircase beyond. The door swung shut. No one had tried to stop him.

Foster blinked again. She was standing to the side of the stage and couldn't remember moving there. The tables were neatly aligned now. The air was hot and humid. One of the children who stood on the fringe of the group around the fat man suddenly fell back to the floor. His leg glistened with blood. It was the boy Bobby Jay had shot when he had fired at Paul.

One of the men—the fat man's helpers, Foster knew without knowing how—knelt fluidly beside the boy and began to examine the pellet wounds.

"*No*!" a small voice rasped. Foster turned to see the boy who had been tied in the center table, the boy who looked unlike the others, shuffle forward, obviously in pain but determined to be with the child with the wounded leg.

"Leave J.D. alone," he said. His lips were swollen and cracked. His voice was feverish and confused. But his meaning was clear. "You leave my friend alone."

The boy from the center reached the kneeling helper and weakly tried to punch him. The helper did not try to duck or move, but remained to take the blows until the boy expended what little energy remained and his small balled fists fell uselessly to his sides.

Then the helper took him gently in his arms, and the boy with the wounded leg said, "It's going to be all right, Jase. Everything's going to be all right."

The rest of the children had fallen silent. The immense man came forward, waddling as if he weren't quite used to walking. Calm poured over Foster in waves. She had an almost dreamlike feeling, as if more things were going on around her than she knew, like a broken film that advanced only in discontinuous jumps. The fat man stared at Foster for a moment. At least, she assumed he did because she couldn't see his eyes through his pitch-black glasses. Then he turned to Hyams and did the same.

She found herself thinking of Detective Ioannou: questions being asked, questions being answered.

And finally the fat man spoke, clearly and without any accent which Foster could identify. "How do you do, Susan Elaine Foster," he said. He extended a surprisingly small, gloved hand.

Foster took the hand. It felt delicately thin and fragile beneath the fabric of the glove. For a moment she wondered if the rest of what he was wearing was padding, or some sort of disguise for his entire body. Hyams shook hands with him, too.

"So many questions," the fat man said. "Is that not right? So many places to begin." He wheezed softly as if he were breathing through a tube beneath his beard. "We understand. We ourselves must answer questions about this." He sighed, exhaling into something? "We are sorry we took so long to arrive. The distances are great and this has been most unexpected."

Hyams snorted. "Unexpected?" the young man repeated. He began to laugh at the understatement.

"Of course, unexpected," the fat man said. He almost sounded indignant. "One at a time is the rule. One at a time is the plan. This has been the wrong number and the wrong time." Inhale. "So many questions." He looked over to where one of his helpers had picked up a crumpled white equipment tarpaulin. The helper brought it back to the fat man, unfolded it, and held it open.

"Dear God," Hyams said as he saw what was on the tarp. Foster shivered with the confirmation the tarp displayed.

It was the image of a child, a child like all the other children of the shroud. The face was distorted in agony, the body obscured by the lines of restraining straps and bloodstains. Wyndham had done what he set out to do. Whatever had happened two thousand years ago in a cave outside Jerusalem had happened again in this studio. But what? Foster thought. And why?

The fat man touched the tarp, caressed it. "Without us nearby, how could the child know how to reform?" he sighed.

The tarp was refolded carefully, reverentially.

The fat man turned back to Hyams and Foster. "We did not know that what you did was possible for you. To begin again from bloodstains. For such a small thing to interfere with such a big plan." He inhaled. "This time, we shall take it with us."

"What do you mean, 'this time'?" Foster asked in awe. Considering all that had happened, the answer seemed obvious. But she couldn't accept it.

"One at a time is the plan," the fat man repeated. "One at a time is the rule. You have seen what they can do. Imagine what would be possible if they became adults here, knowing each other's thoughts and powers." Inhale. "So much planning. So much time spent. You almost spoiled everything."

"Spoiled *what*?" Hyams asked in frustration. "What plans? What rules?"

The fat man only shook his head. "Not yet," he sighed. "I'm sorry." Foster thought she could almost hear a touch of sadness in his voice. And then she felt dislocation and the fat man was talking to a helper and Panati at the other side of the stage.

Juan and Paul were moving to join the other children. Juan hesitated for a moment, then went to Marguerite, who watched over nothing with a glazed look. Foster saw that Juan's eyes were normal now. She wasn't surprised and thought nothing more about the change. After all, the dream friend was here.

Paul looked off to the side of the studio and tensed. Bobby Jay still sat against the wall, rocking back and forth, spittle hanging from his lips. In mad whispers, he condemned everyone to hell, again and again. Paul held out his hand. He approached the reverend. Foster heard a sparking sound.

"No," Louella Jay said in a dead flat voice, stepping in front of the boy. "There's a better way." Foster watched as the woman led Paul to the bank of video consoles on the far side of the stage area and unlocked a cabinet beneath them. She handed Paul a tape, showed him where to place it. The monitors flickered into life. The "Bobby Jay Good News Glory Show" was on the air one last time, with Bobby Jay and his special guests: the girl from props, Hank the cameraman, and Randolph his producer.

Louella showed a large fader switch to Paul and said something to him which Foster couldn't hear. Paul threw the switch without hesitation. Bobby Jay watched a dozen versions of himself without comprehension. Foster saw the images on the monitors and felt nothing for him. Louella walked out of the studio alone. Foster turned back to the fat man.

Dislocation. He was beside her. The shattered glass was gone from beneath the control room window. The studio had the feeling of a room that had been long abandoned.

"We have listened to the explanations you have given the children and we do owe you gratitude for gathering them," the fat man said. "There are so many and each one is different enough from what we had already known that at first we thought we wouldn't find them all." Inhale. "That is why we told them all to gather. We must take them back. They do not belong to your here and now."

Foster's eyebrows drew together so tightly they almost joined. To be this close to understanding, she thought, yet still not know. I don't want to die like this. "But *how* did you tell them?" she persisted. She was ready to beg.

The fat man held out his hand and brushed her face. She felt paralyzed, like a warm column of jelly held up only by the sudden rigidity of her skin. "Like this," the fat man whispered. All support left her. Foster collapsed. Hyams moved too slowly to catch her.

"The plan must be followed," the fat man continued. "Only one at a time and only at the time of our choosing. There have been several times already. It will be a century before we come again." Foster realized she was understanding the fat man's words without hearing them. Hyams was cradling her head, trying to say something to her, but all she was aware of was the fat man, even though she knew that what was happening to her was impossible. Quite lucidly she thought, there still is no such thing as telepathy.

"Accept this gift with our thanks," the fat man said in her mind and Foster's body doubled up in unspeakable agony. She could feel Hyams holding her tighter. She didn't want him to let go. The studio spun around her. The world was breaking into black shards and splinters before her eyes.

Not like this, her mind cried out as she felt herself slide down into senselessness. Don't let it go. Don't give it up. Hold on to life till the last. She fought against the dizziness, the suffocating spin into darkness. She focused on the warmth of Hyams's arms around her, his voice calling to her. She fought desperately against the knowledge that all knowledge was ending.

In those last moments, she listened to the arguments that the dream friend couldn't win and rejoiced that Marguerite was not separated from her cousin and that the Larkin's Mill X-Men were at last reassembled. She heard the joyful dancing of the children's feet as they followed the two helpers from the studio and desperately wanted to go with them.

She remembered thinking that she loved Jim Hyams; remembered hearing him say through his tears that he loved her; remembered realizing sadly that it was what counted most of all, and now it was too late.

And she remembered the one last thing that opened so many doors and closed so many others, that filled her with such excitement and such dread: she heard the fat man's voice as he led the last child through the door, tousled his hair with a friendly laugh, and said with such warmth and such love, "I knew your father."

Then the dream friend's gift finished its work within her, and when the darkness came to Susan Foster, this time, at least, its name was only sleep.

MILESTONES

Time Magazine, September 7, 1992

INAUGURATED. Susan Rutledge, 53, fiery politician who rose to public prominence after a decade spent powerbrokering behind the scenes in the G.O.P.; on September 2, as America's 42nd and first female President. The brief ceremony took place in Walter Reade Hospital an hour before Rutledge's discharge after treatment for superficial wounds received during an assassination attempt on August 28. Rutledge stepped from the hospital into one of the most volatile presidential campaigns in modern times, promising to conduct a full review of the FBI and vowing to give full support to her predecessor's forward-thinking initiatives in foreign policy and defense. (See cover story.)

DIED. Allan ("Number One") Fremont, 63, 41st President of the United States, and beloved embodiment of the ongoing retrenchment of traditional American ideals in the public sector; of multiple head wounds apparently suffered in the tragic fire which destroyed America's Glory (the country's largest Christian Bible college) on the Labor Day weekend. His badly charred body was discovered after rescuers spent three days sifting through the still smoldering ruins of an unused television studio. Mystery still surrounds Fremont's final movements and an investigation has been called to examine why half his secret service contingent was unaware of his location, while the other half perished with him in the fire. (See cover story.)

DIED. Robert ("Bobby Jay") Jablonski, 48, controversial but charismatic evangelist, star of the popular syndicated Christian talk show, "Bobby Jay Good News Glory Show," who led the past decade's fundamentalist revival movement in both the public and political sectors of the United States; of a self-inflicted gunshot wound administered while videotapes alleged to show his participation in sex parties and the murder of his show's producer played on television sets throughout the hotel complex at America's Glory. Fire marshalls are investigating the theory that the conflagration which subsequently destroyed the entire site spread from a fire deliberately set in Jablonski's private quarters. He is survived by his wife, Louella, who is also alleged to have appeared in the tapes, and who is facing arson charges stemming from the incident. (See cover story.)

Maryland Examiner, September 1, 1992

Young offender missing from Yorkwoods

(York Townships) A thirteen-year-old young offender committed to the Yorkwoods Institute for a period of observation escaped on the night of Saturday, August 29, a spokesperson for the Institute announced today.

Dr. Oscar Monroe, Director of Youth Services, admits that Institute personnel are stumped over the youth's vanishing act.

"At first we thought he managed to slip off to somewhere else in the building during Saturday night's power failure," Dr. Monroe said. "But when the lights came back on, he was just nowhere to be found."

Residents are advised to be on the lookout for a thin, dark-haired boy with dark complexion and black eyes. He was last seen wearing blue jeans, a red shirt, and white sneakers. He is believed to be dangerous.

Dr. Monroe does not believe the boy's disappearance is in any way related to the similar disappearance of another boy from a convalescent home in Connecticut, also during a power failure on the night of August 29. Dr. Monroe went on to say that he does not expect the boy will be able to get too far "because he's lugging a twenty-one-inch hospital TV set, which he somehow disconnected from a ceiling mount. I doubt he'll get too far with that thing."

Psychiatrist Dr. Leonard Hadrian, in charge of Yorkwoods criminal wing, is on vacation and unavailable for comment.

THE CHILDREN OF THE SHROUD

APRIL 2017

Foster felt her husband's arm wrap around her as she stood on the balcony, staring out over Miami. It was dusk. Strings of jeweled expressway lights shone dimly through the red haze. The air was hot. The Florida Ocean Barrier Commission would be issuing flood alerts any day now, she supposed.

"What are you thinking?" Jim asked. He nuzzled the base of her neck. Squeezed her tight.

She ran her fingers across his head, smiling to herself when she finally found the small fringe of hair that remained. The years had been kind to everything but Jim's hairline.

"I was thinking about Francis," she sighed.

Jim nodded. He knew that, she thought. He always knows.

They shared the near silence of the early evening. Forty floors below, the traffic flowed by with the soft hum of battery-driven motors. The hybrids couldn't switch over to internal combustion until they were outside the city limits.

"I think about him, too," Jim said eventually. "Sort of came to like him there at the end."

"A long time ago," Susan said, patting Jim's arm. She looked up at the first few stars. "Depending on the velocities, with dilation, he might still be alive out there," she said softly. She wanted to believe it.

"*If* that's the answer," Jim replied. "I remember he had a real strange look on his face and they didn't find a body so I hope and I pray that Francis went with them. But we still don't know where it was they went. Or how."

"Or why."

The topic was old ground for them. Probably not a day had passed without the memories of those few weeks, those last hours, rising up within them. Susan knew that for herself, every time she took a shower she had to brush her fingers across the unmarked skin of her abdomen where once, she remembered far too clearly, the ominous red scar of her exploratory surgery had run.

"Sometimes I hear what the fat man said to us, the way he said it to us, and I feel like we're all in an ant farm or a . . . a petri dish," she said.

"I know." It was old ground.

"It makes me mad."

"Yes."

"I keep thinking if only I had thought to pull off those glasses, rip off his beard, anything, just so I'd *know*."

Jim chuckled and kissed Susan's cheek. "And he probably would have said, 'You almost spoiled everything,' and turned us all into frogs or something."

"Well, I wish we had spoiled everything." She turned to her husband and said what she always said whenever they talked about the children: "It's just not fair!"

Her tight mood continued through dinner. Jim understood and left her to her thoughts. Susan knew she had been lucky in that one respect. But she didn't like the feeling of having to settle for anything less than exactly what she wanted.

After dinner, Susan tried to work in the den. There were at least three feature proposals she could be developing but she couldn't quite bring herself to turn on her processor. For a while she looked at the photos on the wall, hanging beside Jim's English degrees. Ioannou and Heaslip stared out from Jim and Susan's wedding shots. Heaslip had been the only one to wear a tuxedo that day. There was a badly faded print of Francis as a young man that Andre Delambre had stolen from the university for her. When she decided that the past wasn't doing her any good, she went into the kitchen for more coffee. The reedy, solid-state voice of the television set said: "Incoming Bulletin. Incoming Bulletin."

"I bet it's a flood warning," Susan called into the living room. She heard the receiver hum as Jim told the set to turn on.

"It's network," he called back to her, then added ominously, "Something's happened in Geneva."

Susan swallowed hard. Three times in the past twenty-five years the world had been to the brink. Three times it had barely managed to turn back. And each crisis had first been precipitated by a breakdown in Geneva. Bravely, she walked into the living room. Jim was sitting forward in his chair.

"A walkout?" she asked, peering at the screen.

Jim ssshed her.

Wendy Kingsburgh, the NBC anchor in Geneva, stood on the grand outdoor stairway leading into the palace, permanent site of ongoing negotiations between the NATO Alliance and the Warsaw Pact. It was night there. A spotlight flattened the features of the trusted correspondent, but it didn't hide the tears in her eyes. Her lips were moving rapidly but there were transmission difficulties. Perhaps deliberate interference? The picture flipped several times. A crowd of people rushed down the palace steps.

"Oh no," Susan whispered. She sat down on the arm of Jim's chair, took his hand. Again she remembered standing in the old studio, a madman in a small control room above her. They were seconds from the final insanity, then. She felt the same fear, the same helplessness. Her own words came back to her: *not like this*.

The sound rushed with static and was finally brought on line.

"—has finally happened," Kingsburgh shouted into her microphone. A huge roar was building behind her. It sounded like a riot had broken out in the palace.

Susan squeezed Jim's hand. Not like this, please, not like this.

"A full disarmament treaty has been signed!" the anchor yelled across the world.

"What?"

"You can hear the wild shouts and celebration here behind me, viewers. It's an incredible scene." Kingsburgh held one hand over an ear and peered over her shoulder at the swarm of people moving behind her.

"What?"

"Our bureau chief has been informed that the treaty was officially ratified at fifteen hundred hours Geneva time. A joint—

I say again—a *joint* press conference via satellite has been called for eighteen hundred hours with both the President of the United States *and* the Soviet Premier." Kingsburgh looked over her shoulder again. Millions of people around the world heard her joyous laughter.

The scene cut to a meeting room within the palace. Champagne corks flew. The negotiating teams were shaking hands amid the stacks of paper. Cheers echoed as the camera was jostled by the crowds. The anchor's voice returned.

"This is the timetable, viewers. I say again for those who have just tuned in, this is the timetable for a complete"—laughter again—"complete disarmament treaty ratified moments ago by representatives of the Soviet Union and the United States—" The screams of delight, the wild cheers, were like every Times Square New Year's Eve at once. "Orbital weapons platforms are to be downgraded immediately. Lunar bases will be placed on standby awaiting observer and dismantling teams. ICBMs—" Kingsburgh's voice disappeared beneath the cries of the crowd. The television scene jiggled and swerved through the meeting chamber as if the camera were trying to swim upstream.

With tears in her own eyes, Susan slipped from the arm of the chair into Jim's lap and kissed him. Their noses were running; their smiles stretched muscles they never knew they had. Faintly through the balcony windows, they could hear a chorus of car horns and even church bells swell. There were no words for the joy and relief they felt, all humanity felt. They turned back to the television. They both gasped at the same time.

"Record!" Jim shouted to the VDR, but his voice was so stuffed up, the machine didn't acknowledge him. Susan scrambled from his lap and ran her fingers over the buttons, trying to find the proper one. She pressed it.

"There!" Jim said excitedly, "on the Soviet side!"

Susan operated the VDR keyboard to freeze the images Jim called up and display them in the upper corners of the screen.

"You see it too, don't you?" he said. He was almost panting as he spoke. The horns and bells outside were joined by fire and police sirens.

Susan nodded. She couldn't speak.

She zoomed up the freeze frames.

"*Five* of them!" Jim laughed outrageously. "On both sides!" He pounded the arms of his chair.

Susan manipulated the five faces into the center of the screen. They were slightly different in hairstyles and weight, but they shared the same dark eyes, the same dark hair, the same long nose. Two negotiators on the Western side, three on the Eastern. Children of the Shroud! With only one slight difference to them, one minor, genetic difference which affected only one small portion of one tiny chromosome. They were women.

Susan was on her feet. Tears of joy, tears of laughter rolled down her face. Jim was beside her.

"Why didn't they get the call to be together?" he asked in shock.

"The fat man said the children were each so different, he didn't know if he could find them all. I wonder how many others he left behind?"

"But why didn't you find them in Wyndham's records?"

"He sorted all his files by sex. I remember seeing that the first night I went through the records. He sorted all of them by sex!" She clapped her hands. "We did it! We spoiled everything!"

"He said he's coming back in seventy-five years," Jim cautioned. "He said there were plans. He said there were rules."

Susan laughed. The windows were vibrating. The whole world cheered. "The rules just changed," she said.

The true enemy of knowledge and science
is irrationalism,
not religion.

STEPHEN JAY GOULD

AUTHOR'S NOTE

The details given in this book by Susan Foster concerning the technology of cloning are firmly based in the real world, with one exception: as of the date of this writing, cloning of mammalian cells has not been acknowledged by a legitimate body. The problems inherent in mammalian cloning, as described by Foster, are ones of technique, not of science. An announcement of success in this field is simply a matter of time. Dinosaurs are well down the road, but by no means an impossibility.

Additionally, the information given concerning the Shroud of Turin is based on current studies. As Andre Delambre reports, much controversy surrounds these findings and a bitter debate has developed between researchers who believe the shroud is a fraud and those who believe it is the burial cloth of Jesus Christ. The carbon-14 dating test, which could determine the date of origin for the shroud within a few decades, has, as of this writing, yet to be undertaken. Enough material has already been removed from the shroud for the purposes of other tests to allow the dating test to proceed. A carbon-14 dating of less than 1,800 years would conclusively indicate the shroud is a fraud. Unfortunately, a dating of approximately 2,000 years would not prove the shroud to be authentic since no universally acceptable explanation has been found to account for the image it carries, which some investigators claim could only be caused by an intense, and inexplicable, scorch. To quote Dr. Heywood Floyd, "its origin and purpose are still a total mystery."

ABOUT THE AUTHOR

Garfield Reeves-Stevens is a Canadian writer whose novels include *Bloodshift*, *Dreamland*, *Children of the Shroud*, *Nighteyes*, and *Dark Matter*.

With his wife, Judith, he has cowritten the *Science Around Me* series of science and technology textbooks for children, the ongoing fantasy novel series—*The Chronicles of Galen Sword*, and two Star Trek novels—*Memory Prime*, and *Prime Directive*.

The Reeves-Stevens' live in Los Angeles.